Poultry Production

BY

Leslie E. Card, Ph.D.

Professor of Animal Science, University of Illinois, Urbana, Illinois

Ninth Edition, Thoroughly Revised,

With 198 Illustrations and 4 Plates, 2 in Color

LEA & FEBIGER

PHILADELPHIA   1961

Printed in the United States of America

Library of Congress Catalog Card No. 61-9366

Preface to the Ninth Edition

EACH succeeding edition of Poultry Production has seen increasing emphasis placed on the results of research, and on the interpretation of new findings as they apply to poultry practice. This approach is especially important for an industry which has been influenced by so many technological developments in recent years as has the poultry industry. But this is not a "how-to-do-it" book. It stresses the fundamental principles underlying successful poultry practice, and shows why a knowledge of them is essential to a full understanding of the subject.

As in the eighth edition, there are no lists of references such as had been included previously. The decision to omit them was made with some reluctance as one means of keeping the price of the book at a reasonable figure.

My colleagues at the University of Illinois have offered many suggestions and pertinent criticisms. Dr. H. M. Scott and Dr. D. J. Bray, who have used the book in their classes, have been particularly helpful.

Dr. Bradley M. Patten and The Blakiston Company very kindly permitted the use of four illustrations from the fourth edition of "Early Embryology of the Chick," and The Company of Biologists, Ltd., Cambridge, England, granted permission to reproduce from the *Journal of Experimental Biology* the illustrations used in Plate II.

Several illustrations were made available through the courtesy of the publishers of *Poultry Tribune, U. S. Egg and Poultry Magazine, Broiler Business, Poultry Processing and Marketing, Pacific Poultryman,* and *American Poultry Journal.* Credit has been indicated in all such cases.

The organization of the book has not been changed except for omission of the chapter formerly entitled "Management Practices," and separation of the material on marketing into a chapter on Marketing Eggs and one on Marketing Poultry.

L. E. C.

URBANA, ILLINOIS
January, 1961

Contents

A Personal Note to Students

Textbooks are traditionally descriptive, factual and conservative, and they too often make dry reading. The author is expected to write as if talking *about* his subject rather than *to* his readers. This results in a formal style which does not help the "meeting of minds" between author and reader.

I have gone along with precedent in the fourteen chapters which follow, but because I believe that you who study this book are entitled to something more than this, and because many of you are presumably advanced undergraduates in Land-Grant Colleges of Agriculture, I want to tell you why I have stressed certain subjects and have treated others very briefly. I also want to give you some idea of the opportunities which may be open to you when you graduate.

During twenty-five years of teaching undergraduate students at the University of Illinois I have observed that certain subject matter topics, year after year, were difficult for students to grasp. Some of these topics I have tried to clarify in this revision by a new, or at least a different, approach. Others have been expanded to include more background material.

Those of you who have elected a course in poultry husbandry—yes, even those who are taking poultry as a required course—are fortunate in that this, like most subjects in agriculture, deals with living things. The pertinent information is constantly changing—it is not static. That is why textbooks must frequently be revised or rewritten.

Up to the turn of the century most poultry books dealt with breeds and varieties and with the art of feeding and management. There was no science of poultry production, nor was there a poultry industry as we know it today. Mammoth incubators and the coal stove brooder had not been invented. There was no information about the inheritance of egg production. Almost nothing was known about vitamin requirements of chickens, or about the efficiency with which chickens could transform feed into poultry meat. No one was studying the cost of egg production, and there were no egg and poultry processing plants.

All this has changed. We now know far more about the genetics of the fowl and about the nutritional requirements of the growing chick than is known about any other animal species of economic importance. Conversely, breed and variety have become of minor importance except as they affect economic production and returns. Very few poultrymen today are concerned about the number of points on a single comb, about a few black feathers on a Barred Plymouth Rock, about whether a White Plymouth Rock is "pure bred," or about a little down between the toes of baby chicks. But they are very much concerned about how fast the feathers grow, how well they cover the chicken, whether gains are rapid and economical, and whether the production index of a flock is 200 or more eggs.

This ninth edition of Poultry Production differs from most other texts in the field in several ways:

1. It minimizes the discussion of breeds and varieties.
2. Endocrine secretions and the stimulus of light are presented as fundamental factors influencing the performance of both growing chicks and laying hens.
3. Poultry breeding and improvement are discussed in terms of the interaction of heredity and environment and the relation of this concept to selection methods.
4. Poultry housing is considered from the point of view of both biology and engineering as they relate to climatic control and management efficiency.
5. The significance of individual amino acids and of the fundamental nature of energy requirements in poultry feeding is dealt with in considerable detail.
6. The continuing trends toward increased specialization, larger production units, and integration of the industry, are recognized as being inherent in the economic development of this important branch of agricultural production and marketing.

If this seems confusing and a bit difficult, it is only because poultry science has been making rapid advancement. You are to be congratulated on having the opportunity to participate in that advancement. And as you become familiar with the vast literature bearing on the whole subject of poultry and egg production, you will realize that neither interpreting nor condensing this material into a book to be covered in a single quarter or semester has been an easy task. I have tried to do both of these things in such a way as not to mislead any reader. How well I have succeeded, only you and your instructor can judge.

Opportunities for College Graduates.—Opportunities in the poultry business are closely related to the food needs of the population.

Psychologists often refer to human wants and desires, but food is a need that is important to most people three times a day. The simple fact that births in the United States are occurring at the rate of one about every ten seconds furnishes ample evidence of the continuing opportunity which exists in all branches of the food industry. The poultry business benefits because poultry and eggs are important items of human food.

Because of increased efficiency in agricultural production, and because of the increasing demand for many new kinds of goods and services, the long-time trend in population shifts has been away from farms into cities and towns. As long as this continues, it means that numerically there will be more opportunities for employment in the cities and towns than on farms, and many agricultural college graduates must look in that direction because there are not enough places for them on farms.

Many employers in both large and small businesses related to agriculture prefer to hire college-trained men who have a farm background. The reasons are simple. A college graduate is favored because he had the energy and vision to spend four years in study and preparation for a job. A farm background usually means that he is willing to work and that he knows how; that he is resourceful, and can improvise when necessary, to meet a new situation. It means also, especially if it included 4-H or F. F. A. experience, a character background which makes for good citizenship—a most valuable asset in any business. Of course along with these qualities, the college graduate is expected to know something about poultry management, poultry nutrition, poultry genetics, or poultry and egg marketing, as the case may be.

Some of the best job opportunities are in sales and service with feed manufacturers, poultry equipment and supply firms, hatcheries, and specialty companies manufacturing or dealing in products which are needed by various branches of the poultry industry. There are numerous opportunities in the processing field because of the tremendous volume of poultry and eggs handled every year. In choosing a job in any one of these fields, it is well to find out about the local reputation of the particular business firm or local branch. Is the local manager thought well of in the community? Are the present employees enthusiastic about their work?

There are also a great many jobs which call for some knowledge of poultry as part of a broad agricultural training. Assistant county agents, teachers of vocational agriculture, and service men with farm supply companies are examples.

Becoming a Poultryman.—The poultry business is safer and saner today than it was twenty years ago. There are fewer complications, because of more and better knowledge about feeding, breeding and management. As evidence of this, large production units are becoming the rule rather than the exception in most sections of the country.

If you want to get into the poultry business for yourself, there are several possibilities. You can follow the sound and time-honored procedure of going to work for someone else while gaining experience and accumulating sufficient capital to start your own business. In some of the commercial broiler areas you can, with even limited experience, get started on a basis in which the financial risk is largely assumed by a feed dealer, hatcheryman or processor who advances the money for chicks, feed, and perhaps for equipment. The operator supplies all labor in exchange for a share in the returns.

Acquiring a hatchery with limited capital is more difficult. There are fewer opportunities for new hatcheries today than there were twenty years ago, and a prospective owner may have to purchase an entire plant and good will. You might, however, be so fortunate as to find an owner who is about ready to retire and who would take you in as a partner, giving you the opportunity of buying the business as you can.

You might make similar arrangements for the purchase of a commercial egg farm. Or you might have a chance to take over the managership of such a farm on a salary and profit-sharing basis, with the understanding that an opportunity to purchase would be given later. Whatever the arrangement, you as the new operator must remember that it takes time, energy and money to establish a successful business. You must therefore be willing to put in several years of your own time and energy if you are to develop a new business or acquire one that is already established.

Whatever your future objective—whether it is to become identified with the four-billion-dollar poultry industry or simply to be a better-informed consumer of its products—I trust that your study of this book may be both interesting and profitable. If you gain nothing else, you should have a better conception of the magnitude and significance of the poultry industry and an understanding of why so many men are proud to be a part of it.

L. E. Card

Poultry Production

Chapter 1

The Poultry Industry

THE business of producing poultry and eggs, like many other phases of commercial farm production, is concentrating in fewer hands. This is not a new development but it has been accelerated in recent years by increasing and prolonged cost-price pressures which in turn have provided the incentive for many technological developments in the industry. Census reports provide a clear indication of the long-time trend, as shown by the following brief tabulation.

	Percentage of all farms reporting chickens sold	Average number sold per farm	Percentage of all farms reporting eggs sold	Dozens sold per farm
1929	50	91	62	505
1939	41	119	*	*
1949	32	343	45	995
1954	22	940	35	1,576
1959†	21	1,950	29	3,040

*Not reported
†Estimated from incomplete data

There has been geographical concentration also. Over half of the poultry farms reported in 1954 were found in ten States (See Table 1). Furthermore, 22 per cent of the commercial broilers sold in 1954, and 11 per cent of all chicken eggs sold, came from the ten leading counties. This trend has continued. According to estimates made by the U. S. Department of Agriculture, over half of the commercial broilers produced in 1959 were raised in the five States of Georgia, Arkansas, Alabama, North Carolina and Texas.

Poultry production exists as an industry because poultry and eggs are prized as human food. Chickens are often raised as a hobby, feathers are put to many different uses, and great quantities of eggs are used in the preparation of therapeutic vaccines, but all these things are distinctly secondary to the use of poultry and eggs as human food. Furthermore, the business of producing, processing, transporting, storing, financing, and serving food gives employment to more persons in this country than do all other businesses combined. Poultry meat and eggs are important commodities in the food business.

TABLE 1.—THE TEN LEADING STATES IN NUMBER OF POULTRY FARMS* AND IN TOTAL VALUE OF POULTRY PRODUCTS SOLD, 1954. (FROM THE U.S. CENSUS OF AGRICULTURE, 1954).

Rank	State	Number of poultry farms	Rank	State	Poultry products sold (millions)
1	Pennsylvania	11,851	1	California	$188
2	California	11,574	2	Pennsylvania	115
3	Georgia	10,742	3	Minnesota	103
4	Texas	8,940	4	Iowa	96
5	New York	6,963	5	Georgia	95
6	North Carolina	6,718	6	Texas	80
7	New Jersey	6,679	7	New Jersey	80
8	Indiana	5,937	8	New York	78
9	Ohio	5,877	9	Indiana	70
10	Arkansas	5,267	10	Ohio	70
Ten-State Total		80,548	Ten-State Total		975
United States		154,257	United States		$1,919

*A poultry farm, as defined by the Census, is one on which 50 per cent or more of total sales was realized from poultry products.

TABLE 2.—THE TEN LEADING STATES IN GROSS POULTRY INCOME FROM CHICKENS, EGGS, AND COMMERCIAL BROILERS, 1959. BASED ON ESTIMATES BY THE U.S. DEPARTMENT OF AGRICULTURE.

| Rank | State | Millions of Dollars | | | |
		Chickens	Eggs	Broilers	Total
1	Georgia	7.9	54.5	153.0	215.4
2	California	9.7	137.3	32.0	179.0
3	Pennsylvania	11.6	109.0	28.1	148.7
4	North Carolina	8.3	61.9	68.9	139.1
5	Texas	5.1	61.3	55.4	121.8
6	Iowa	8.0	97.8	2.5	108.3
7	New Jersey	4.5	72.7	6.9	84.1
8	Indiana	6.1	56.0	21.5	83.6
9	Minnesota	5.4	72.6	3.0	81.0
10	Ohio	5.9	59.5	9.0	74.4
United States		155.4	1,617.7	922.4	2,695.5

Changes in population can have significant effects on the poultry business. In 1930 California shipped more eggs to New York, Chicago and Philadelphia than it did to either of its own markets, San Francisco and Los Angeles. Since 1950 it has shipped almost no eggs east, and its own poultry industry has greatly expanded in order to meet the needs of its rapidly growing population. In 1959 California surpassed Iowa to become the leading state in total number of eggs produced.

TABLE 3.—THE RANK OF THE FIRST TEN STATES IN PERCENTAGE OF TOTAL FARM CASH RECEIPTS DERIVED FROM POULTRY AND EGGS, 1959, WITH COMPARISONS FOR EARLIER YEARS. (DATA FROM U.S. DEPARTMENT OF AGRICULTURE.)

Rank	State	1959	1949	1939	1929
1	Delaware	55	71	57	33
2	New Hampshire	41	47	33	27
3	Maine	39	26	14	12
4	New Jersey	29	39	23	23
5	Connecticut	29	31	23	18
6	Georgia	28	13	5	5
7	Massachusetts	26	36	24	19
8	Maryland	26	30	18	18
9	West Virginia	25	31	18	20
10	Rhode Island	22	27	19	19
	United States	9	11	10	10

TABLE 4.—THE TEN LEADING COUNTIES IN CHICKENS AND EGGS SOLD IN 1954, WITH COMPARISONS FOR 1949. (FROM U.S. CENSUS REPORTS.)

Chickens Sold			Eggs Sold		
County	Rank		County	Rank	
	1954	1949		1954	1949
Sussex, Del.	1	1	Los Angeles, Calif.	1	2
Washington, Ark.	2	4	Monmouth, N. J.	2	3
Benton, Ark.	3	3	San Bernardino, Calif.	3	6
Wicomico, Md.	4	7	Sonoma, Calif.	4	1
Scott, Miss.	5	49	Ocean, N. J.	5	4
Hall, Ga.	6	12	Lancaster, Pa.	6	5
Cherokee, Ga.	7	5	Cumberland, N. J.	7	8
Worcester, Md.	8	2	San Diego, Calif.	8	11
Rockingham, Va.	9	9	Orange, Calif.	9	26
Forsyth, Ga.	10	13	Atlantic, N. J.	10	15

GROWTH OF THE INDUSTRY

The poultry industry has shown a tremendous growth in the last twenty-five years, largely because of a complete and fundamental change in viewpoint. Instead of keeping chickens as a hobby or a sideline, for pleasure and some incidental profit, thousands of flock owners have come to look upon the poultry enterprise on their farms as an economic unit, a means of livelihood, a source of income by which to raise and educate a family and acquire a certain degree

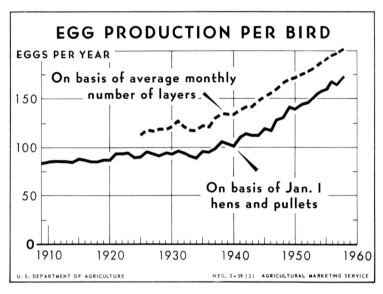

Fig. 1.—Annual rate of lay has been increasing steadily for about 20 years.

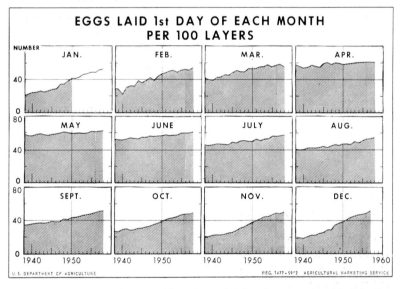

Fig. 2.—The increase in rate of lay since 1940 has been most marked in the months of October, November, December and January.

of economic independence. Instead of keeping chickens, they have made the chickens keep them.

In January, 1925, the U. S. Department of Agriculture began reporting the number of eggs produced each month for each 100 layers on farms. For twelve years the annual total ranged a little above or below 120 eggs for each hen and pullet in farm flocks. Then in 1937 there began a steady and almost continuous rise in production which brought the 1959 figure to 206, 70 per cent above the average for the first twelve years of record.

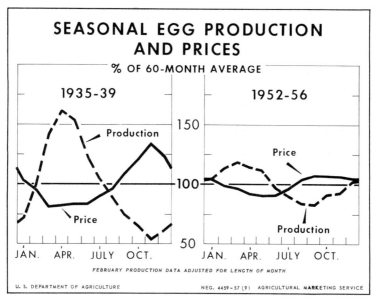

FIG. 3.—Seasonal variation in both egg production and prices has been much less in recent years than formerly.

There are several reasons for this spectacular rise, and the increased production has, in turn, been responsible for many other marked changes in the poultry industry. In 1928, about 43 per cent of the chickens raised on farms were hatched under hens, and only 23 per cent were bought as baby chicks. By 1938, 66 per cent of the chickens raised were purchased as baby chicks. In 1959, this figure had risen to 96 per cent and, in addition, commercial hatcheries produced over 1,800 million chicks for the commercial broiler trade. This change has enabled producers to start their chicks earlier than is usually possible when all must be hatched on the farm where they are grown. The pullets raised from these early chicks are ready to lay in September or October instead of in November or December.

Early hatching by commercial operators meant that breeding

flocks had to be in production well in advance of the usual hatching season. This was accomplished in part by the early hatching of a previous year, in part by better feeding and management methods, and in part by selection and breeding for the ability to lay well. These methods will be discussed in some detail in later chapters.

TABLE 5.—STATES IN WHICH TOTAL EGG PRODUCTION INCREASED BY AS MUCH AS 50 PER CENT IN 1959 OVER 1949, OR DECREASED BY AS MUCH AS 20 PER CENT. CALCULATED FROM DATA REPORTED BY THE U.S. DEPARTMENT OF AGRICULTURE.

Increases		*Decreases*	
State	*Per cent change*	*State*	*Per cent change*
Florida	258	Nevada	60
Georgia	145	Oklahoma	35
South Carolina	102	Wyoming	34
North Carolina	96	Missouri	30
Arizona	77	Colorado	30
California	75	New York	27
Alabama	61	West Virginia	24
Mississippi	56	Virginia	23
Maine	50	Maryland	22
U.S. Total	10	Kentucky	20

TABLE 6.—EGG PRODUCTION PER LAYER, BY MONTHS, FOR INDICATED YEARS. (DATA FROM U.S. DEPARTMENT OF AGRICULTURE.)

Month	*1929*	*1939*	*1949*	*1959*
January	5.9	8.1	12.8	16.6
February	7.5	9.7	13.6	16.0
March	13.6	14.9	17.5	19.1
April	16.7	17.0	18.1	19.1
May	16.5	17.0	18.2	19.6
June	14.0	14.6	16.2	18.2
July	12.7	13.2	15.0	17.9
August	11.1	11.7	13.6	16.8
September	8.7	9.3	11.8	15.4
October	6.3	7.4	11.2	15.6
November	4.1	6.1	10.9	15.2
December	4.1	6.8	12.2	16.3
Totals	121.2	135.8	171.1	205.8

The increase of 70 per cent in annual production per layer from 1937 to 1959 was gained chiefly by improved performance in the months of September through February. The increase in these six months added about five dozen eggs to the annual average, whereas the increase during the other six months added only two dozen. (See Table 6).

The longtime upward trend in egg production per layer is shown also in the records of official egg-laying tests. The following tabulation is for the Storrs (Connecticut) Test which has been in continuous operation since 1911.

Test	Year	Average number of eggs per layer
1st	1911–12	154
5th	1915–16	162
10th	1920–21	160
15th	1925–26	162
20th	1930–31	183
25th	1935–36	192
30th	1940–41	209
35th	1945–46	215*
40th	1950–51	230†
45th	1955–56	231†

*51 weeks
†50 weeks

Prior to 1937, egg consumption per person in the United States was about 300 eggs a year. With increased production per layer, more eggs of better quality became available, and the American public responded by increasing consumption till it reached a maximum of 402 in 1945. In the last fifteen years there has been a gradual decline to about 90 per cent of that figure.

With increased production, fresh eggs are available to more people throughout the year. From 1925, the first year of record, through 1939 (see Table 6) there were six months of the year when the average number of eggs per hen was fewer than 10, but by 1949 it was better than 10 in all twelve months, and in 1959 it exceeded 15 eggs in all twelve months. This leveling out of production has tended to level out the price. The peak monthly price is much closer to the springtime average price than it was even twenty years ago. Because of more uniform production, fewer shell eggs go into storage. Peak holdings in 1959 were only 10 per cent of what they were thirty years earlier.

Coincidental with the nation-wide increase in average egg production was an even more spectacular rise in the production of commercial broilers. Broilers were being grown on a fairly extensive scale in the Delmarva section (adjoining counties in Delaware, Maryland and Virginia) in the late twenties. In 1934, when the U. S. Department of Agriculture began reporting commercial broilers separately from farm-raised chickens, the U. S. total was 34 million, about 4 per cent of the total chicken meat supply. Broiler production increased, by successive 5-year intervals, to 106 million in 1939, 274 million in 1944, 513 million in 1949, 1,048 million in 1954, and 1,731 million in 1959. Commercial broiler sales in 1959 amounted to 84 per cent of the total pounds of chicken meat sold.

2

This rapid expansion has been possible largely because of the nation-wide increase in average egg production. Since fewer hens were needed to produce the nation's eggs, fewer farm-raised chickens were grown relative to human food needs, and about one-third of the crop consisted of pullets instead of straight-run chicks of both sexes. This left a gap to be filled by commercial broilers.

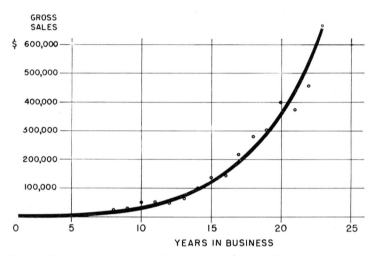

Fɪɢ. 4.—Developing a successful business takes years of hard work, but after 23 years this breeder-hatchery was doing better than a half-million-dollar business annually.

But production alone was not enough. New methods of processing, packaging and distribution, especially the retailing of fresh-killed and frozen ready-to-cook broilers, and the fact that such broilers were widely available at a favorable price when compared with other meats, favored an increase in consumption. During the five years from 1935 through 1939, chicken meat consumption, converted to a ready-to-cook basis, averaged 13.8 pounds per person per year. Ten years later, during 1945–1949, it had risen to 19.4 pounds, an increase of 41 per cent. Most of the increase was broilers. This increase has continued. The average for 1955–1959 was 25.7 pounds, with the 1959 figure at an all-time high of 28.8 pounds.

Since broiler production has been concentrated in new areas, as contrasted with the production of farm-raised chickens, many new processing plants have been built in the broiler areas, even when other well-equipped plants in areas of farm production had to be shut down and devoted to other purposes because of an inadequate local volume of poultry. Similarly, large tonnages of manufactured feeds have moved in new directions to accommodate broiler growers.

The same sort, of changes have occurred in respect to baby chicks, equipment for growing chickens, and services of various kinds. As the broiler business became firmly established, many bankers have come to look upon "chicken paper" as among their best risks.

This brief review of developments should be sufficient to indicate the many opportunities for employment in the various phases of the poultry industry. A profitable exercise for any group of poultry students is to make a list of the many kinds of jobs which must be done in order to keep the industry operating efficiently.

THE NATURE OF POULTRY AND EGG PRODUCTION

There are many ways of measuring both the size and the significance of the poultry industry. Several different charts and tables are therefore included in this chapter to give the reader some conception of the nature of the poultry business as an important part of American agriculture. No single ranking of the states will tell the whole story of their relative importance. Georgia now leads in total gross poultry income and in number of commercial broilers raised, but Delaware outranks all other states in the per cent of total farm income realized from poultry products. California produces more eggs than any other state, but per square mile of land area New Jersey produces more than twice as many eggs as her nearest competitor.

TABLE 7.—THE TEN LEADING STATES IN NUMBERS OF CHICKS HATCHED BY COMMERCIAL HATCHERIES, 1959 AND 1955. BASED ON ESTIMATES BY THE U.S. DEPARTMENT OF AGRICULTURE.

Rank	State	Chicks hatched (millions) 1959	Rank	State	Chicks hatched (millions) 1955
1	Georgia	345	1	Georgia	201
2	Alabama	156	2	California	104
3	Arkansas	154	3	Texas	102
4	North Carolina	145	4	Indiana	100
5	Texas	134	5	North Carolina	92
6	California	114	6	Missouri	91
7	Mississippi	114	7	Arkansas	77
8	Maryland	106	8	Pennsylvania	76
9	Indiana	92	9	Maryland	71
10	Missouri	87	10	Virginia	71
United States		2,385	United States		1,853

Largely because of the many technological problems involved, the industry is fairly well concentrated in certain geographical areas. The ten leading states, as listed in Tables 7, 8, 9 and 10, accounted for 61 per cent of all the chicks hatched, 49 per cent of the farm-raised chickens, 52 per cent of the eggs produced, and 74 per cent of the commercial broilers raised in 1959.

TABLE 8.—THE TEN LEADING STATES IN NUMBERS OF FARM CHICKENS RAISED, EXCLUDING COMMERCIAL BROILERS, 1959 AND 1955. BASED ON ESTIMATES BY THE U.S. DEPARTMENT OF AGRICULTURE.

Rank	State	Number raised (millions) 1959	Rank	State	Number raised (millions) 1955
1	California	31.5	1	Iowa	34.6
2	Iowa	28.6	2	California	28.9
3	Minnesota	20.8	3	Minnesota	24.5
4	Pennsylvania	20.3	4	Pennsylvania	23.2
5	Georgia	17.5	5	Illinois	22.3
6	North Carolina	16.6	6	Missouri	20.1
7	Missouri	15.5	7	Indiana	19.2
8	Texas	15.3	8	Wisconsin	17.7
9	Illinois	14.6	9	Ohio	15.9
10	Indiana	14.5	10	Texas	15.7
	United States	398.7		United States	461.9

TABLE 9.—THE TEN LEADING STATES IN NUMBERS OF EGGS PRODUCED, 1959 AND 1955. BASED ON ESTIMATES BY TNE U.S. DEPARTMENT OF AGRICULTURE.

Rank	State	Number of eggs (millions) 1959	Rank	State	Number of eggs (millions) 1955
1	California	5,236	1	Iowa	4,859
2	Iowa	5,042	2	California	4,404
3	Minnesota	3,803	3	Minnesota	4,287
4	Pennsylvania	3,625	4	Pennsylvania	3,654
5	Illinois	2,970	5	Illinois	3,064
6	Ohio	2,463	6	New Jersey	2,433
7	Indiana	2,410	7	Ohio	2,366
8	Wisconsin	2,401	8	Wisconsin	2,328
9	Texas	2,384	9	Indiana	2,289
10	New Jersey	2,379	10	Texas	2,249
	United States	62,401		United States	59,496

TABLE 10.—THE TEN LEADING STATES IN NUMBERS OF COMMERCIAL BROILERS RAISED, 1959 AND 1955. BASED ON ESTIMATES BY THE U.S. DEPARTMENT OF AGRICULTURE.

Rank	State	Number raised (millions) 1959	Rank	State	Number raised (millions) 1955
1	Georgia	303	1	Georgia	122
2	Arkansas	164	2	Texas	80
3	Alabama	158	3	Arkansas	77
4	North Carolina	137	4	Delaware	70
5	Texas	115	5	North Carolina	60
6	Mississippi	108	6	Maryland	58
7	Maryland	93	7	Alabama	58
8	Delaware	85	8	Virginia	55
9	Maine	58	9	California	49
10	Virginia	54	10	Mississippi	37
	United States	1,731		United States	1,078

Over one-half of the farms reporting chickens in 1930, and again in 1940, had flocks of fewer than 50 each, and the average for these 3,000,000 farms was 23 chickens per flock. But the other half of the flocks are getting larger, and an increasing percentage of total egg production is coming from flocks of 400 and more hens. By 1954, 27 per cent of the chickens reported were in flocks of 800 or more, with an additional 13 per cent in flocks of 400 to 799. These two groups accounted for 54 per cent of all eggs sold, but represented less than 5 per cent of the nearly 3.5 million farms reporting layers in that year.

Fig. 5.—The poultry industry holds several important trade conventions and conferences each year. This is a view of the exhibit hall at the Fact Finding Conference in Kansas City. (*Courtesy of U. S. Egg and Poultry Magazine.*)

Large production units are becoming the rule rather than the exception in many areas. Brief reference to the hatchery business will illustrate the point. A hatcheryman who today needs 40,000 breeding females in his supply flocks has probably been encouraging his flock owners to expand their operations, and may have under contract no more than 40 flocks averaging 1000 hens each. Twenty years ago he probably would have had to deal with 200 flock owners having flocks of 200 hens each, in order to operate the same total capacity. Of course part of this change has come about because progressive hatcherymen realize that their flock owners are, in a very real sense, a most important part of their business, and compensate them accordingly.

Large commercial egg farms are becoming common in many parts of the country. There are farms in the Middle West, as well as along the east and west coasts, on which 100,000 to 200,000 layers are housed annually. Many commercial broiler growers market upwards of 60,000 broilers a year. There are about 100 large hatcheries in the country, each with sufficient incubator capacity to set 500,000 or more eggs at one time, and perhaps 4,000 smaller operators. And there are breeding farms, perhaps more accurately described as breeder-hatcheries, on which the gross annual income is in excess of $500,000. Poultry and egg production is truly big business.

OTHER PHASES OF THE POULTRY INDUSTRY

This book is concerned primarily with those things that have to do directly with production, and other phases of the industry can be given but brief mention. It is important to remember, however, that the poultry industry as it exists today involves a great deal more than the farm production of poultry and eggs for food or other purposes.

The business of producing chicks for sale has enjoyed a remarkable growth since March 15, 1918, when shipments of day-old chicks were first admitted to the mails. The appearance, in 1922, of room-type mammoth incubators of large capacity gave added impetus to the business and made rapid expansion an easy matter. The number of commercial hatcheries in the United States increased from an estimated 250 in 1918 to more than 10,000 in 1927. The number of hatcheries has since decreased, to around 4,000 in 1959, but their average capacity is much greater than formerly, and many operate on a year-round basis. Weekly placements of broiler chicks in the 22 important broiler producing states average about 25 million throughout the year. The incubating of eggs and the hatching of chicks has literally been taken off the farm, and this change has had marked effects on many other practices in the industry.

More than 40 million breeding hens are tested annually for pullorum disease, and comparable numbers of chickens must be vaccinated for the prevention of such diseases as fowl pox, laryngotracheitis and Newcastle disease.

A necessary accompaniment of commercial hatching is artificial brooding. Without modern brooding equipment it would have been impossible for the industry to reach anything like its present size.

Under the impetus of a demand growing out of war conditions, the business of drying eggs mushroomed from almost nothing to plants with an annual capacity of around 400 million pounds. This is sufficient to take the total egg production of about 125 million hens.

Adequate rations are essential to such expansion, and in this direction the industry has made such strides that more is known about the nutritional requirements of the chicken than about those of any other farm animal. This, and the fact that several different nutrients can now be produced synthetically at low cost, makes it possible to produce a tremendous tonnage of feed which is vastly superior to the most carefully prepared mixtures of a few years ago. Of the more than 30 million tons of manufactured feeds produced each year, about two-thirds, or 20 million tons, are poultry feeds.

Both changing poultry practices and increased production call for new equipment beyond the ordinary replacement needs of the industry. Incubators, brooders, feeding equipment, egg cases,

Fig. 6.—A view of the trading floor on the Chicago Mercantile Exchange.

chick boxes and many other articles must be made in increasing numbers as the industry grows. Leg bands, time clocks, battery brooders, laying batteries, egg cartons, glass substitutes, hardware cloth, insulating boards and automatic feeders have been needed to meet changing practices. Many new kinds of labor saving equipment have been introduced into poultry and egg processing plants. Refrigerator units are needed by thousands of retail stores offering pan-ready poultry for sale. New demands take the place of old needs as new ideas develop and older practices are discarded.

Allied Interests.—It is easy to see that feed, equipment and supplies must be manufactured to meet production needs. Just as important, though perhaps not so readily apparent, are the needs for processing equipment, cold storage warehouse facilities, trucks for the bulk handling of feed and for the transportation of live and dressed poultry and eggs, laboratories for the production of embryo-propagated vaccines, and facilities for getting information about poultry and eggs to the consuming public by way of the press, radio and television.

TABLE 11.—THE TEN LEADING STATES IN EGG PRODUCTION PER PERSON AND PER SQUARE MILE OF LAND AREA, 1959. BASED ON PRODUCTION ESTIMATES BY THE U.S. DEPARTMENT OF AGRICULTURE AND THE 1960 POPULATION CENSUS.

Rank	State	Eggs per person	Rank	State	Eggs per square mile (Thousands)
1	South Dakota	2222	1	New Jersey	317
2	Iowa	1844	2	Connecticut	147
3	Nebraska	1368	3	Massachusetts	94
4	Minnesota	1121	4	Iowa	90
5	North Dakota	811	5	Pennsylvania	81
6	Kansas	779	6	Rhode Island	80
7	New Hampshire	758	7	Indiana	67
8	Maine	678	8	Delaware	60
9	Wisconsin	612	9	Ohio	60
10	Indiana	520	10	Illinois	53
	United States	348		United States	21

TABLE 12.—THE TEN LEADING STATES IN BROILER PRODUCTION PER PERSON AND PER SQUARE MILE OF LAND AREA, 1959. BASED ON PRODUCTION ESTIMATES BY THE U.S. DEPARTMENT OF AGRICULTURE AND THE 1960 POPULATION CENSUS.

Rank	State	Broilers per person	Rank	State	Broilers per square mile (Thousands)
1	Delaware	192	1	Delaware	42.6
2	Arkansas	93	2	Maryland	9.4
3	Georgia	77	3	Connecticut	5.5
4	Maine	60	4	Georgia	5.2
5	Mississippi	50	5	Arkansas	3.1
6	Alabama	49	6	Alabama	3.1
7	North Carolina	30	7	North Carolina	2.8
8	Maryland	30	8	Mississippi	2.3
9	Virginia	14	9	Maine	1.9
10	Texas	12	10	Virginia	1.4
	United States	10		United States	0.6

The Chicago Mercantile Exchange, at 110 North Franklin Street, provides a trading floor where buyers and sellers can meet each business day to trade in eggs, tom and hen turkeys, butter and other commodities. This provides a futures market which is necessary for hedging operations, and which automatically indicates from day to day the combined judgment of a large group of buyers and sellers as to the value of the various commodities traded. Because of the limitations surrounding trading in futures, the overall effect is a highly desirable stabilizing of the market. The maximum daily price range for eggs, for example, is 2 cents a dozen above or below the previous day's settling price. The New York Mercantile Exchange provides similar trading facilities in that city.

TABLE 13.—THE MORE IMPORTANT CHARACTERISTICS OF SOME REPRESENTATIVE BREEDS OF CHICKENS

Breed	Standard weight, pounds		Type of comb	Color of earlobe	Color of skin	Color of shank	Shanks feathered?	Color of egg
	Cock	Hen						
American Breeds:								
Plymouth Rock	9½	7½	Single	Red	Yellow	Yellow	No	Brown
Wyandotte	8½	6½	Rose	Red	Yellow	Yellow	No	Brown
Rhode Island Red	8½	6½	Single and rose	Red	Yellow	Yellow	No	Brown
Jersey Black Giant	13	10	Single	Red	Yellow	Black	No	Brown
New Hampshire	8½	6½	Single	Red	Yellow	Yellow	No	Brown
Asiatic Breeds:								
Brahma (Light)	12	9½	Pea	Red	Yellow	Yellow	Yes	Brown
Cochin	11	8½	Single	Red	Yellow	Yellow	Yes	Brown
Langshan (Black)	9½	7½	Single	Red	White	Bluish-black	Yes	Brown
English Breeds:								
Australorp	8½	6½	Single	Red	White	Dark slate	No	Brown
Cornish (Dark)	10	7½	Pea	Red	Yellow	Yellow	No	Brown
Dorking (Silver-gray)	9	7	Single	Red	White	White	No	White
Orpington (Buff and White)	10	8	Single	Red	White	White	No	Brown
Sussex	9	7	Single	Red	White	White	No	Brown
Mediterranean Breeds:								
Leghorn	6	4½	Single and rose	White	Yellow	Yellow	No	White
Minorca (S. C. Black)	9	7½	Single	White	White	Dark slate	No	White
Ancona	6	4½	Single and rose	White	Yellow	Yellow	No	White
Andalusian (Blue)	7	5½	Single	White	White	Slaty blue	No	White

THE BREEDS OF CHICKENS

Of the nearly 200 varieties of chickens listed in the American Standard of Perfection, not more than five were of commercial importance in 1950, and only two—the White Leghorn and the White Plymouth Rock—can so qualify in 1960. New Hampshires accounted for about 100,000 breeders in NPIP flocks in their home

Fig. 7.—Single Comb White Leghorns (Mediterranean). (*Courtesy of Poultry Tribune.*)

Fig. 8.—Barred Plymouth Rocks (American). (*Courtesy of Poultry Tribune.*)

state and in Indiana, and Rhode Island Reds accounted for over 90,000 in Massachusetts in 1958–59. Nowhere else did they represent a significant number on a statewide basis.

On the other hand, cross-mated flocks, which accounted for only 2 per cent of the 11 million head of breeding stock in NPIP hatchery supply flocks in 1941–42, increased gradually to 16 per cent of 34 million head in 1952–53, and then rapidly to 64 per cent of the 40 million head in these flocks in 1958–59.

FIG. 9.—White Plymouth Rocks (American). (*Courtesy of Poultry Tribune.*)

FIG. 10.—Rose Comb Rhode Island Reds (American). (*Courtesy of Poultry Tribune.*)

With increased emphasis being placed on performance—whether it be growth or egg production—poultrymen have become less and less concerned about the supposed "purity" of the breeds with which they work. If dominant white plumage and early feathering are needed in White Plymouth Rocks, they do not object to introducing these characters by the use of White Leghorns if necessary, in spite of the rigorous selection which must follow the original introduction. They are not disturbed by a few black feathers in a white fowl, by an extra point on a single comb, or by a little down between the toes, *provided* growth and egg production are satisfactory. This change in attitude, like the growing interest in cross breeding and in the production of hybrid chickens, has developed as a part of present-day commercial poultry and egg production.

Fig. 11.—New Hampshires (American). (*Courtesy of Poultry Tribune.*)

Fig. 12.—Dark Cornish (English). The Cornish is often crossed with other breeds to produce a desirable meat type chicken. (*Courtesy of Poultry Tribune.*)

TABLE 14.—CHICKENS IN NATIONAL POULTRY IMPROVEMENT PLAN HATCHERY SUPPLY FLOCKS AND THEIR DISTRIBUTION BY VARIETIES, 1949–50 AND 1958–59. AS REPORTED BY THE U.S. DEPARTMENT OF AGRICULTURE.

	North Atlantic	East North Central	West North Central	South Atlantic	South Central	Western
	Per Cent					
New Hampshire:						
1949–50	49	26	21	68	44	39
1958–59	2	4	2	1	2	4
White Leghorn:						
1949–50	15	24	32	6	15	42
1958–59	19	25	25	5	6	29
White Plymouth Rock:						
1949–50	3	23	13	1	11	2
1958–59	16	15	4	7	10	6
Barred Plymouth Rock:						
1949–50	15	8	2	2	7	1
1958–59	2	1	–	–	–	–
Rhode Island Red:						
1949–50	10	2	2	2	3	5
1958–59	2	1	1	1	–	1
Cross Mated:						
1949–50	7	12	25	18	15	9
1958–59	57	40	48	85	75	53
Incross Mated:						
1949–50	–	–	–	–	–	–
1958–59	2	12	17	1	4	6
Other:						
1949–50	1	5	5	3	5	2
1958–59	1	2	2	–	2	–
	Millions					
Total number:						
1949–50	7.6	8.6	9.0	5.8	2.6	2.6
1958–59	7.6	5.9	7.0	11.5	6.0	1.9

Chapter 2

The Structure of the Chicken and the Formation of the Egg

THE FOWL AS A LIVING ORGANISM

In comparison with most other animals, birds are often spoken of as fast-living creatures. Structurally, too, they are among the most highly specialized of vertebrates, many of their modifications being in the nature of adaptations for flight. Their coating of feathers is sufficient to set them apart from all other forms, but they are also characterized by being warm-blooded, by having a high metabolic rate, and by the fact that development of the young takes place, for the most part, outside the body of the mother.

The body temperature of the fowl is higher than that of other domestic animals, and because of a more or less regular diurnal variation the recorded temperatures show a greater range than is found in other farm animals. The reported temperatures range from a minimum of 105° to a maximum of 109.4° F., depending upon the time of day the observations were made. The average noon figure is about 107° F. The minimum temperature during each twenty-four hour period occurs between 10 P.M. and midnight, whereas the maximum occurs some time during the afternoon.

The fowl is a rapid breather and its pulse rate is high. Records taken of the heart-beat of the chick embryo indicate that the pulse rate rises rapidly from about 130 to about 230 beats per minute, during the first nine days of incubation. It then rises but little during the next two or three days, and remains remarkably uniform during the remainder of the incubation period.

The heart rate again rises sharply during and immediately after hatching, and by the end of twelve hours it is about 300 beats per minute, where it remains reasonably constant. This rate is also characteristic of the adult fowl.

There is a definite relationship between body weight and heart rate. Small fowls such as Leghorn females have a resting heart rate of about 330 beats per minute, while large fowls such as Rhode Island Red males average below 250. There is also a regular diurnal variation in the normal heart rate, associated with the normal diurnal variation in temperature. Any excitement will cause an immediate and pronounced acceleration in heart rate. Dropping

(30)

a day-old chick has been shown to cause the heart rate to increase from 300 to 560 beats per minute.

Feathers.—Feathers help to protect the bird from physical injury, and are also of a great deal of aid in keeping the body warm. The wing feathers are, of course, essential to flight. The annual renewal of the feather coat constitutes a considerable physiological expense to the fowl, since the feathers make up from 4 to 9 per cent of the empty live weight, depending on the age and sex of the individual.

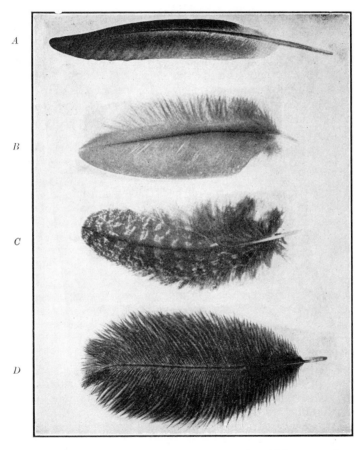

Fig. 13.—Different types of feathers. (*A*) Primary of Pigeon—an important flight feather with a stiff vane. (*B*) Under wing covert of a Great Blue Heron; downy portion overlapped by an adjoining feather. (*C*) Wing covert of Owl; the downy edge makes possible the all-important noiseless flight of this bird. (*D*) Feather of Ostrich; the power of flight has been lost, and the entire vane is downy. (*From "The Bird," by C. William Beebe; courtesy of Henry Holt and Company.*)

Though the body surface of most birds is almost entirely covered by feathers, there are only a very few species in which the feathers actually grow from the entire surface of the skin. In most species, including the fowl, the feathers are arranged in definite areas or feather tracts. Several of these tracts, or *pterylæ*, are paired, as may be seen readily by examining a picked carcass.

The parts of a typical body feather are the quill, which is continued throughout the vane of the feather as the shaft or rachis; the barbs, branching from the shaft; the barbules, branching from the barbs; and the barbicels, branching from the barbules. Except for size differences, most of the variation in the form and structure of feathers is due to differences in the mode of structure of the barbules and their branches.

The order of formation of the shaft of the feather is strictly apico-basal, and the order of age of the barbs is naturally the same. Similarly, in each barb, the apex at the margin of the feather is the first formed, and the central end attached to the shaft is the last. Thus there are two time gradients in each feather: from the apex to the base along the shaft, and from margin to center along the barbs.

The rate of growth of the shaft is approximately uniform throughout its length, at least during the formation of the vane of the feather. The rate of growth of the barbs, on the other hand, diminishes from the apex to the base of each, that is, from the margin of the feather to the shaft. This form of growth plays a large part in determining the pigmentation and general pattern of the feather. The time required to form the vane of a breast feather is approximately twenty days from the time of plucking an old feather.

The large feathers of the wings and tail are definite in number, and are molted and replaced, as a rule, in a regular order. As will be pointed out in the discussion of judging fowls for egg production, this fact can be used as a basis of estimating the length of time that certain birds have been out of production.

There are well-known differences between the sexes in the appearance of feathers in the neck, back, saddle, and tail sections. These are among the secondary sexual differences that are characteristic of birds. In certain "hen-feathered" breeds the feathers in these sections are essentially alike in both sexes. The Campine and the Sebright Bantam are examples.

The Skin.—A description of the skin and its specialized development in the form of comb, wattles and ear lobes, and the scales on the shanks and toes might easily be developed into an extended discussion. It is sufficient here to point out that there is a close relation between gonad development and activity, and the size and appearance of the comb and wattles. The practical application of this fact will be pointed out in the discussion of judging fowls for egg production.

The several different shank colors found in fowls result from different combinations of pigments in the upper and lower layers of skin.

Yellow shanks are due to the presence of lipochrome pigment in the epidermis, with the absence of melanic pigment. Black and its variations depend upon the presence of melanic pigment in the epidermis. It is probable that the darkest type of shank occurs when melanic pigment is present in both the dermis and the epidermis. Yellow in the dermis is obscured by black in the epidermis.

Blue, or slaty blue shanks occur when melanic pigment is present in the dermis, and neither type of pigment is present in the epidermis. With black in the dermis and yellow in the overlying epidermis, the shank appears willow green in color. White shanks are the result of complete absence of both types of pigment.

The Skeleton.—The skeleton of the fowl is compact, light in weight, and very strong. Many of the long bones are hollow, which helps to make them light; and many of them are fused together forming very strong structures to which the large muscles used in flight are attached. The keeled sternum is characteristic of the superorder *Neognathæ*, to which the domestic fowl belongs.

Questions are often asked about the rumpless fowls that sometimes are found in flocks of otherwise normal specimens. This condition may be either hereditary or accidental. In either case it is due to the absence of the last few vertebræ, including the pygostyle.

The Muscles.—The particular point of interest about the muscular system of the bird is the special development of the large muscles of the breast region. The greater part of this muscle group appears to be on the body proper because of the extensive attachment to the sternum. The muscles in this region weigh about as much as do all the rest of the muscles together, and make up about one-twelfth of the weight of the entire body.

The Respiratory System.—The respiratory system of birds is quite different from that of mammals. The lungs are firmly attached to the thoracic wall, and the active part of respiration is expiration. In mammals the more vigorous part of breathing is inspiration.

Connected with the lungs are four pairs of air sacs placed on either side of the body, and ranging in position from the neck to the abdomen, with a single median sac located in the cavity of the thorax. Besides opening into the lungs, these sacs communicate directly with the cavities of most of the bones of the body, with the exception of those of the forearm and hand of the wing and those below the hock-joint of the leg.

The voice of the fowl is produced in the syrinx, or lower larynx, located where the trachea divides into the two bronchi. The syrinx is the only part of the respiratory tract that is capable of producing sound, the upper larynx serving only to modulate the voice. The syrinx is essentially the same in both male and female. The normal hen does not crow because she lacks the psychological incentive to do so. If this incentive is provided experimentally, by suitable injections of the male sex hormone, hens so treated will crow.

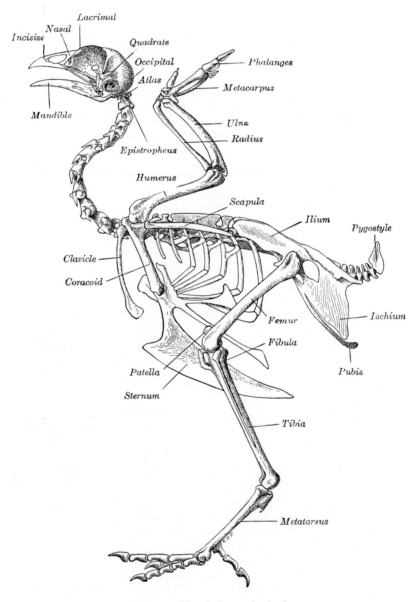

FIG. 14.—The skeleton of a fowl.

The Digestive System.—The structure of the alimentary canal of the bird suggests that the digestive process is rapid and that it resembles both the carnivora and herbivora in certain particulars. The relative shortness in length is a carnivorous characteristic, while the thorough pulverizing of the feed in the gizzard corresponds to mastication in the herbivora.

Mouth Parts.—The distinctive character of the mouth of the bird is the absence of lips and teeth. These parts are replaced by a horny mandible on each jaw, forming the beak.

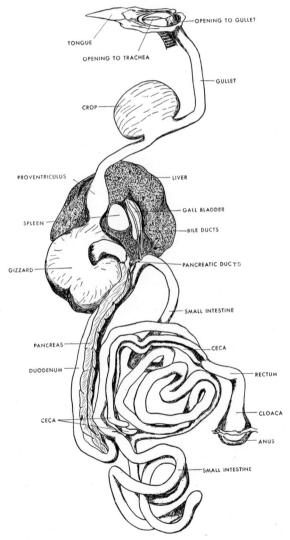

Fig. 15.—The digestive system of the fowl. (*Courtesy of F. B. Adamstone.*)

The tongue in fowls and turkeys is shaped like the barbed head of an arrow with the point directed forward. The barb-like projections at the back of the tongue serve the purpose of forcing the grain toward the entrance to the gullet when the tongue is moved from front to back. In water fowl the tongue is wider, softer and more flexible.

Gullet and Crop.—The gullet or esophagus is distinguished by its enormous expansibility. Immediately before entering the body cavity it is enlarged to form a pouch called the crop, which acts as a storage for the coarse feed eaten, much as does the paunch of ruminants.

Glandular Stomach.—Beyond the crop the gullet contracts until well within the body cavity, when it expands somewhat to form the glandular stomach (proventriculus), from which it passes immediately into the gizzard.

The glandular stomach, which is little more than a thickening of the gullet wall, does not appreciably detain the feed, but surrounds it with an acid gastric juice which passes with it into the gizzard. Gastric digestion continues through the duodenum until inhibited by the alkaline bile.

The Gizzard.—The gizzard is oval in form, having two openings on its upper side, one communicating with the proventriculus and the other with the small intestine. It is depressed on each side, being situated behind the liver and partly covered by the lateral lobes of that gland. It is composed of two pairs of red, thick, powerful muscles covered internally with a thick, horny epithelium.

The gizzard is normally without movement when it is in an empty condition, but it begins rhythmic movements as soon as food passes into it. The number of muscular contractions per unit of time increases in proportion to the hardness of the feed. When food is withheld until the fowls become hungry, the proventriculus and gizzard are found to be vigorously and continuously contracting, the usual rate of contraction being about 2.5 times a minute for the fasting fowl. After the ingestion of food this rate increases to about 3 times a minute.

The chief function of the gizzard is to grind or crush the coarse feed. This crushing process is absolutely necessary for the digestion of grains, and is most efficient only when aided by the presence of grit and gravel taken in through the mouth and always present in a normal bird. The gastric juice is incapable of digesting the cellulose walls of the grains and does not act until the grains are reduced by the gizzard to a more or less homogeneous pulp. The constant action of the gizzard may be heard by holding a little chick that has been supplied with grit, to the ear.

The gizzard functions as a filter, in such a way that fine material enters the duodenum in about one minute after ingestion by a fowl that has been starved, while coarse material is retained much longer to be ground by the contractions of the gizzard.

Pancreas.—Immediately after its attachment to the gizzard the intestine is folded in a long loop called the duodenum, the sides of which are parallel and enclose the pancreas. The pancreas plays a very important part in the work of digestion, and is relatively longer in birds than in mammals. It secretes a fluid known as the pancreatic juice, that contains proteolytic, amylolytic and lipolytic enzymes which vigorously hydrolyze proteoses, peptones, starches and fats. The pancreatic juice empties into the duodenum just anterior to the bile ducts.

Liver.—Two ducts convey the bile from the liver to the terminal part of the duodenum. The one from the right lobe of the liver is enlarged to form the gall-bladder in which the bile is temporarily stored. The one from the left lobe has no such enlargement. They enter the duodenum together, the cystic duct from the right lobe being slightly posterior to the other.

Intestine.—The walls of the small intestine secrete the intestinal juice, which contains erepsin and sugar-splitting enzymes. Erepsin is an enzyme which carries to conclusion the work of digesting the proteins. The sugar-splitting enzymes have the power of converting disaccharides into simple sugars which can be assimilated by the body.

Besides its digestive function, the small intestine also acts as an organ of absorption, taking in the soluble nutrients and inorganic salts.

Ceca.—At the juncture of the intestine and the rectum are two blind pouches, given off from either side, called ceca. These are usually 4 to 6 inches in length, and more or less completely filled with fecal matter. Their function is not fully understood, though it appears that they aid in the digestion of fiber.

Rectum and Cloaca.—The rectum terminates the digestive canal, being a short and somewhat enlarged continuation of the intestine. It opens into the cloaca, a chamber common to the digestive and genito-urinary passages, which opens externally at the vent.

The Urinary System.—Brief mention is made of the urinary system in order to point out that in birds the urine is discharged into the cloaca and excreted along with the feces. There is no liquid urine voided. The white, pasty material appearing in the droppings is largely uric acid, whereas the nitrogen in the urine of mammals is mainly in the form of urea.

THE ENDOCRINE GLANDS

Both the appearance and functioning of the fowl are profoundly affected by the secretions of the endocrine glands. These comparatively small but extremely important bodies, sometimes referred to collectively as the regulatory system, merit special consideration. They are described as endocrine, or glands of internal secretion,

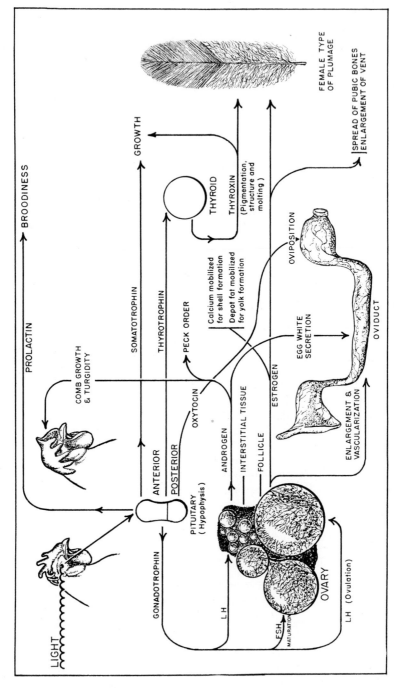

Fig. 16. — Diagram showing the principal effects of endocrine secretions, and their inter-relationships, in the female fowl. For adrenal effects, see Figure 17.

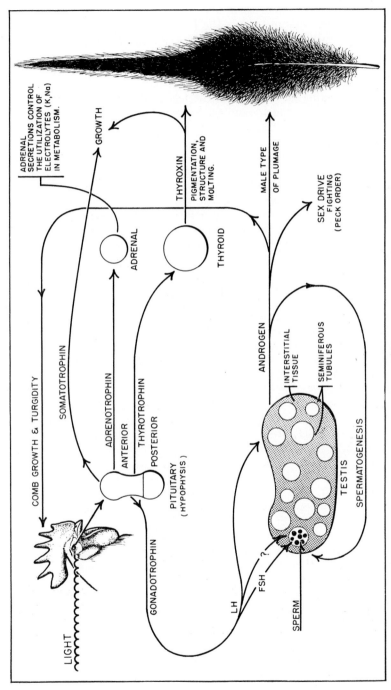

FIG. 17.—Diagram showing the principal effects of endocrine secretions, and their inter-relationships, in the male fowl.

because the products of their cells are not carried away through a duct, but are disseminated in the blood stream to all parts of the body. The different secretions of specific glands have their own names but the term *hormone* (meaning rousing, or setting in motion) is commonly used for any endocrine secretion and is applicable to all of them.

The endocrine glands include the testes, the ovary, the thyroid, the parathyroids, the hypophysis or pituitary gland, the thymus glands, the adrenal or suprarenal glands, the pineal gland, and the islets of Langerhans.

Some of these glands are thus far known to produce only a single hormone, but one of them produces as many as five or six different kinds and it is probable that, as their study progresses, additional hormones will be discovered. Abnormal functioning of a gland may result in production of a hormone either in excessive amounts, or, more usually, in subnormal quantities. Both of these conditions give some idea of the effects of the hormone in question and for that reason they are frequently induced in experiments seeking to determine more about the functions of the endocrine glands. The usual procedure in such work is either to remove all or part of the particular gland being studied, or to add in some way an excessive amount of its active principle.

Hormone Control of Egg Production.—There are very few endocrine effects which result from the simple and direct action of a single hormone. Instead, the physiological and psychological activity of the chicken, particularly the female, is dependent upon a very complex interrelation of glandular effects.

A good example is the complex hormonal control of ovulation and egg formation. A follicle-stimulating hormone (commonly abbreviated FSH) from the anterior lobe of the pituitary gland causes the growth of the ovarian follicles with their contained ova. When a follicle has reached ovulatory size, another hormone from the pituitary gland (luteinizing hormone or LH) is released and causes ovulation. The exact manner in which LH produces its effect upon the ovary is not known, but it has been well established that in the absence of LH, ovulation will not occur.

The oviduct also is under hormone control and it is stimulated, at exactly the right time, to pick up or engulf the released ovum. Hormone secretions from the ovarian follicle are responsible for the enlargement of the oviduct to functioning size, for the spread of the pubic bones and enlargement of the vent, and for the mobilization of depot fat for yolk formation and of calcium for shell formation. Egg white secretion is apparently under the control of a hormone secreted by the ovarian interstitial tissue.

Formation of the egg shell is at least partially under the control of hormones secreted by the parathyroid glands and here also, timing—both as to the beginning and end of shell formation—is remarkably exact. And finally, a hormone from the posterior pituitary comes into play to cause the fully formed egg to be laid. The inter-relationships are shown diagrammatically in Figure 16.

Normal functioning of the whole process of egg production is completely dependent upon extremely fine adjustment and synchronization of all the foregoing events. If any gland begins to function "on its own," without awaiting the proper signal, such freaks as yolkless eggs, soft-shell eggs, and eggs within eggs are likely to result.

Fig. 18.—Sex dimorphism in structure of feathers. From left to right the paired male and female feathers are from the wing bow, neck and saddle regions. The male feathers (on the right in each pair) appear more pointed and lacier because of the large areas free from barbules toward the tip of the feathers. (*Photo by Dr. W. F. Lamoreaux, Cornell University.*)

A striking example of the extent to which physiological activity is subject to endocrine control has been provided by workers at Illinois. Leghorn hens placed in individual cages without food but with water always available were injected daily with 2 milligrams of crude chicken pituitary extract. They continued to lay for a period of eight to ten days, literally because they couldn't help it, drawing on body tissues for both maintenance and the formation of eggs, and losing about a pound each in body weight during that time.

Not all of the known endocrine effects in the fowl are shown in Figures 16 and 17. The thyroid gland, for example, in addition to influencing body growth and feather formation, is partially responsible for more or less regular seasonal changes in egg production, body weight, and egg weight. The stimulus for this latter effect comes, presumably, from the varying amount of light to which hens are subjected with the changing seasons, although the picture is complicated by the unfavorable effect of high air temperature on egg size.

One should also remember that not all of the postulated endocrine effects have been, or can be, so completely demonstrated as to leave no question in the mind of a skeptical reader. To prove conclusively that the hormone oxytocin, shown in Figure 16 as being responsible for oviposition, is in fact the only endocrine secretion which gives a hen the urge to seek a nest and lay an egg which has been fully formed, would require surgical techniques beyond those available at present.

a   b   c

Fig. 19.—Effects of thyroxin on color and structure of saddle feathers in Brown Leghorn males. a, Is normal; b, was injected with 1.0 mg. of thyroxin every seventh day; c, was injected with 1.5 mg. of thyroxin every sixth day. Extension of the black is accompanied by formation of barbules in the affected areas. (After Lillie and Juhn in Physiol. Zoöl., Vol. 5.)

If one could remove the posterior lobe of the pituitary gland and if such a hen then formed normal eggs but laid them only after appropriate injections of oxytocin, the demonstration could be considered complete. Actually we know only that a large dose of oxytocin given intravenously will cause expulsion of a hard-shelled egg within 3 minutes. It seems reasonable to postulate that in the normal hen there is an accumulation of oxytocin sufficient to provide the necessary stimulus to laying.

Furthermore, the time of laying of a particular egg will be delayed one or more days if the follicle from which its yolk came is surgically removed shortly after ovulation. Removal of other parts of the ovary has no such effect. The ruptured follicle may therefore be responsible either for release from the pituitary of the necessary amount of oxytocin to cause normal egg laying to occur, or for the temporary removal of whatever mechanism is usually in effect to prevent premature laying.

Time of oviposition may also be affected by external influences. The mere handling of hens shortly before normal laying would have occurred may delay oviposition long enough for a second egg to be forming in the oviduct before the preceding one is laid.

Stimulation and growth of the ovary result in increased production of the ovarian hormones which, strangely enough, include both a male and a female sex hormone. The male sex hormone is responsible for the red, waxy comb and wattles of the normal laying hen, while the female sex hormone controls the typically feminine secondary sex characters such as normal female plumage, absence of spurs, and female sexual behavior.

If, as sometimes happens, a hen develops an ovarian tumor of sufficient size to destroy that part of her ovary which secretes the female hormone, she will gradually assume male characteristics. Her comb and wattles become large and coarse, her new plumage after a molt will be almost exactly like that of a male, and she may even crow.

Both egg laying and ovulation are also subject to the external influence of light and darkness. As will be pointed out in discussing the formation of the egg, ovulation normally occurs about thirty minutes after laying. But if laying happens to take place as late as 4:00 P.M., release of the next ovum does not occur until some ten or twelve hours later, unless the hen's normal lighting schedule has been reversed or she is being kept under continuous twenty-four-hour light of constant intensity. Hence no egg will be laid the following day.

If lights are used all night, one might expect the hens to lay both night and day, but this does not happen because there is normally a marked difference in light intensity between the daylight hours and the night hours. If, on the other hand, hens are kept in individual cages in a room from which all natural daylight is excluded, and are subjected to constant twenty-four-hour illumination, they will lay "round the clock"—depositing about half their eggs at night. There is no onset of darkness to delay ovulation and terminate a clutch.

If instead of twenty-four-hour illumination, hens in an artificially lighted room have light from 6 A.M. to 6 P.M. and no light the other twelve hours, they will lay all their eggs in the daytime. But if their lighting schedule is suddenly reversed, so that they get light from 6 P.M. to 6 A.M., and no light during the solar day, they will, in about three days time, shift over so that all of their eggs are laid at night.

Time of laying may be influenced also by the feeding schedule. If hens are kept under continuous light, with natural daylight excluded, and are fed only from 8 A.M. to 4 P.M., most of their eggs will be laid during those hours. On the other hand, if feeding is from 8 P.M. to 4 A.M. the hens will adjust to this sort of schedule by laying most of their eggs during the new feeding period.

The Use of Artificial Light.—The response of healthy fowls to the influence of light is both prompt and of considerable magnitude, and many poultrymen make use of artificial light to obtain partial control of flock egg production. The nature of the response and the extent to which egg production can be controlled are perhaps most easily explained and understood by considering the effect of light on pullets.

In northern latitudes spring-hatched pullets are subjected to continually increasing natural day length during the first weeks of growth when this sort of change can have its maximum effect on feed intake and consequently on rate of growth. Later in the summer the gradually decreasing length of day operates to prevent precocious sexual maturity and such undesirable results as the onset of laying before body size is sufficient to permit pullets to lay eggs of suitable market size.

December-hatched pullets, on the other hand, if exposed to natural daylight only, will approach laying age at a time when the natural day length is increasing. They will respond to this stimulus by maturing early and beginning to lay in the spring before they have attained normal adult body weight. A high percentage of their eggs will be small and therefore worth less than average market price.

The foregoing comparison suggests immediately that the primary effect of light is on sexual maturity. Unless one keeps this point in mind he can easily be led into faulty conclusions about the use of artificial light and its application to practical egg production control. A related point of extreme importance is that the effect is brought about by changing day length rather than by any specific amount of light. Increasing day length results in earlier maturity. Decreasing day length results in later maturity.

A practical problem is how to control age and weight at sexual maturity in December-hatched pullets, for example, so that their egg-laying performance will be commercially profitable. The key to the solution is found in subjecting them to decreasing day length from the time they are hatched until they are ready to lay—just the opposite of what would happen to them under natural daylight. This could be accomplished by starting the chicks out on a 16-hour day, and gradually reducing the day length to about 6 hours by the time the pullets are $5\frac{1}{2}$ or 6 months old, at which time they could be returned to normal daylight conditions. There is no reason why this procedure would not be effective, but it would involve the expense of constructing suitable quarters from which all natural daylight could be excluded during the latter part of the growing period.

A much simpler and equally effective procedure is to start the December-hatched chicks out on a 24-hour day and gradually reduce the amount of artificial light, perhaps by weekly decrements of 25 minutes, so that by the time the pullets are 24 weeks old they will be getting a 14-hour day—not much longer than the natural day at that season. No special construction problems are involved as there will be no need to exclude natural daylight at any time.

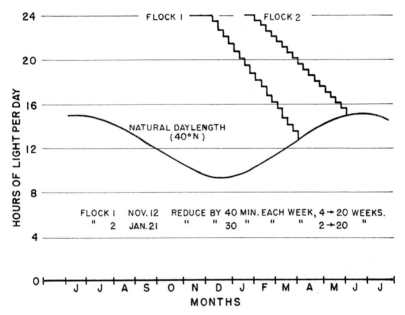

Fig. 20.—Examples of light patterns which can be used to delay sexual maturity when pullets are grown at 40° north latitude. (*Courtesy of T. R. Morris.*)

Careful studies of this sort conducted by English workers have shown that the delay in sexual maturity amounts to about $1\frac{2}{3}$ days (40 hours) for each one-hour change in day length, and that the maximum delay which can be obtained by this method is about three weeks. This is sufficient to accomplish the desired objectives with regard to body weight and egg size. Note, however, that the total change in day length is calculated for the entire period from hatching time to the date of first egg.

The amount of delay which could be accomplished with June-hatched pullets would be small and of little economic importance because a control flock of June-hatched pullets under natural daylight would also be subjected to decreasing day length from hatching time to maturity. For pullets hatched in other months the effect would be intermediate, but presumably somewhat greater and also more important for pullets hatched between October and January than for those hatched in September or February.

In summary, a schedule of decreasing day length provided by artificial light can be used to delay sexual maturity—specifically to prevent precocious maturity—so that average egg size is much improved in fall and winter-hatched pullets. Total feed intake to 500 days of age is only slightly increased over that of the controls, and there is a compensatory increase in rate of lay during the later months of production which equals and may exceed the early loss in eggs resulting from delay in maturity.

Artificial light can also be used to bring non-laying pullets or hens into production at some desired time, or to postpone the normal drop in rate of laying during the fall months. The necessary stimulus is provided by exposing the fowls to additional light beyond that available during natural daylight hours. The initial response from increased lighting will be obtained in from seven to ten days.

A common procedure is to use enough artificial light—in the early morning, in the evening, or in combination—to provide a 13- or 14-hour day. Considerable latitude in total day length is permissible, provided only that it is kept constant or is slowly increasing. One must always remember that a decrease in day length is detrimental. With large flocks a continued decrease in day length or a complete interruption of the lighting schedule can be economically disastrous in terms of egg production. A precise optimum constant day length has never been established and indeed may be non-existent.

It was once thought that the favorable effect of artificial light was gained simply by providing a longer feeding day for the hens, but this has long since been shown not to be true. The stimulus of light by way of the optic nerve activates the pituitary gland so that secretion of FSH is increased, and ovarian activity follows in due course.

The light stimulus can be provided in various ways, and the time span within the twenty-four hour day is not necessarily critical. All-night light of low intensity, sufficient to permit the hens to find feed and water at any time, is fully as effective as morning or evening light of greater intensity. Flashes of bright light ten seconds long operated once each hour will provide the necessary stimulus, but there is no practical advantage to be gained from using such a procedure.

When morning or evening light is used to extend the normal day, the minimum intensity of light should be sufficient to provide one foot-candle of illumination at the feeding level. Brighter lights may be used, but no greater stimulus will result . Color, too, seems to be unimportant and ordinary incandescent lamps with reflectors are therefore suitable under most practical conditions. A common recommendation is to provide one 40-watt lamp, with reflector, for each 200 square feet of floor space.

Effect of Light on Growth.—Rate of growth is also subject to the indirect effect of light. Spring-hatched chickens in high northern latitudes tend to grow more rapidly than do those brooded farther south, provided both lots are exposed to all available natural daylight, simply because the more northerly latitudes provide a longer summer day. Numerous tests involving various schedules of intermittent lighting, as well as continuous 24-hour light, indicate that the important consideration is feeding time. Exposure to light under conditions of restricted feed intake has no measurable effect on rate of growth.

The maximum effect of increased feeding time, as provided by artificial light, and assuming that there is no other limitation on feed intake, will be obtained (*a*) under continuous 24-hour light, and (*b*) during the early weeks of growth. Twenty-four hour light provides the maximum opportunity for feed consumption, and it can be used to advantage by commercial broiler growers.

As body weight increases, more and more feed will be required for maintenance, with proportionately less being available for the formation of new body tissue. There is little to be gained, therefore, by continuous lighting after twelve weeks of age. On the contrary, there may be a real disadvantage in that pullets so reared often develop an abnormal eye condition amounting to partial or even complete blindness. The best commercial practice may therefore be to use a 16-hour day until the pullets are twelve weeks old, and natural daylight thereafter. The increase in weight over unlighted controls at 10 or 12 weeks of age is of the order of 10 per cent.

Other Endocrine Effects.—Several other endocrine effects in the fowl have been well established. The feeding of large doses of either fresh or desiccated thyroid, for example, is followed by rapid molting. It has been shown that the thyroid gland increases in size during that portion of the year when molting normally occurs. Thyroxin, the active principle secreted by the thyroid, also affects the color and form of feathers.

Prolactin, secreted by the anterior lobe of the hypophysis, and so named because it induces milk secretion in mammals, is the controlling factor in broodiness in the fowl. Not only do laying hens, when dosed with prolactin, stop laying and quickly become broody, but male birds given sufficiently high doses likewise become broody, and will brood chicks just like a normal broody hen. The effect disappears quickly when injections of prolactin are stopped, and within a very few days such males are likely to kill the chicks which they previously cared for and defended.

Secretions of the adrenal glands are concerned in metabolism of carbohydrates and of sodium and potassium, and in the regulation of blood-pressure. Hormones secreted by the islets of Langerhans, which are scattered through the pancreas, presumably control the level of blood sugar in the fowl as in mammals.

Another example of a complex chain of events set in motion by the initial action of a single hormone, is the chemical or hormone pseudo-caponization of cockerels. This involves the use of synthetic estrogens which are closely related to the female sex hormone.

A 15-milligram pellet of stilbestrol, implanted subcutaneously, will cause a remarkable change in the appearance of a Leghorn cockerel within ten to fifteen days. The comb loses its bright red color, and shrinks in size, until the cockerel resembles a capon in general appearance. There is an immediate increase in feed consumption, accompanied by a greatly increased deposition of fat. The same changes occur, of course, in any breed of chickens. The Leghorn is mentioned simply because the comb changes are more striking than in breeds with smaller combs.

The greater deposition of fat cannot be completely explained at present, but it seems to be due to the demonstrated ability of estrogens to cause an increase in the amount of fat circulating in the blood stream, an effect which is known to occur in the laying hen as a result of normal secretion of the female sex hormone.

The pseudo-caponizing effect of estrogens, on the other hand, is fairly well understood. The estrogen—in this case stilbestrol— has an inhibiting effect on the pituitary gland, thus shutting off the normal secretion of the gonadotrophic hormones. Lack of these will cause the testes to decrease in size, and will deprive them of the stimulus to secrete the male sex hormone, testosterone. Lack of testosterone will, in turn, result in regression of the secondary sex characters (comb, wattles, ear lobes, mating instinct, and crowing) because of the absence of endocrine encouragement. In time, the "maleness" is so completely submerged by the effect of estrogen, that the pubic bones are spread as in a laying hen, the skin over the abdomen becomes soft and velvety, and the coarse feather follicles characteristic of the adult male are no longer evident.

A secondary effect, not yet fully explained, is interference with calcium metabolism to such an extent that the long bones become brittle and very easily broken. Results similar to those following implantation have been obtained by feeding appropriate amounts of synthetic products such as the dimethyl ether of diethylstilbestrol.

Soon after estrogen treatment is stopped, the pituitary gland recovers its ability to function normally, gonadotrophic hormones are again secreted, the testes increase in size and begin to secrete testosterone, and the secondary sex characters reappear in a short time.

Many other endocrine effects are being studied experimentally. and new information is constantly being brought to light. More and more of the hormones are being prepared synthetically, as their chemical nature is determined. The sex hormones are related to the fats, whereas all the others are protein in nature. Certain protein compounds have been found to have effects which are very similar to those brought about by the natural hormones. Thyroprotein, for example, has a thyroxin effect, whereas thiouracil has an opposite effect. Experiments already carried out suggest that it may eventually be possible to control growth, fattening, and reproduction in the fowl to a much greater extent than at present, largely through the administration of synthetic hormones.

Some knowledge and understanding of the principal hormones is important in the practice of selection for physiological characters. Success in selection which is aimed at improving winter egg production when artificial lights are not used depends in part on being able to identify, by their performance, individuals which have a naturally high rate of secretion in respect to the gonadotrophic hormone which stimulates ovarian activity. Non-broody hens, and presumably males, which do not transmit broodiness to their daughters are those which have an inherently low secretion rate for prolactin—the hormone which causes broody behavior. Selection for the ability to fatten easily and quickly may well depend on the extent to which one is able to identify, albeit by indirect means, those individuals which have a higher than average level of estrogen secretion.

REPRODUCTION AND THE FORMATION OF THE EGG

The Reproductive System of the Male.—The male fowl possesses two testes which are situated high up in the abdominal cavity, along the back, near the anterior ends of the kidneys. These never descend into an external scrotum, as is the case with other farm animals. In form they are more or less ellipsoid, and in color light yellow, frequently having a reddish cast caused by the numerous much-branched blood-vessels on the surface.

In gross structure the testis consists of a large number of very slender, much-convoluted ducts, from the linings of which the sperm are given off. These ducts, called seminiferous tubules, appear in groups separated by delicate membranes which extend inward from a membrane surrounding the organ. They all lead eventually to the vas deferens, a tube which conducts the sperm outside the body.

Each vas deferens opens into a small papilla, which together serve as an intromittent organ. These are located on the dorsal wall of the cloaca. The so-called rudimentary copulatory organ of the fowl has no connection with the vasa deferentia, and is located on the median ventral portion of one of the transverse folds of the cloaca. It is this rudimentary organ, or male process, which is used in the classification of baby chicks according to sex on the basis of cloacal examination.

The Reproductive System of the Female.—In early embryonic

4

life there are two gonads in the female, as in the male. Normally, only the left one develops, the right persisting, if at all, only as a functionless rudiment. A few cases have been reported, however, in which both a right and left ovary and oviduct were present and functioning in a mature pullet. More recently it has been shown that an occasional strain may show a rather high incidence of persistent right oviducts.

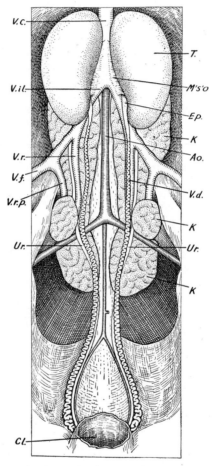

Fig. 21.—The reproductive and urinary organs of the male fowl: *T.*, testis; *V.d.*, vas deferens; *K.*, kidney; *Ur.*, ureter; *Cl.*, cloaca. (*Courtesy of L. V. Domm.*)

The functioning ovary is a cluster of many follicles, each of which is independently attached by a very slender stalk. Each sphere is a more or less developed ovum or yolk enclosed in a thin membrane or follicle. The spheres vary in color from pale straw color to deep reddish-yellow or orange, and in size from that of a mature yolk about 40 mm. in diameter down to those so small as not to be visible to the unaided eye.

The Oviduct.—Associated with the ovary, and corresponding to the vas deferens of the male in certain functions, though having quite a different origin and developmental history, is the oviduct. In a laying hen the oviduct appears as a large, much-coiled tube

Fig. 22.—Ovary from a hen in laying condition, showing ova of various sizes and a ruptured follicle from which an ovum was recently released. (*Courtesy of Cornell University.*)

occupying a large part of the left side of the abdominal cavity. It is covered with a net-work of blood-vessels, and is in more or less continuous movement during the time that an egg is being formed.

The oviduct is divided into five rather clearly defined regions. Beginning at the end nearest the ovary, these are: (1) the funnel or infundibulum; (2) the magnum, where the thick white is secreted;

(3) the isthmus, which secretes the shell membranes; (4) the uterus or shell gland; and (5) the vagina, which leads into the cloaca.

The Formation of the Egg.—The egg of commerce consists of the true egg, or reproductive cell, *i. e.*, the yolk with its germinal disc, and the surrounding envelopes of white, shell membranes and shell. The yolk is formed in the ovary, but the balance of the process occurs in the oviduct.

Formation of the Yolk.—During the early stages of yolk formation, the oöcytes grow very slowly by the gradual accumulation of light yolk. When a diameter of about 6 mm. is reached, certain ova, but only a few at any one time, suddenly begin to grow at an enormously increased rate. They add about 4 mm. to their diameter

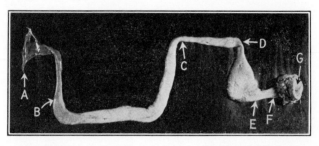

FIG. 23.—The oviduct of the hen.   *A–B*, infundibulum; *B–C*, magnum; *C–D* isthmus; *D–E*, uterus; *E–F*, vagina; *G*, cloaca.   (*After Scott.*)

every twenty-four hours, until full size of about 40 mm. in diameter is reached. An ovum within seven to nine days of laying contains less than 1 per cent of its final complement of yolk, yet those few days suffice to supply the missing 99 parts.

It is during this period of rapid growth that the concentric layers of light and dark yolk are formed. The thickness of each pair of light and dark layers, representing the growth in a twenty-four-hour period, is from 1.5 to 2 mm. The visible white and yellow bands result from periodic deposition of differing amounts of carotinoid pigment. Although yolk deposition continues at a nearly constant rate throughout the twenty-four-hour day, that formed at certain periods is light in color because no dietary pigment is available.

As the yolk enlarges, the germinal disc remains on the surface, and thus leaves behind a trail of white yolk which forms the neck of the flask-shaped mass of white yolk which is a part of every normal egg.

Ovulation.—When the yolk comes to full size it is released from the ovary by the rupture of the follicle along the stigma. In most instances the ovum probably is discharged into the body cavity and is later engulfed by the funnel of the oviduct through repeated

PLATE I

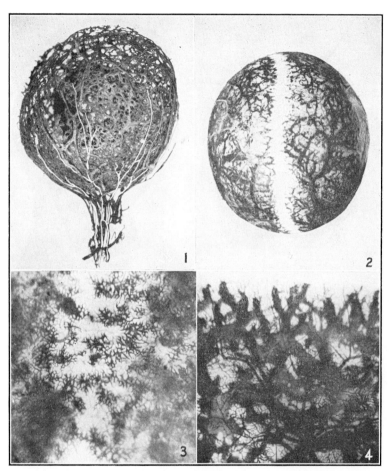

VASCULAR SYSTEM OF THE OVARIAN FOLLICLE.
(After Nalbandov and James.)

1. Vinylite resin cast of the vascular system of a mature follicle and its stalk. Arteries white and veins dark.

2. Injected pre-ovulatory follicle. Note that no large blood vessels extend across the stigma.

3. View from inside a follicle showing that vascularization of the stigma consists primarily of a fine capillary network.

4. India ink injection of the vascular system of a pre-ovulatory follicle viewed from the inside. The stigma is at the upper edge of the picture.

advances and recessions of the edge of the infundibulum over the surface of the ovum. Once completely enclosed, it appears to be forced along by wave-like contractions of the muscles of the oviduct.

Fertilization of the Egg.—Fertilization follows almost immediately after ovulation, the spermatozoa having made their way through the entire length of the oviduct after mating has occurred.

Since the sperm must penetrate the vitelline membrane, which surrounds the yolk, in order to reach the germinal disc, it is of interest to point out that the true vitelline membrane on the freshly ovulated yolk has been found to be only 4 microns thick. After a short time in the oviduct, the membrane becomes swollen and thickened, as a result of contact with the secretions of the oviduct. It is also augmented by mucin secretions which thicken and strengthen it as a protection against rupture of the yolk. The complete vitelline membrane from the yolk of a laid egg is about 48 microns thick.

Secretion of the Dense White.—During its passage through the magnum, or albumen-secreting region, the yolk acquires the mass of firm white which makes up about one-half of the total white, by volume. The remainder of the white is not added until after the shell membranes have been formed and the egg has entered the uterus. It has been shown by analyses of egg white at different stages of egg formation that this latter addition is largely water and that no nitrogen is added to the egg in the uterus.

Formation of the Shell Membranes.—The shell membranes are formed in the isthmus. It is an interesting fact that these membranes should be so formed as to enclose the yolk and thick white rather loosely. They do not plump out until the egg receives its final quota of fluid in the uterus.

Formation of the Chalazæ.—The two whitish cords, known as chalazæ, which extend out from the yolk toward the ends of the egg, though obviously formed from material secreted in the upper part of the oviduct, do not become visible until after the egg has entered the uterus. Their formation appears to be partly the result of a change in the colloidal structure of the layer of white adjacent to the yolk, and partly the result of rotation of the white around the yolk while the egg is in the uterus. Chalaza formation has been artificially induced in eggs removed from the anterior portion of the uterus.

Formation of the Shell.—The shell of the hen's egg consists mostly of calcium carbonate, the reported percentages varying from 93 to 98. This material is deposited in the uterus, and there is considerable shell material deposited on the membranes before the egg has acquired its full quota of white.

The rate of shell deposition is relatively slow during the first three hours. It then increases rapidly until about the fifth hour, after which a constant rate is maintained until the twentieth hour (approximately the time of laying).

While the egg is in the hard-shell stage in the uterus it is possible to locate it by external palpation. This method can be used in keeping egg records except during the breeding season when pedigreeing is being done. At the Utah Station it was found that the whole flock could be handled early each morning and the individual hens which would lay during the day determined with accuracy.

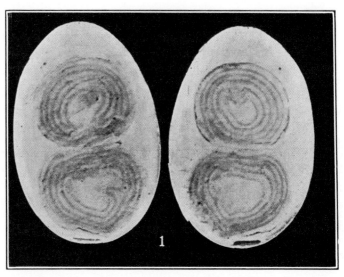

Fig. 24.—A double-yolked egg, showing how the yolk is formed in concentric layers. The hen was fed a small amount of a fat-soluble dye (Sudan III) on each of five successive days. (*After Gage and Fish.*)

A 5-pound hen laying 300 eggs in a year must deposit in the egg shells about 3.75 pounds of calcium carbonate (1.5 pounds of calcium). Since this is about thirty times the amount of calcium in her entire body, it is obvious that such a hen must be supplied with an abundance of calcium in her feed.

There is considerable evidence to support the view that much of the calcium used in shell formation is first deposited in the long bones and that often no more than 10 to 40 per cent of the calcium in a particular egg comes directly from the feed. For short periods of time all of the calcium may come from the bones, as is normal in wild birds which lay only a few eggs. If, however, laying hens are suddenly deprived of all food calcium their eggs promptly show thin shells, and egg laying stops in ten to fourteen days. It seems entirely possible that some of the complications which often accompany high egg production develop because some hens are unable to replace calcium in their bones as rapidly as it is withdrawn for shell formation.

Laying of the Egg.—Eggs are normally formed small end caudad, that is, with the small end first as they move down the oviduct. This is true of wild birds as well as of the fowl. But curiously enough, if the hen is not disturbed in the act of laying, most eggs are laid large end first. This has puzzled poultry workers for many years. Not until an English investigator made use of radiographic techniques and published his findings in 1951 was the series of events made clear.

TABLE 15.—THE APPROXIMATE LENGTH OF THE VARIOUS PARTS OF THE OVIDUCT AND THE TIME INTERVALS INVOLVED IN EGG FORMATION

Section of oviduct	Approximate length in centimeters*	Approximate time for the yolk to traverse each section†
Infundibulum (and chalaziferous region) .	11.0	$\frac{1}{4}$ hr.
Magnum	33.6	3 "
Isthmus	10.6	$1\frac{1}{4}$ "
Uterus	10.1⎫	20$\frac{3}{4}$ "
Vagina	6.9⎭	
Interval between laying and next ovulation	....	$\frac{1}{2}$ "

* Illinois data on 70 White Leghorns.
† Adapted from Warren and Scott (1935).

TABLE 16.—AVERAGE TIME SPENT IN DIFFERENT PARTS OF THE OVIDUCT BY EGGS REQUIRING VARIOUS PERIODS FOR THEIR FORMATION. (AFTER WARREN AND SCOTT, 1935.)

Item	Hens with interval lengths of (hours)					
	25	26	27	28	29	30
Time from laying of one egg to entrance of isthmus by next egg .	4.3	4.6	4.2	4.7	5.2	5.3
Time spent in uterus	18.0	18.4	19.9	19.8	20.8	21.6
Time from first indication of shell to laying of the egg . . .	13.8	14.7	15.6	16.4	17.0	17.9
Number of eggs observed . . .	9	25	20	42	44	21

As can be seen in Plate II, the fully-formed egg is turned horizontally (not end-over-end) through 180 degrees just prior to laying. In order for this to happen the egg must drop from its normal position high up between the ischia to a point opposite the tips of the pubic bones. This is necessary because the normal egg is too long to turn in a horizontal plane within the pelvic arch. The position of an egg after it has turned and is ready to be laid is shown in Figure 6 of Plate II. Rotation of the egg is accomplished in a matter of one to two minutes. Should the hen be disturbed as she raises herself slightly from the nest when the egg is about to turn, she is very likely to expel it immediately and in that event it will be laid small end first. There is also some variation among hens and no doubt among breeds in the consistency with which they lay eggs large end first. It is not known whether hereditary factors are involved.

No valid reason has been advanced for the fact that eggs are formed small end caudad. As for the reversal prior to laying, it seems reasonable to assume that muscular pressure required for expelling the egg is more effectively applied to the small end.

Time Intervals in Egg Formation.—Careful observations made on anesthetized birds at the Kansas Agricultural Experiment Station, together with autopsy records of hens in laying condition, have made it possible to estimate with considerable accuracy the time required to form the various parts of the egg. These time intervals are summarized in Table 15, along with average lengths of the various parts of the oviduct as determined on 70 White Leghorn hens at the Illinois Station.

The time between laying and the next ovulation, as observed at the Kansas Station, ranged from fourteen to seventy-five minutes, and there is also some variation in the rate of passage through the different sections of the oviduct. Hens which have small clutches, with long intervals between eggs, and low intensity, also have long delays in ovulation. Poor production of low-intensity hens is caused not only by the longer period of egg formation but also by a longer delay in ovulation between clutches.

Records on 119 Rhode Island Red pullets for one year at the Massachusetts Station showed an average interval of 26.5 hours

---

LEGEND FOR PLATE II

RADIOGRAPHIC VIEWS OF EGG SHELL FORMATION IN THE HEN.

(*After Bradfield and Fozzard in the Journal of Experimental Biology, Vol. 28.*)

1. Radiograph of a hen taken $6\frac{1}{2}$ hours after an egg had been laid. The new yolk has been surrounded by both the white and the shell membranes and has passed into the shell gland (uterus). The first faint outlines of the calcareous shell can barely be detected.

2. The same egg three hours later.

3. The same egg 12 hours after the previous egg had been laid.

4. The same egg still later, $23\frac{1}{2}$ hours after the previous egg had been laid. The gradual increase in shell thickness, as shown by X-ray absorption, is clearly evident.

5. A different egg which was observed at frequent intervals during the last few hours before it was due to be laid, so that the rotation could be followed. This radiograph was taken half way through the rotation, and the egg is therefore seen end-on. The picture was slightly blurred by the breathing movements of the hen. Note the lowered position of the egg in the body cavity. The time required for rotation is between one and two minutes.

6. The same egg shown in views 1, 2, 3 and 4, but $25\frac{1}{2}$ hours after the previous egg had been laid, and $\frac{1}{2}$ hour before it was itself laid. In the preceding views (1 to 4), the pointed end is caudad, but here the egg has rotated through 180° so as to bring the blunt end caudad.

7. Calcium carbonate suspensions used for comparison.

PLATE II

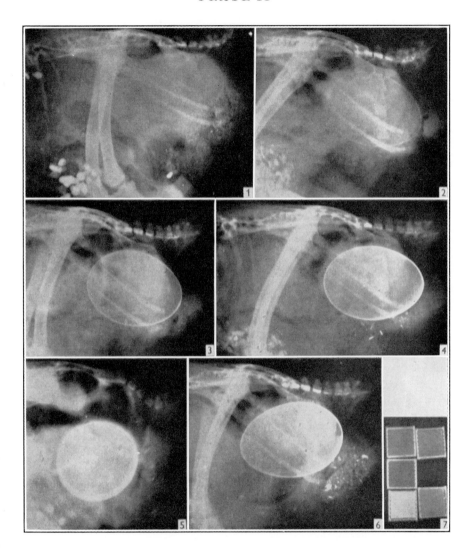

between successive eggs in the same clutch. The shortest interval observed for any one hen was 23 hours in April, and the longest was 31.7 hours in February. The average interval for all birds was shortest in April (25.7 hours) and longest in February (27.7 hours).

Shape, Size, and Color of Eggs.—The normal or characteristic shape of the egg is determined in the magnum, but the specific shape may be modified by abnormal or unusual conditions in either the isthmus or the uterus.

Eggs laid by a hen after the anterior half of her isthmus had been removed were, for the most part, more irregular in shape than eggs laid before the operation. In another hen the isthmus was torn longitudinally and then closed with catgut sutures. After the operation this hen laid eggs with characteristically wrinkled shells, suggesting that the specific shape of the shell membranes, as determined in the isthmus, has a direct influence on shell shape.

Operations on the uterus showed clearly that shape of the egg may also be affected by that portion of the oviduct. Eggs laid by a hen after cotton was placed at the sides of the uterus had a depression reaching more or less around the egg.

That there is great variability in the size of hens' eggs is well known, but the specific causes of this variation are not so well established. It is obvious that the weight of the egg is equal to the sum of the weights of its parts, and that anything affecting the weight of any of the parts may be expected to have some influence on the weight of the entire egg. The small size of the eggs laid by pullets at the beginning of the laying period is due in part to the smaller size of yolk in such eggs, as well as to the lesser amount of albumen. The shell is, of course, formed to fit the egg contents.

The position of an egg in the clutch affects its weight. The second egg of a two-egg clutch is nearly always smaller than the first egg, and in clutches of several eggs, the first egg is usually the heaviest with a progressive decrease in the weight of the egg laid on each successive day. This decrease is almost entirely the result of a decrease in the amount of white, since yolk size appears to be very nearly constant, for any given hen, for all clutch positions.

The color of eggs is in large measure a characteristic of individual hens, all eggs laid by a hen tending to be of the same color except for a gradual change from a darker to a lighter shade during a continuous period of daily laying.

The Completed Egg.—The gross parts of an egg are shown diagrammatically in Figure 25. Taking these in the order of their formation they are: (1) the germ spot, or blastoderm; (2) the yolk; (3) the white; (4) the shell membranes; and (5) the shell.

The Germ Spot.—The germ spot is closely associated with the yolk. Because its development can be traced back to a point where the cell of which it is a part is yolkless, that is, when no yolk material has been laid down, and also because of its importance as the living part of the egg, it is described separately. Technically it is referred to as the germinal disc in an infertile egg, or prior to fertilization, and as the blastoderm following fertilization, but before development has proceeded very far. It later gives rise to an embryo which ultimately becomes a chick.

The Yolk.—From the standpoint of the packing-house breaking room, the yolk of an egg is a globular mass of more or less highly colored, palatable and very nutritious semi-liquid, for which there is a considerable commercial demand, and without which pastries

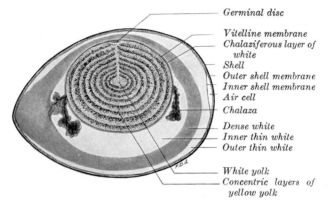

FIG. 25.—Composite diagram showing, in vertical section, the parts of a fresh pullet egg. (*Courtesy of F. B. Adamstone.*)

may not reach their full perfection. In a technical sense the yolk of the kitchen and of commerce, with its germinal disc, or blastoderm, *is the egg*, though it is customary to refer to it as such only when surrounded by its complement of white, shell membrane and shell.

It is enclosed in a transparent membrane known as the vitelline membrane, which is responsible for its maintaining a nearly spherical shape. The material making up the body of the ovum, serves as the chick's first and last food during prehatching life, and its first after it escapes the shell.

The White.—Immediately surrounding the yolk, and adhering closely to the vitelline membrane, is a layer of very dense white called the chalaziferous layer. This is prolonged toward the ends of the egg in two whitish, opalescent, convoluted strands called chalazæ, because of a fancied resemblance to hailstones. These prolongations are twisted in opposite directions. The line describing the long axis of the egg passes through them in an egg that has been rotated recently, so that the position of the yolk is central.

Surrounding the chalaziferous white is a spiral layer of faintly pigmented dense albumen referred to as the thick white, which comprises from 40 to 60 per cent by weight of the total white of the egg. The dense white, as a whole, will not flow readily, but holds together in a flattened mass when poured out upon a plate, if the egg is new-laid. This layer of firm white holds an inner layer of liquid white, as can easily be demonstrated by drawing the point of a knife through the firm white of an opened egg. This suggests

Fig. 26.—Appearance of a new-laid egg of AA quality. Note how both the yolk and the thick white "stand up."

an explanation for some of the "watery white" eggs of commerce, since rough handling may conceivably bring about a rupture of the layer of dense white, thus causing an apparent liquefaction of the egg. The spiral formation of the white may be noted by carefully dissecting an egg boiled to medium hardness.

Surrounding the thick white in turn is more liquid white (also frequently referred to as "thin," "watery" or "fluid"), which is mucilaginous in character. The difference between the dense and liquid white is easily seen when a new-laid egg is broken into a dish.

Although these four layers of white are readily distinguished in a fresh egg, it is of interest to observe how and when they become differentiated. There is normally no evidence of an inner thin layer until after the forming egg has left the isthmus. The same is true of the chalazæ.

Through a combination of enzyme action, some dilution of the thick white by the uterine secretion (which approximates normal saline solution in density), and rotation of the egg in the uterus, there is brought about the differentiation of the egg white into the inner or chalaziferous layer; the chalazæ; the inner thin white, which is completely enclosed in the dense layer; the thick or dense

white, which retains the egg shape when broken out into a saucer:
and the outer thin white.

The continued break-down of the thick white, with corresponding increase in the amount of thin white, is one of the major changes
involved in the deterioration of egg quality.

The Shell Membranes.—Surrounding the white of the egg are
two white papery membranes referred to as the inner and outer
shell membranes.   Both are composed of matted organic fibers
crossing one another in all directions.   The outer membrane is
about three times as thick as the inner one, average measurements
having been reported as 0.05 and 0.015 mm., respectively.

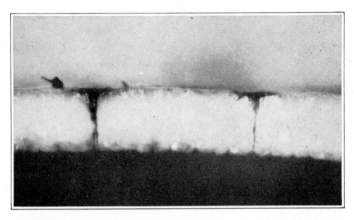

Fig. 27.—The edge of a broken shell, showing two pores partially filled with
the external cuticle or bloom (enlarged 60 times).   (*Courtesy of California
Agricultural Experiment Station.*)

These membranes normally adhere to each other quite closely,
except at the large end of the egg where usually they are separated
to form the "air cell."   The air cell is quite small when the egg is
first laid, but progressively increases in size as the egg cools and as
water later escapes from the contents by evaporation through the
membranes and the shell.

The position of the air cell is quite variable. though usually so
situated at the large end that the line describing the long axis of
the egg will pass through it at some point.   Occasionally, however,
it is found at the small end, or at various positions between the ends.

The Shell and Its Cuticle.—The inner shell layer consists of knob-
like crystals of calcite.   If an egg is removed from the oviduct at
the proper stage of development, the shell will be found to consist
entirely of this crystalline material.

As shell formation proceeds, there is deposited a chalky layer
which comprises about two-thirds of the entire shell.   This layer

consists of very small calcite crystals of irregular shape, arranged so that their long axes are about perpendicular to the shell surface.

Extending through the egg shell are pores or channels which permit gaseous exchange to take place. In fresh eggs the number of open pores is normally small, but under the influence of high temperature, the number of visible pores is greatly increased. As many as 8000 pores have been observed in a single egg.

When an egg is first laid, it appears moist because it is coated with mucus. This quickly dries, leaving a residue called the cuticle, which partially seals the pores of the shell.

TABLE 17.—APPROXIMATE CHEMICAL COMPOSITION OF THE EGG AND ITS PARTS.

	Entire egg	Egg contents	Yolk	White	Shell and membranes
Water	66%	74%	48%	88%	2%
Dry matter	34	26	52	12	98
Protein	12	13	17	11	6
Fat	10	11	33	—	—
Carbohydrates	1	1	1	1	—
Ash	11	1	1	—	92

Composition of the Egg.—The physical composition of a 2-ounce egg, by weight, is about 10 per cent shell, 30 per cent yolk, and 60 per cent white. The white consists of outer thin white 23 per cent (range from 10 to 60), dense white 57 per cent (range from 30 to 80), inner thin white 17 per cent (range from 1 to 40), and chalaziferous white 3 per cent.

Large eggs contain proportionately more white and less yolk than small eggs. The percentage of shell remains very nearly constant, except that the first eggs laid by pullets carry relatively more shell and less yolk than is characteristic of eggs in general. The last egg of a clutch, at least for clutch sizes of 2 to 7, usually has a thicker shell than the egg which preceded it, presumably because it has spent a somewhat longer time in the uterus.

The approximate chemical composition of the egg and its parts is shown in Table 17.

Chapter 3

Principles of Poultry Breeding

PRODUCTIVE poultry breeding has made tremendous progress since the beginning of the present century. Hens with a first-year production of 300 eggs are as common as 200-egg hens were twenty-five years ago. Egg size has been brought under practical genetic control, slow feathering has been eliminated from many flocks, and many other characters have been improved by selection. It is quite evident, however, as was indeed inevitable, that the rate of progress is slowing down, especially with respect to the egg production of superior flocks.

Further improvement will depend on a refinement of selection methods and practices. As we learn more about poultry breeding, it becomes more complex and more difficult. There is no simple, easy, rule-of-thumb method by which a flock average of 300 eggs a year may be attained. Once the basic principles are understood, the most fruitful plan is to apply those principles in a flexible system which permits the breeder to take full advantage both of new information and of families or individuals of exceptional merit whenever they are found. But continued progress will require all the skill of which poultrymen are capable.

HEREDITARY BASIS OF IMPROVEMENT

It is probably correct to say that all characters in the fowl are influenced by both heredity and environment. With some characters the influence of environment is very slight, so slight that there is never any question as to the proper classification of an individual with respect to the character in question. Certain other characters may be so greatly influenced by environment that it is difficult to demonstrate any hereditary influence at all. Those of the first sort — comb type, for example — are said to have a high degree of heritability, because the amount of individual variation which is traceable to environment is extremely small, even non-existent in the case of single comb in the sense that there is never any difficulty about classifying a particular comb as single. Comb size, as influenced by environment, is another matter. Characters at the other extreme are said to have a low degree of heritability because the amount of individual variation traceable to heredity is small, while that traceable to environment is very large.

(66)

For single comb, then, it is sufficient to know that it is one form of a character which is highly heritable, that it is recessive to the type of comb called rose, and that selection for the single type is immediately and completely effective. In other words, if a male and a female possessing single comb are mated together, they will breed true for that character. All of their offspring will have single combs, and they in turn will likewise breed true for that particular character.

Single comb is said to be recessive to rose comb because, if an individual with a single comb is mated to one which is pure for rose comb, the single comb character will not appear in the next generation. All of the offspring will have rose combs, but if any two of these are mated together, the single comb character will reappear in about one-fourth of *their* offspring. This is an example of the familiar 3:1 Mendelian ratio between simple dominant and recessive characters. Of those individuals which show the dominant character, about one-third will be true-breeding rose, while two-thirds (one-half of the entire generation) will be like their parents. The true-breeding individuals, either rose or single, are said to be *homozygous*, while the remaining rose-comb individuals are described as *heterozygous*.

Many simple characters in poultry are inherited in the same manner as rose and single comb, while certain others are much more complex. We shall consider a number of characters for purposes of illustration, proceeding from the simple to the complex and, in a very rough way, from high heritability to low.

Market poultry with yellow skin is prized in some areas, while in others the preference is for white skin. Genetically, white and yellow skin color constitute a pair of characters just as do rose and single comb, white skin being almost completely dominant to yellow. As every poultryman knows, yellow skin is subject to bleaching until it is practically indistinguishable from skin that is genetically white. Feeding fowls on a ration which is entirely devoid of the pigment xanthophyll will cause the yellow color to disappear after a time. Females which lay continuously will lose all of their yellow color, even though their ration may be high in xanthophyll for the entire time. On the other hand, white-skinned fowls will not develop yellow color even when fed rations high in such xanthophyll-containing feeds as yellow corn and green forage. Here, then, is an example of a character which in a technical sense exhibits high heritability, but only if observed at the right time and under specified conditions.

Plumage colors in poultry are, in general, characterized by a high degree of heritability. Environmental influences such as inadequate rations may cause some variation, but seldom enough to interfere with accurate classification of individuals with respect to plumage color. An interesting example, which serves also to illustrate incomplete dominance, is the Blue Andalusian. These fowls never breed true for color. The offspring of blue parents occur in the ratio of 1 black to 2 blue to 1 blue-splashed white. The blacks behave genetically like any other blacks, while the blue-splashed whites are homozygous, and the blues heterozygous, for a gene which dilutes black plumage color. The heterozygous individuals are distinguishable by appearance, and the phenotype ratio is therefore 1:2:1 instead of 3:1. It so happens that the blue heterozygote is the desired type. Breeders may therefore maintain stocks of black and blue-splashed white fowls in order to obtain 100 per cent blue offspring when these two kinds are crossed.

The common 3:1 ratio may be modified in other ways as, for example, by any one of several lethal or semi-lethal genes which interfere with or prevent normal hatching. The short-legged mutation known as creeper is caused by a gene which in homozygous condition completely prevents hatching and in heterozygous condition reduces it slightly. Here again the observed creeper condition in mature fowls is the heterozygous form. When creepers are mated together, the resulting offspring consist of creepers and normals in the ratio of approximately 2:1. Some of the heterozygous creepers die just before hatching, while all of the homozygotes die earlier, and the common 3:1 ratio is therefore changed not to 1:2:1 but to 0:2:1. The creeper condition is regarded by most poultrymen as undesirable. It can be eliminated by the simple procedure of discarding creepers and breeding only from normal fowls. Recessive lethal genes, on the other hand, pose more of a problem because individuals carrying such genes in heterozygous condition cannot be distinguished from normals by appearance. They can be detected only by suitable breeding tests to be explained later.

SEX DETERMINATION AND SEX LINKAGE

To return to plumage color for another example, all fowls so far as is known, carry either the gene for silver or the gene for gold. The gene for silver gives the plumage a silver (white) background on which various black patterns are superimposed, while the gene for gold causes a gold (red, brown or buff) background for such patterns. The presence of either gene may be masked by solid black or by the presence of genes which inhibit color. In the inheritance of characters of the sort previously chosen as examples, it makes no difference in the progeny whether it is through the sire or the dam that the dominant gene of a given pair is introduced. But in the case of genes for silver and gold, and indeed for several other gene pairs in the fowl, it makes considerable difference. This is because the genes for silver and gold are carried on the sex chromosomes, of which the male fowl always has two and the female only one.

Every fertilized egg receives a sex chromosome from the male parent, but whether or not the egg contains a sex chromosome from the female which laid the egg is purely a matter of chance. Approximately half of them do, while the other half do not. If the egg carries a sex chromosome it will, when fertilized, give rise to a male chick. If the egg does not contain a sex chromosome it will, after fertilization contain only one, and will therefore produce a female chick. By this simple device the sexes are maintained in approximately equal numbers.

FIG. 28.—The Blue Andalusian is a heterozygous form which never breeds true for color. (*Courtesy of Poultry Tribune.*)

Because females produce eggs both with and without a sex chromosome and thereby determine, albeit entirely by chance, which are to become males and which are to develop into females, the females are said to be *heterogametic*. Other chromosomes, often called *autosomes*, invariably occur in pairs so that an individual not only has the same number of chromosomes in all its body cells as every other individual of the same species, but has a pair of genes for every character in question, one from its sire and one from its dam. If the genes are alike, the individual is *homozygous* for that gene and will breed true in respect to it. If the genes are unlike, the individual may transmit either to any individual offspring and is therefore *heterozygous* with respect to the character. It is only in the case of the sex chromosomes, and then only in the female, that an individual may receive but a single gene for a particular character. Genes of this sort, that is, all genes which are carried on the sex chromosomes, are called *sex-linked* genes, and the characters which they determine are called sex-linked characters. Barring as found in Barred Plymouth Rocks is another example.

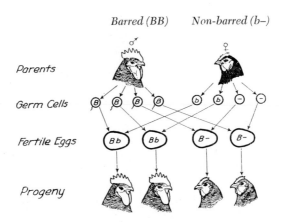

Fig. 29.—Showing the transmission of a dominant sex-linked character, barring (dominant to non-barring) when introduced by a male pure for the character. Compare with Figure 30.

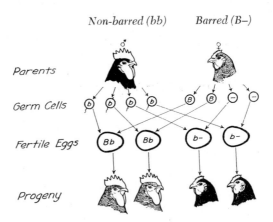

Fig. 30.—Showing the transmission of a dominant sex-linked character, barring (dominant to non-barring) when introduced by a female showing the character. Compare with Figure 29.

Making Use of Sex Linkage.—The manner in which sex-linked characters are transmitted makes it possible to use some of these characters for rapid and accurate sex identification of day-old chicks. The only requirement is that the character be one that can be seen at hatching time. Any silver female, when mated with a gold male, produces chicks in which the males are genetically silver and the females gold. Unless they are obscured by some form of dark down color, it is therefore a simple matter to separate the silver (male) chicks

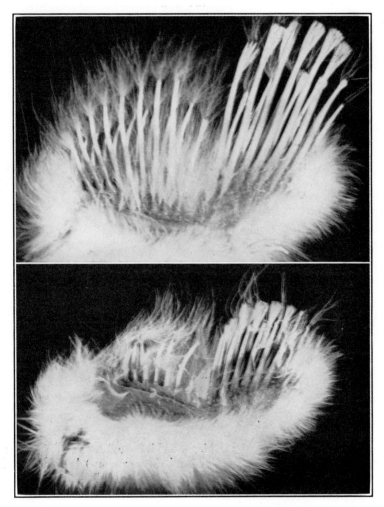

Fig. 31.—Slow feathering is dominant to rapid feathering and sex-linked. The difference is apparent in newly hatched chicks. In the rapid-feathering chick (*above*) the primaries and secondaries are longer than the coverts. In the slow-feathering chick (*below*) the primaries and coverts are about equal in length.

from the gold females. If the cross is made the other way around, silver male and gold female, all of the chicks will be silver and the recessive gold will not appear, provided the male parent is homozygous for the gene for silver.

Exactly the same procedure can be followed with respect to the genes for barring and non-barring. If barred females are bred to non-barred colored (usually black or red) males, the resulting male chicks will be barred, as evidenced by a characteristic white head

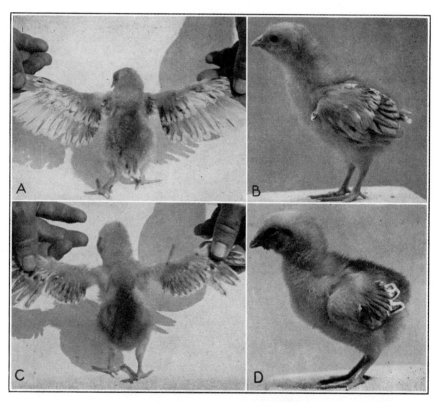

FIG. 32.—Showing the difference between rapid feathering (*above*) and slow feathering (*below*) at ten days of age.

spot appearing on the black down, while the females will be solid black in head color. If a pure-bred (homozygous) barred male is used with non-barred females, all of the chicks will be barred.

Another sex-linked gene affects rate of feathering in chicks, and it can be used in the same manner. Leghorns and some other breeds are characteristically rapid feathering, whereas most of the American and other heavy breeds are slow feathering. Slow feathering is dominant to rapid, and if the cross is to be used for sex-identification it is therefore necessary to mate rapid-feathering males with slow-feathering females. At hatching time the rapid-feathering female chicks from such a cross show well-developed primaries and secondaries which not only extend well beyond the down, but which are also longer than the associated wing coverts. In the slow-feathering male chicks, by

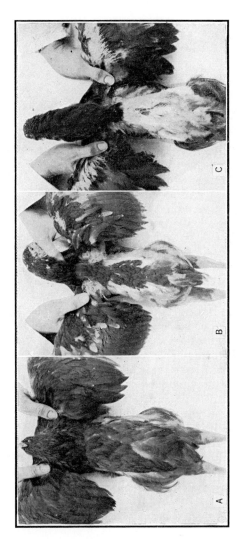

Fig. 33.—In breeds or strains which lack the sex-linked recessive gene for rapid feathering, there is often great variation in rate of back feathering caused by autosomal genes. (*Courtesy of Massachusetts Agricultural Experiment Station.*)

contrast, the primaries are much shorter, are of about the same length as the coverts, and the secondaries are either absent or very poorly developed. Later on, at about ten days of age, the rapid-feathering chicks show well-developed tail feathers, wing feathers extending to the tail, and a small tuft of feathers on each shoulder. The slow-feathering chicks show no tails and much shorter wings. These differences are shown in the accompanying pictures. (Figs. 31, 32.)

It must be remembered that feathering is influenced by other genes as well, and that even more serious to broiler growers in particular is the type of slow feathering which is autosomal rather than sex-linked. It has been shown that family selection for good back feathering at eight weeks of age is rather quickly effective. The characteristic differences in back feathering are shown in Figure 33. Various other modifying genes affect both rate and condition of feathering, but they are less important than the ones which have just been discussed.

QUANTITATIVE CHARACTERS

All of the characters thus far considered belong in what may be described as an "either or" category. There is no gradation by almost imperceptible degrees from rose comb on the one hand through some intermediate form to single comb at the other extreme. But with most of the economically important characters, variation is of the continuous type found in all quantitative characters. Egg size, for example, varies all the way from something under 45 grams to as much as 75 grams. It would not be difficult to find eggs among those produced by almost any large flock which would represent every weight, by one-gram intervals, from 45 to 75 grams. If enough eggs were weighed, it would undoubtedly be possible to find also individual eggs weighing 45.1, 45.2, 45.3 grams each, and so on by one-tenth-gram intervals up to 74.7, 74.8 and 74.9 grams. How then is one to describe and classifly eggs according to weight for the purpose of determining how egg weight is inherited? Classifications must obviously be made in some arbitrary manner. And after the upper and lower limits have been chosen for small, medium and large eggs, how is one to determine what genes are involved, and how many pairs of such genes there are? Clearly, this is not so simple a problem as the inheritance of rose and single comb.

For our purpose it is not so important to determine exactly how many pairs of genes are involved, as to recognize that variation in egg size is the result of the influence of more than one pair of genes, that the exact number cannot easily be determined, and that selection for egg size is therefore a somewhat different problem from selection for comb type or plumage color.

A great many things have been learned about egg size, and some of this knowledge can be useful to poultry breeders. We know that egg size is correlated with body size, especially among the smaller breeds of chickens. Selection for large egg size within a breed or variety tends to increase body size at the same time, though not all large fowls lay large eggs. Even seasonal changes in body weight and egg weight tend to be associated so that a spring and fall maximum for each is fairly well defined, at least during the first laying year.

Since the quantity of feed nutrients which must be digested, metabolized and deposited in 300 small eggs is less than for the same number of large eggs, it is easier to develop families and strains of high-producing fowls if no attention is paid to egg size. Conversely, selection for large egg size places a handicap on the rate of improvement which can be made in egg production, but market demands make it almost mandatory on poultry breeders to strive for egg production performance which not only includes a reasonable minimum average egg weight of between 24 and 25 ounces to the dozen, but which involves a minimum number of small eggs from each pullet.

It has been repeatedly demonstrated that selection for increased egg size is rather quickly effective, so that the present market standard of a 2-ounce minimum for individual eggs can be attained within a period of two to four years of family selection. This is perhaps comparable to the problem of increasing average flock egg production to about 160 eggs a year. Whether it would be any easier to increase average egg weight to $2\frac{1}{2}$ ounces than to increase average egg production to 240 has apparently never been determined. For practical purposes, however, we can say that egg size, within the limits of present market desirability, has a fairly high degree of heritability.

Body size is another quantitative character in which many poultrymen have a direct interest. For our purpose it is important to distinguish between adult weight, and various intermediate weights which may vary widely because of differences in rate of growth to the age at which weight is measured. By no stretch of the imagination could we expect a chick hatched from an egg laid by a bantam hen and fertilized by a bantam male to grow to the size of an adult Plymouth Rock, but the percentage rate of growth of bantams and Plymouth Rocks for a short time after hatching might not be so very different. Rate of growth as reflected by average weight at, let us say twelve weeks of age, is greatly influenced by environment, including the kind and amount of feed consumed. Final adult weight on the other hand, is largely determined by genetic influences, though the time required to reach the maximum may show wide variation, depending on the effects of environment.

Crosses between large and small breeds of chickens, such as Leghorn and Brahma or Hamburg and Cornish, always produce offspring which at maturity are intermediate in size, usually averaging somewhat above the midpoint between the parental stocks. On the other hand, crosses between breeds which are of about the same size often produce offspring which outstrip their parents in rate of growth to ten or twelve weeks of age. This characteristic is important to producers of commercial broilers.

There can be no doubt that both adult weight and rate of early growth are highly variable within breeds as well as among breeds, or that they are influenced directly and indirectly by a great many different genes. And yet each is readily influenced by selection. Even mass selection with no reference to family performance will bring about a significant change. This can only mean that both of these quantitative characters have rather high heritability.

EGG PRODUCTION

To the vast majority of poultrymen no other character is quite so important as annual egg production. It is now often calculated by a method which includes the effect of adult mortality. Dividing the total number of eggs laid during the year by the number of pullets or hens housed at the beginning of the year gives a value known as the hen-housed average or the production index. A high death loss during the year will lower the index, even though the surviving hens may have laid exceedingly well.

No other character with which we are concerned is subject to such wide variation within a practical range as is egg production. Hens may lay all the way from 175 eggs to 350 eggs a year and still make money for their owners. No other character involves a combination of genetic and environmental influences which present an improvement problem so intriguing, so challenging, and at the same time so difficult of solution as does the complex character egg production. As indicated at the beginning of this chapter, tremendous progress has been made in improving egg laying performance, and yet no one has the faintest idea how many pairs of genes are involved. Neither do we know how to set up a selection and breeding program that can be guaranteed to push egg production to any predetermined high level. It will be worth while to examine the entire question in some detail. For this purpose we shall use the egg production of survivors rather than the production index.

Analysis of Laying Performance.—There are authentic individual records of 350 or more eggs in twelve months, and there are also records of hens laying no eggs at all in the same length of time. Whether the performance of any given hen falls in the upper or lower part of this range will depend upon the rate at which she lays, and on how much of the time she is in laying condition. For the purpose of analyzing the performance record, it makes no difference whether the stimulus to laying is of genetic or environmental origin. Normally, of course, both sorts of stimuli are at work.

Intensity or Rate of Laying.—Some hens lay only on alternate days, some lay two days out of three, some lay three days before skipping a day, and a few lay every day for one hundred or more consecutive days.

The eggs laid by a hen on consecutive days are referred to as a *clutch,* and clutch size is therefore one of the hereditary characteristics which helps to determine the annual egg record. It is of course influenced to some extent by environment, as well as by natural variation, so that no hen can be expected to lay exactly 4 eggs in every clutch throughout the year. Nevertheless, differences in average clutch size are definitely correlated with annual egg yield.

CLUTCH SIZE	1	2	3	4	5	6	7	8	9	10	11	12	13	14	15	16	17	18	19	20	21	22	23	24	25	26	27	28	29	30	TOTAL
1	x		x		x		x		x		x		x		x		x		x		x		x		x		x		x		15
2	x	x		x	x		x	x		x	x		x	x		x	x		x	x		x	x		x	x		x	x		20
3	x	x	x		x	x	x		x	x	x		x	x	x		x	x	x		x	x	x		x	x	x		x	x	23
4	x	x	x	x		x	x	x	x		x	x	x	x		x	x	x	x		x	x	x	x		x	x	x	x		24
5	x	x	x	x	x		x	x	x	x	x		x	x	x	x	x		x	x	x	x	x		x	x	x	x	x		25
6	x	x	x	x	x	x		x	x	x	x	x	x		x	x	x	x	x	x		x	x	x	x	x	x		x	x	26
7	x	x	x	x	x	x	x		x	x	x	x	x	x	x		x	x	x	x	x	x	x		x	x	x	x	x	x	27
8	x	x	x	x	x	x	x	x		x	x	x	x	x	x	x	x		x	x	x	x	x	x	x	x		x	x	x	27
9	x	x	x	x	x	x	x	x	x		x	x	x	x	x	x	x	x	x		x	x	x	x	x	x	x	x	x		27
10	x	x	x	x	x	x	x	x	x	x		x	x	x	x	x	x	x	x	x	x		x	x	x	x	x	x	x	x	28

Fig. 34.—Effect of clutch size (number of eggs laid without a skip) on the total number of eggs laid in a 30-day period. An average clutch size of three or more is essential to making a high annual egg record.

If a hen lays in clutches of single eggs, the most that she can lay in a thirty-day month is 15 eggs. If she lays 2-egg clutches, her maximum record in thirty days is 20 eggs, an increase of $33\frac{1}{3}$ per cent. Should she lay in 3-egg clutches throughout the month she could make a total of 23 eggs, which is a further increase of 15 per cent over the 2-egg clutch maximum. Further increases in clutch size to 4 eggs and 5 eggs, respectively, add only one more egg each time to the maximum thirty-day total. The practical problem is, therefore, to increase average clutch size in a flock to a minimum of 3 eggs.

Intensity may also be measured by the number of eggs in a ten-day, thirty-day, sixty-day, or one hundred-day period. Thus one standard of selection might be a minimum of 25 eggs in each of two consecutive winter months. Many variations are possible, depending on the preference of the individual breeder and the particular form in which his records are kept.

For an exact analysis it is better to use a third measure, which is called *net rate.* It is calculated by first eliminating pauses of seven

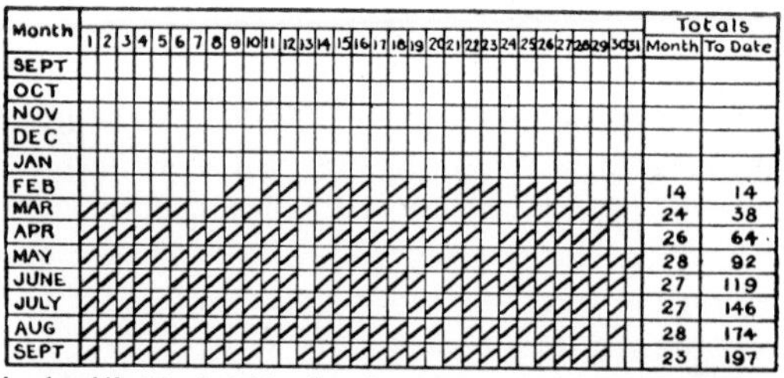

A, Leg band No. 896; hatching date Apr 10, 1934; age at first egg, 305 days

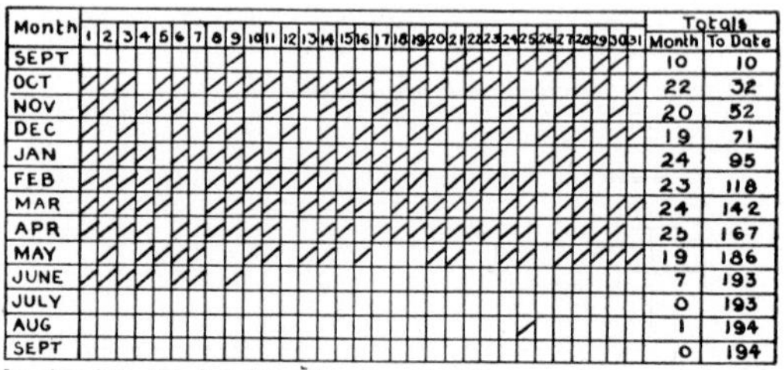

Month	Month total	To Date
SEPT		
OCT		
NOV		
DEC		
JAN		
FEB	14	14
MAR	24	38
APR	26	64
MAY	28	92
JUNE	27	119
JULY	27	146
AUG	28	174
SEPT	23	197

B, Leg band No. J18; hatching date Mar 20, 1934; age at first egg, 173 days

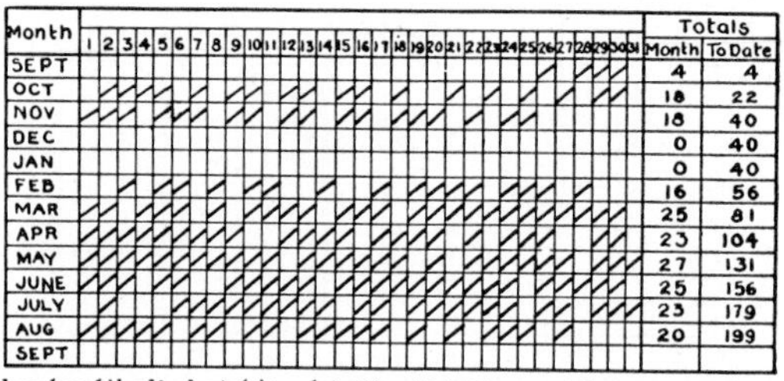

Month	Month total	To Date
SEPT	10	10
OCT	22	32
NOV	20	52
DEC	19	71
JAN	24	95
FEB	23	118
MAR	24	142
APR	25	167
MAY	19	186
JUNE	7	193
JULY	0	193
AUG	1	194
SEPT	0	194

C, Leg band No. J1; hatching date Mar 20, 1934; age at first egg, 190 days

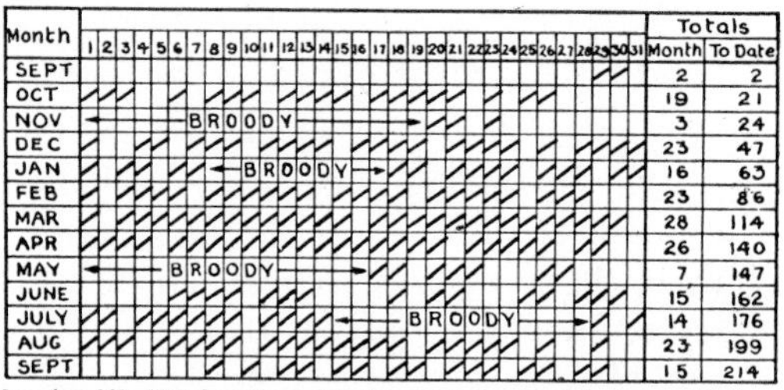

Month	Month total	To Date
SEPT	4	4
OCT	18	22
NOV	18	40
DEC	0	40
JAN	0	40
FEB	16	56
MAR	25	81
APR	23	104
MAY	27	131
JUNE	25	156
JULY	23	179
AUG	20	199
SEPT		

D, Leg band No. J318; hatching date Mar. 20, 1934; age at first egg, 193 days

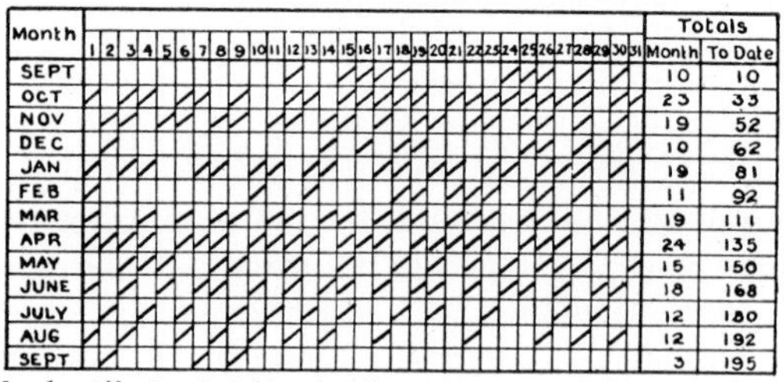

Month	Month total	To Date
SEPT	2	2
OCT	19	21
NOV	3	24
DEC	23	47
JAN	16	63
FEB	23	86
MAR	28	114
APR	26	140
MAY	7	147
JUNE	15	162
JULY	14	176
AUG	23	199
SEPT	15	214

(chart D contains BROODY periods marked in NOV, JAN, MAY, and JULY)

E, Leg band No. J10; hatching date Mar. 20, 1934; age at first egg, 176 days

Month	Month total	To Date
SEPT	10	10
OCT	23	33
NOV	19	52
DEC	10	62
JAN	19	81
FEB	11	92
MAR	19	111
APR	24	135
MAY	15	150
JUNE	18	168
JULY	12	180
AUG	12	192
SEPT	3	195

FIG. 35.—Each of these hens laid approximately 200 eggs, yet each shows a different fault which prevented the record from being higher. *A*, Late maturity; *B*, poor persistency; *C*, winter pause; *D*, broodiness; *E*, low rate. (*Courtesy of California Agricultural Experiment Station.*)

(78)

days or more within the period under consideration, say December and January, and calculating the percentage of the remaining days on which the hen lays. This is logical because it has been well established that pauses are inherited separately from rate. The net rate of two birds may be exactly the same, whereas their gross rate—calculated without taking pauses into account—can be very different.

Breed **White Leghorn**

Hatching Date **MAR. 27** 1934

Maturity **182 DAYS**

INDIVIDUAL EGG RECORD 　1

Years 19**34** to 19**35**

Leg Band No. **J 422**

Wing Band No.

Mating No.

Date	Month	To Date
July		
Aug.		
Sept.	4	4
Oct.	21	25
Nov.	22	47
Dec.	21	68
Jan.	24	92
Feb.	23	115
Mar.	28	143
Apr.	29	172
May	30	202
June	27	229
July	30	259
Aug.	29	288
Sept.	25	313

FIG. 36.—The record of a "300-egg" hen. Compare with Figure 35. (*Courtesy of California Agricultural Experiment Station.*)

Age at First Egg.—Length of the laying year for pullets is greatly influenced by the time laying commences. This may be measured either in terms of age in days when the first egg is laid or, if date of hatch is not too variable, by the calendar date on which the first egg is laid.

Since there is no necessary relation between age at beginning to lay and the time of beginning the fall molt, which normally marks the end of the laying year, it is obvious that the pullet which begins to lay at an early age is likely to have a longer laying year than one which matures slowly and begins to lay at a later age. In many flocks this difference between the earliest and latest maturing pullets is more than one hundred days, and it may be more than one hundred and fifty days. Extreme cases might show a spread of two hundred days between individual pullets.

Early maturity is hereditary, and is one of the easiest characters to establish in a flock, especially if attention is given to the selection and use of males from early-maturing dams. Environmental factors such as date of hatch, and other management practices, may have considerable influence on the age at which laying commences.

Persistency.—Length of laying year is influenced not only at the beginning by the date of the first egg laid, but also at the end by the date of the last egg. The tendency to continue laying well into the fall or winter is known as persistency, and it has much the same effect at the end of the year as early maturity does at the beginning.

Lack of persistency is easily determined, as a rule, by the beginning of an early molt, because the fall molt normally marks the end of the laying year. Some hens molt as early as June and others as late as December, so that it is easily possible to have a difference of one hundred and eighty days in length of laying year on account of this one factor.

The common practice of culling laying flocks in late summer or early fall is based on the fact that persistency is highly correlated with total annual egg production. Culling out the early molters automatically removes many of the low producers from the flock.

Continued selection for persistency tends to strengthen the "urge to lay" to such an extent that flocks so selected are less likely to be thrown out of production by minor errors in management. In fact persistency may become so well established that it is necessary to use rather drastic measures in order to cause certain flocks to molt in time to be ready for the production of hatching eggs in January or February.

Pauses in Laying.—A pause in laying, as here used, refers to a cessation of laying of one week or more. From the standpoint of selecting for an improved laying performance, there are at least three types of pauses with which the poultry breeder has to deal. These are: (1) environmental; (2) broody; and (3) winter pauses.

The environmental pauses are those brought about by mismanagement, accidents, unusually severe weather, and the like. From the standpoint of the present discussion they are of interest only because it is sometimes puzzling to determine whether a given bird stops laying because of a hereditary bias, or because she has been mishandled. It is not always possible to tell.

At the same time it must be observed that even a susceptibility to environmental changes probably has a genetic basis, for daughters of some individuals are thrown out of lay easily, while daughters of others will stand a good deal of abuse before stopping.

Broodiness, like many other physiological functions in the hen, is under endocrine control. Increased secretion of prolactin by the pituitary gland causes the hen to go broody. It is of importance in selection and breeding for egg production because a hen normally stops laying when she goes broody. The days lost on account of broodiness may have a marked effect on the annual egg record, especially if the hen goes broody several times and is slow about coming back into production.

Rapid progress can be made in reducing broodiness in a flock if all broody females and all male relatives of such females are discarded. Any outside stock brought in for breeding purposes, even if from a flock with a history of nonbroodiness, should be tested by mating to a few individuals in order to avoid introducing broodiness on a large scale.

Sex-linked genes for broodiness have been found in certain breeds, and must be taken into account in a careful breeding program.

Some hens show pauses in laying without ever going broody. Such pauses are most common during the winter months, but may occur at other times of the year.

Relative Importance of the Various Factors.—An attempt to evaluate the relative importance of the several characters with respect to their effect on first-year egg production has been made by Hays of the Massachusetts Station. He used the records of 1220 Rhode Island Red pullets during the five-year period from 1938 to 1943, during which hatching dates were kept constant and egg size was well above 24 ounces to the dozen.

The five factors studied, and minimum standards for each, were as follows:

1. Early maturity—215 days or less.
2. High winter intensity—clutch size 3 or more.
3. Non-winter pause—shorter than eight days.
4. Non-broody—no broody periods.
5. Persistency—laying year at least 280 days.

The flock was essentially early maturing and non-broody, so that these two factors had different values than they probably would have in an unselected flock. Using the average production of pullets showing all five characters as a standard, a lack of persistency reduced the annual egg record by 55 eggs, a lack of high intensity reduced it by 31 eggs, winter pause caused a reduction of 24 eggs, broodiness 17 eggs, and late maturity 7 eggs.

The combined effect of several characters on the annual egg record in these 1220 pullets is of particular interest. The data are shown in Table 18.

TABLE 18.—RELATION OF FIVE DESIRABLE CHARACTERS TO ANNUAL EGG PRODUCTION IN RHODE ISLAND REDS. (*Massachusetts Agricultural Experiment Station.*)

No. of desirable characters	No. of pullets	Per cent of total	Average egg production
0	. . . .	. .	. .
1	10	1	125
2	69	6	157
3	393	32	188
4	439	36	224
5	309	25	252
Average	1220	100	215

The foregoing analysis of laying performance is suggestive rather than final. It suggests the kinds of building blocks out of which a good performance record is made, and the subdivisions which are likely to be important in selection. It is obvious that if a given female matures at an early age, lays at a high rate, has no pauses, and is a persistent layer, she will inevitably have a high annual egg record. This will be true whether we are able to understand the underlying genetics and physiology or not. But if such hens are to make up a high percentage of any flock, it will be because some breeder has delved deeply into the problem of selection and improvement.

The seasonal distribution of egg production may vary widely among hens making the same total annual egg record. This, together with the well-known influence of many environmental factors on egg production, makes it clear that (1) there is no simple formula for explaining the inheritance of egg production, and (2) the heritability of egg production is not very high.

When we say that the heritability of egg production is not very high, we are simply saying that there is no accurate way of sorting the genetically high producers from those which laid well mainly because the environment was such that they could do so, or the genetically poor layers from those which had low records because of an unfavorable environment. It means that our basis of selecting breeding stock must be something other than mere evidence of having laid 300 or more eggs in twelve months. Family selection and the progeny test must be brought into play if we are to have any success in identifying individuals with desirable genotypes. But the opportunity is there as long as there is any appreciable heritability left for the character in which we are interested.

HATCHABILITY

The final character chosen for discussion in this chapter is hatchability. By definition, it is usually taken to mean the percentage of fertile eggs which hatch under artificial incubation. It is influenced by many things such as age of breeding stock; rate of egg production of the breeders and the rations they have been fed; season of year; size of eggs; character of egg shells; length of holding time after laying, and conditions under which eggs for hatching are held; temperature, humidity and other conditions in the incubator; as well as by genetic influences working through the hens that laid the eggs or the males that fertilized them.

The emphasis here is on the environmental rather than the genetic influences. It is true that there are some 16 lethal genes which either reduce or prevent hatching. It is also true that the indirect effect of certain other genes which influence egg size and shell quality may reduce the percentage of eggs which hatch. But by and large, the problem of improving hatchability is a problem of improving the environment. Hatchability for a given flock in any given season may be improved by eliminating individual hens which show poor hatchability early in the season, but it is futile to select as future breeders hens which give high hatchability, and sons of such hens, with the expectation that average hatchability of a flock will thereby be greatly improved by reason of inheritance. Some writers have referred to specific genes for hatchability, but all available evidence supports the view that heritability of this character is very low. Except for selection against the lethals, and against such indirect effects as large and small egg size and poor shell texture, genetics has little place in the improvement of hatchability. The problem of rations which are nutritionally adequate, and the management methods which help to insure a high percentage hatch will be discussed in later chapters.

SYSTEMS OF BREEDING

Only a small fraction of all the chickens on farms and ranches ever become a part of any planned system of breeding. Most of them, however, are influenced in some degree by the systems in use by breeders, and in particular by the selection and improvement procedures carried out by commercial hatcheries. Seldom is any one system used exclusively by a breeder, and it is probable that the most successful breeders make use of all the accepted systems from time to time and in combination.

Inbreeding.—A simple and easily understood definition of inbreeding is that it involves the mating together of closely related individuals. The closest inbreeding which the poultryman can use is continued brother × sister mating for several successive generations. A lesser degree of inbreeding results from the mating of father × daughter, mother × son, half-brother and sister, or cousins.

Some degree of inbreeding is essential to the development of uniform stocks. Close inbreeding makes for greater uniformity but, since undesirable genes as well as desirable genes are concentrated in the inbred line, the overall effect is frequently disappointing. Close inbreeding by itself is, therefore, not often profitable.

It must be clearly understood that maintaining a closed breeding flock, even if the total number of females in any one year is no more than 100, is not necessarily inbreeding in the accepted sense. So long as the breeders are chosen more or less at random, and several males are used each year, there is very little risk of any sort of trouble which can be ascribed solely and specifically to inbreeding. On the contrary, the success of many breeders can be attributed in part to the fact that they have chosen to follow the closed flock plan.

Outbreeding.—Outbreeding is essentially the mating together of individuals which are less closely related than the average of the flock with which the breeder is working. The poultryman often speaks of it as introducing new blood. With flocks in which several desirable characteristics are well established, it should be done very cautiously, if at all.

There are numerous instances in which a strain has been ruined by the unwise introduction of new stock in such a manner as to involve the whole flock. Test matings, involving a small fraction of the flock, should always be made before risking the entire breeding program, assuming that one has highly productive stock with which to start.

Outbreeding often increases the average performance of the individuals in the next generation—average egg production, for example —so that the breeder may think he is making real progress. The trouble is that the breeding value of his best birds is lowered by making them more heterozygous than they were before, thus lessening the chances of being able to carry on their good qualities to the next generation. If the stock is not to be used for future breeding, there is no objection to such a change in genetic make-up.

Crossbreeding.—For the same reason that outbreeding frequently improves the average performance of the first generation, crossbreeding of totally unrelated breeds sometimes produces rather startling results. The new combination of genes often results in a high degree of heterosis or hybrid vigor. This usually is apparent in rapid growth, uniformity, and sometimes in increased egg production. Whatever is gained in these lines with respect to individual performance is offset by lowered breeding value. Hence crossbreeding is most useful when applied to the production of stock which is to be grown for meat purposes, or kept no more than a year or two for egg laying, and then sold without any attempt to use it for breeding.

Crossing of Inbred Lines.—There has been much recent interest in the crossing of highly inbred lines belonging to the same or different breeds, on the supposition that such a procedure might duplicate for poultry some of the known advantages of hybrid corn. The chickens so produced are commonly referred to as hybrids, and the system of breeding used is often called hybridization.

When highly inbred lines from two different breeds are crossed, the resulting chicks have a much higher degree of heterozygosity than do chicks from a mating between random samples of the same two breeds. This increases the predictability of results, whether good or bad, so that one can make additional matings between the same two inbred lines with the expectation of getting substantially the same results.

Present commercial practice is to make use of four-way crosses involving two inbred lines within each of two breeds. The lines within each breed are crossed, and these two crosses are then brought together to produce the commercial hybrid chick. Production and maintenance of the inbred lines is costly, and many of them have to be discarded after trial because they do not combine well with other lines.

The egg production of such hybrid chickens as have been commercially available has been good enough to make certain that still more of them will be produced.

Reciprocal Recurrent Selection.—As already mentioned, close inbreeding gradually makes a population more homozygous for both desirable and undesirable genes. Very frequently the concentration of unfavorable genes puts an end to the inbreeding program, at least in some of the lines. In fact there is some reason to believe that continued brother × sister matings for several generations are possible only because of natural and controlled selection *against* this very homozygosity, so that the eighth or ninth generation is not as closely inbred as the calculated coefficient of inbreeding would indicate. It may even be that a certain amount of heterozygosity is a basic essential of being alive. Many geneticists are of the opinion that the best performance comes not from individuals which are homozygous for a large number of desirable genes, but rather from individuals which are somewhat if not highly heterozygous.

The concept of increased heterozygosity as a condition favorable to high egg production has led to another idea which some breeders are attempting to apply to poultry. It is to discover and measure the "combining ability" of both strains and families in terms of strain or breed crosses. Within a breed it means finding strains or lines which combine well together to give production better than can be obtained from any one of the strains alone. Each strain would then have to be continued by matings within its own stock, but with individuals used in such matings selected on the basis of their abiliy to combine well with one or more of the other lines or strains. Because three or four such strains would no doubt be combined in various ways, and because selection would be based on combining ability rather than on family performance within each strain, this plan of breeding is being referred to as reciprocal recurrent selection. It is too new to be properly evaluated, but it has interesting theoretical possibilities. It is mentioned here primarily to indicate that poultry breeders are keenly interested in any and all techniques which offer some promise of increasing the effectiveness of selection.

Making a Breeding System Work.—No matter what system is used, the breeding value of a given individual must be judged either from its own performance or from the performance of its relatives. This means that the breeder must use great care to avoid confusing the effects of environment with those of heredity. Variations caused by environment can be very large in such characters as egg production, and they can be very important economically, but they do not change the hereditary makeup of the individuals so affected. They are therefore not transmitted to the next generation. They can be reproduced only by repeating the environmental conditions which produced them originally.

Improvements brought about by heredity, on the other hand, tend to be permanent, and the cost of making them may be returned many times over in future generations. This means that different characters in any selection program should be given emphasis in proportion to both their heritability and their economic value.

It is important to remember that while the gene is the actual unit of inheritance, the individual fowl is the smallest unit that can be saved or rejected for breeding purposes. This is bound to temper one's judgment as to the value of inbreeding, for example, except for specific purposes. Inbreeding is, in fact, a much stronger force for lowering annual egg production than selection is for increasing it. The effect of close inbreeding in a small flock could not be overcome by any amount of selection pressure in the direction of increased egg production.

Successful breeding systems of the future will no doubt be applied principally to large flocks which consist of many fairly large families of full or half sisters. They will be designed to take full advantage of all known methods of improvement, including some complex selection indexes. They will also include careful consideration of such things as the optimum proportion of pullets to older hens and of cockerels to older males in the breeding flock, because these things are important in determining both the intensity of selection for desired characters and the interval between generations. Selection methods are discussed in more detail in the next chapter.

Chapter 4

Selection and Improvement

SELECTION, as used in connection with breeding, refers to the choosing of parents for the next generation. Its skilled performance is the foundation of constructive breeding practice. One should remember that selection will be operating no matter what system of breeding is used, even though in the simplest case it may be reduced to mere chance. Furthermore, selection can not change or alter any genetic process any more than will trap-nesting or pedigree breeding. All that it can do, if successful, is change the gene frequency by preventing the poorer individuals from being hatched, and thus carry the breeder more rapidly in the direction of his ultimate goal.

SELECTION METHODS

Selection of individual males and females for breeding may be based on:
1. The past—in which the pedigree of the individual is examined for several preceding generations.
2. The present—in which the appearance or performance of the individual and its sibs (sisters and brothers) is used in making final judgment.
3. The future—in which the breeding worth of the individual is judged by the appearance or performance of its descendants, usually only its sons and daughters.

Two or more of these bases may sometimes be used in combination, especially the second and third. The constructive breeder attempts by selection to segregate individuals which are pure for certain desirable genes and, through intelligent mating, to assemble in new individuals still more desirable combinations of genes.

Pedigree Selection.—A good individual with a good ancestry is to be preferred to an equally good individual with a poor ancestry, but it should be emphasized that a good ancestry only improves the chances for desirable breeding performance; it is no guarantee of such performance. Since genes and chromosomes occur in pairs, and are halved for any individual in each generation, it is immediately apparent that a particular remote ancestor can have very little influence on the genetic makeup of an individual which is being considered in selection. It can be shown by suitable calculation that an ancestor which appears but once in the tenth preceding generation will have contributed less than one-tenth of one per cent to the total genetic makeup of the individual. A similar ancestor in the fifth generation will have contributed, on the average, only a little more than 3 per cent.

Pedigree selection is of value in a broad sense in that one would certainly choose a breeding cockerel whose dam had laid 250 eggs

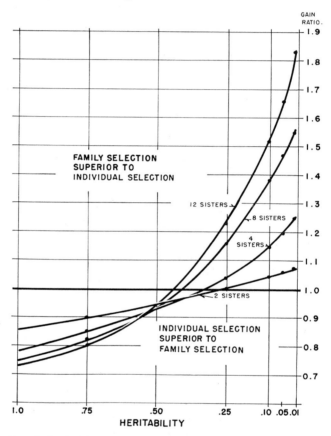

FIG. 37.—As heritability decreases, family selection becomes more and more important, especially when large families of full sisters are available. The curves show the ratio of expected gains from family selection alone over individual selection alone. (*Adapted from Lerner.*) Note: single comb has an heritability of 1.0; the production index about .05.

in preference to one whose dam's record was only 150. But one should also remember that two cockerels from the 250-egg hen may give widely differing performance as measured by the egg production of their daughters. Furthermore, a difference between 250 eggs and 150 eggs in a dam's record may be important in selection, where-

environment on the expression of the genetic character may be and frequently is very great.

Mass selection, based on phenotypic performance, may be effective through the low to medium range of a given quantitative character and quite ineffective in the upper range. Egg production is a good example. There can be no doubt about the effectiveness of individual or mass selection in improving average egg production up to 160, 180, or perhaps 200 eggs per pullet per year—the exact limit depending both on the sort of stock with which one is working and the environment under which it is kept. But continued dependence on mass selection can only lead to disappointment when it ceases to bring any further progress.

A great deal of improvement in poultry flocks has been the result of widely applied mass selection practices, particularly in the elimination of such undesirable individuals as slow growers, poor layers, and those which detract from a reasonably uniform appearance of flocks. Many flocks can still be improved by this method of selection, but as performance moves up the scale it is necessary to use more refined selection methods or accept something less than maximum performance as the end and aim of a breeding program.

Family Selection.—Modern breeding methods involve a great deal more than a detailed record of the performance of individuals. They consider rather the extent to which individuals reflect the performance of a family. The distinction is important. Sons of a 240-egg hen which was one of eight sisters laying between 230 and 260 eggs each are much more likely to transmit desirable genes for egg production to their daughters than are the sons of a 280-egg hen whose sisters finished the year with records of 190 to 230 eggs. But there is still no assurance that the particular son of the 240-egg hen chosen to head a new breeding pen will be able to equal the breeding performance of his sire. Hopes may be built upon ancestry, individuality, and sibs, but the only sure basis for forming a judgment concerning the ability of an individual to transmit genes for desired characters to most or all of its progeny is breeding it. This part of family selection is usually referred to as the progeny test.

By progeny testing is meant a careful analysis of the results secured from various matings in order that future matings may be made with greater assurance of success. Any mating that has given unusually good results should be repeated or, in terms of today's procedure on many breeding farms, continued. The progeny test is also used for the purpose of distinguishing between individuals which are homozygous and those which are heterozygous for some simple character such as rose comb or white skin color. Only one single-comb chick is needed from a mating of two individuals with rose comb to show that *both* parents are heterozygous for rose comb. Similarly, if any of the offspring of two white-skin parents have yellow skin, both parents must be heterozygous for skin color. When it is desired to check a given male to find out whether he is homozygous for rose comb, the simplest procedure is to mate him with a few single-comb hens. If even one chick hatched has a single comb, the male is heterozygous. If, on the other hand, there are no single combs among as many as twelve or fifteen chicks, one can be practically certain that the male is homozygous.

More often, however, a breeder is concerned with the progeny test as a measure of breeding worth in respect to some quantitative character such as annual egg production, egg weight, mature body weight of females, or survival through a full year of egg production. This calls for records which are sufficiently complete to provide the necessary measures. Just what they are will depend on the particu-

Fig. 40.—Trapnesting is speeded up by the use of a portable microphone and a wire recorder. Later the spool of wire is played back in the office where permanent egg records are kept. (*Courtesy of Heisdorf and Nelson Farms.*)

lar characters under observation, but certain details are necessary in any case. Some of these are indicated in the following section.

Blood Group Systems.—In many animal species there are several distinct blood groups, but they are seldom directly comparable to the A–B–O groups in humans. The number of blood group systems so far identified in the chicken is seven, and each group is controlled by a group of genes forming an allelic series. The significance of this for the poultryman lies in the finding that chickens which are heterozygous for certain blood group genes, having received unlike genes from their two parents, possess somewhat better survival characteristics than do homozygous individuals of otherwise similar breeding. Since high survival tends to be associated with such desirable economic traits as high hatchability, high egg production and rapid growth rate, some commercial breeders are using comprehensive blood typing procedures, followed by performance testing of various crosses, to help fix desirable characteristics in the strains with which they are working.

BREEDING AND PERFORMANCE RECORDS

From the preceding discussion of the bases of selection, it should be clear that complete breeding and performance records are essential items in the progressive production-breeder's equipment.

Steps in Keeping a Complete Record.—The steps in keeping a complete record are: (1) marking prospective breeders; (2) recording egg production; (3) recording the matings made; (4) identifying the eggs to be hatched; (5) pedigree hatching; (6) recording fertility and hatchability; (7) marking and recording the chicks; (8) recording livability, rate of growth, rate of feathering, and the like; and (9) making family summaries.

Record systems may be simple or complex, depending on the number of characters under observation, but an elaborate set of records is of little real value unless the data are carefully analyzed. A few simple records well kept and carefully studied will be much more helpful than a complete set which involves so much work that there is no time for its analysis.

Record forms may be purchased, but since no one system of records can be best for all purposes, the breeder will usually do better by developing such forms as best suit his own particular needs.

Making Use of Records.—The records to be kept and the use to be made of them will naturally vary with the objectives which the individual breeder has in mind. The following suggestions will serve as a guide in using family, individual, and progeny test records when the breeding objective is high production of market eggs.

Minimum standards for birds to be saved as breeders should be set for each factor considered, or all birds may be given a grade of A, B, or C on each separate factor and on overall breeding value.

The standards may be raised from time to time as the flock improves. Those indicated here are for purposes of illustration only.

Factors Known Prior to the Hatching Season.—Certain factors can be measured early in the life of the individual, while others must wait for performance of its progeny. Some of those in the first class are:

(a) Family size (5 or more full sisters).

(b) Family egg production (hen-housed average of 215 eggs or better—also known as the production index)

(c) Family egg quality (size—2 ounces within sixty days from first egg; color, shape, and interior quality standards as desired).

(d) Family survival to specified age (95 per cent to six months of age; 85 per cent in laying house, before any culling).

(e) Family record of physical characters (body weight, rate of feathering, *etc.*).

(f) Hen's individual record of egg production.
   Early maturity—185 days or less.
   Non-pause—no winter pause of seven days or more.
   Non-broodiness—no broody periods.
   Intensity—clutch size of 3 or more eggs, or 50 eggs in sixty consecutive days before March first of pullet year.
   Persistency—late molt, and still laying at three hundred and fifteen days from date of first egg.

Factors Based on Hatching Season and Progeny Test.—Although preliminary selection of breeders must nearly always be made before any record of progeny performance is available, a final check on the value of a breeding bird can be made only after its offspring have had an opportunity to perform in the laying house. Some of the additional factors which can then be applied are:

(g) Hen's own record of fertility (90 per cent or better).

(h) Hen's own record of hatchability (85 per cent or better)

(i) Number of daughters raised.

(j) Rate of growth of chicks.

(k) Rate of feathering of chicks.

(l) Daughters' average egg production.

(m) Daughters' average egg quality.

(n) Daughters' record of survival.

SELECTION IN PRACTICE

The foregoing discussion may suggest to some persons that breeding for egg production can easily be reduced to a matter of keeping individual egg records, assembling them into family averages, choosing the better families for breeding, and by so doing to keep on improving flock average egg production year after year. Unfortunately, it is not that simple. Perhaps the chief reason why it cannot be that simple is that no poultry breeder can afford to be satisfied with improving a single trait such as number of eggs. His stock must be of acceptable body size and general appearance; it must live well; the chicks must grow rapidly and feather properly; and the eggs laid by surviving pullets must be of suitable size, shape, color, shell texture and interior quality.

Suppose, for illustration, that a poultryman is satisfied to use in his breeding program any sires which, on the basis of family performance, are above the average of his entire flock. Only about half of all the sires can be above average in any measure of family egg production, for the other half must be below. Similarly, only about half can be above average in respect to family egg size. But the chance for a given sire to be above average in both respects becomes $\frac{1}{2} \times \frac{1}{2}$, or $\frac{1}{4}$. That is, only one in four can be expected to excel in both characteristics. If, now, we add a requirement that a sire excel also in respect to suitable measures of body size, interior egg quality and shell color, we reduce the mathematical chance of finding such a sire to 1 in 32. A small breeder may not even have a total of 32 tested sires in any one season.

There are other important characters for which selection should be practiced. For instance, no sire should be used which did not come from a family of some reasonable minimum size, and he in turn must have a reasonable number of daughters as a basis for evaluating his own breeding worth. And all will agree that choosing males which merely exceed the *average* in respect to the desired qualities does not constitute very rigid selection. If we say that the males chosen must be in the upper 25 per cent of the flock in respect to five different character measurements, then instead of finding 1 in 32, we can expect by chance to find only 1 in 1024 (namely, $\frac{1}{4} \times \frac{1}{4} \times \frac{1}{4} \times \frac{1}{4} \times \frac{1}{4}$). And if we set the requirement at the upper 20 per cent level, we still further reduce the chances to 1 in 3125. At 10 per cent it becomes 1 in 100,000. This is just another way of saying that poultry breeding is difficult and complex, and that progress toward the upper physiological limit in terms of production performance is bound to be slow.

The preceding discussion should make it clear that if high average egg production is the chief aim of a breeding program, each additional character for which selection is made, if at the same time and to the same extent, automatically reduces the intensity of selection which can be applied to the main objective. In the example just used, if 10 per cent of the available males must be saved for breeding purposes, and if family average egg production is the only character considered, the top 10 per cent of the males can be chosen. But if two characters are considered, assuming no correlation between them, only about 1/10 of the males which qualify in the first character will also be in the top 10 per cent with respect to the second. Therefore the remaining 9/10 of the males which must be saved to provide the minimum total number will fall below the desirable standard in one or both measures.

If we select for as many as five characters simultaneously, provided they are not correlated and assuming that we want the best 10 per cent of all males as before, the intensity of selection for any one character is reduced a great deal further, actually to the equivalent of $\sqrt[5]{1/10}$. Hence it is very important when making selections not to give undue weight to those characters which are of minor significance. If a breeder feels that he must select for a certain shade of plumage color, in addition to perhaps five economically important characteristics, he must accept the obvious corollary that progress toward his main objective of high average egg production will be slowed just that much more.

Fortunately, there are some short cuts. A breeder may find it wise to concentrate on one or two characters at a time. He can use production to January 1 as his measure of egg-laying ability instead of insisting on full yearly records; he can use the median instead of the mean for measuring such family traits as age at first egg; he can breed from pullets instead of from older hens in order to get ten generations in ten years instead of only five. All of these will help because they save time, in terms of breeding progress, and because they enable a poultryman with a specified number of breeding pens to increase the selection pressure which he applies to his stock. But even when all these things are taken into account, poultry breeding today is big business. It calls for extensive facilities in the way of physical equipment, large numbers of fowls, and a great deal of labor both in the keeping of detailed records and in their analysis. Some breeding operations involve more than 500 small pens for flock matings headed by individual males. The larger breeding farms make extensive use of punch cards and tabulating equipment in handling thousands upon thousands of individual records.

All of this has come about, not merely as expansion and growth, but in an attempt to discover and apply more refined and precise methods of selection to the business of increasing egg production. As pointed out earlier, poultry breeders have come a long way by the use of a common sense approach to the problem, so that a prospective purchaser of chicks or breeding stock today can obtain at nominal cost the kind of chickens which not so many years ago were known on but few farms in the country. But because better and better performance is demanded, breeders will continue to use all means at their disposal to reach still higher goals.

For many years, while egg production has been increasing from low to mediocre to good, the amount of variation traceable to heredity has been large enough to make selection—even mass selection—highly effective. Concurrently much has been learned about how to improve egg production performance by providing better environment. The stimulus of artificial light, the favorable effect of the best possible rations, the increase in fall egg production resulting from consistently early hatching, the construction of houses of a size and type which will conserve the heat energy produced by the hens themselves and so provide more comfortable winter quarters, have combined to increase the opportunities for improving egg production through the influence of environment. An inevitable result has been that as mass selection approached the limit of effectiveness, the amount of individual variation traceable to environment increased. The indications are that in many of today's better bred flocks the heritability of egg production, that is, the amount of variation directly traceable to heredity, is no more than 30 per cent, and that the heritability of the production index, because it includes the effect of mortality, probably does not exceed 5 per cent.

This low degree of heritability does not mean, however, that poultrymen should discard all selection and breeding efforts to concentrate on methods by which egg production can be further improved through environment. It does mean that the individual has become of little importance in selection except as it helps to make up a family average, or as it is representative of a family with high average performance. It means also that further progress will be slow, even with increased selection pressure. And it means that as this continued progress is made, the heritability figure will decline still further as the barrier to increased egg production through genetic means is raised higher and higher. The detailed theory behind this reasoning is too intricate to be included here, but to the student of poultry genetics it is a fascinating subject.

Regardless of the breeding and selection methods used by specialty breeders, there are many thousands of flock owners who do no breeding but who, for economic reasons, are very much interested in methods of separating high-producing hens from their low-producing flock mates. Routine culling of laying flocks means many dollars saved in feed which would otherwise be consumed by non-layers. In the following sections are given the essential facts about methods of estimating production ability from external examination and appearance of the fowls, without the use of trapnests.

ESTIMATING PRODUCTION QUALITY FROM EXTERNAL APPEARANCE

The Relation of Selection and Culling.—In actual practice the selection and culling of poultry should begin when the chicks are taken from the incubator and should continue as long as they live and make up a part of the flock.

Although frequently used as synonyms, the terms "selection"

and "culling" are strictly opposite in their implication. Selection aims at progress. It is positive and constructive. It deals with the very cream of the flock, including at the most the top 25 per cent, and more commonly only the top 10 or 15 per cent.

Culling, on the other hand, is negative, has no necessary relation to breeding, deals with the least productive fraction of the flock, and is aimed at the prevention of retrogression rather than at progress.

It is unfortunate that the term "cull" should have come to mean one thing to the poultry producer and quite another thing to the buyer of market poultry. In marketing practice a "cull" is an inferior product from a meat standpoint, whereas to the producer a cull hen is simply a non-layer or one that has made a low record. As the term is short and descriptive, it seems likely to persist in both usages, but the distinction between them should be clearly understood.

Physical Characters Related to Laying.—As applied to the laying flock, the judging of fowls for egg production really consists of two distinctly different phases which in practice are nearly always considered simultaneously. These are (1) the separation of the laying from the non-laying hens with the object of disposing of the ones that have stopped for the season, and (2) sorting hens on the basis of their ability to lay eggs throughout the year.

It is significant that the second phase has to do largely with estimating past production, and that most of our knowledge in respect to the judging of laying ability is closely tied up with the fact that high egg production leaves its mark in the way of discernible physical characteristics. To the extent that a good hen in any one year tends to repeat the performance, the selection of high layers on the basis of past production has a commercial value that is not necessarily related to the breeding problem, though it is commonly used as a part of a general improvement program.

Head Type.—The appearance of the head is variable because of differences in size, shape and expression. Some of these differences are undoubtedly related to laying performance, and several different attempts have been made to arrive at more or less exact correlations in order that head types may be accurately classified and used as a basis for the estimation of laying ability. While this objective has not been, and perhaps never will be, wholly realized, it is entirely possible to group head types according to the degree of refinement, and to show some relation between this and the egg records. Hens with coarse, phlegmatic, masculine, or "beefy" heads are not likely to lay very many eggs. Those with clear-cut rugged, alert heads that are at the same time fine in quality, are likely to be among the best layers in the flock.

Body Type.—Type or shape of body is essentially a breed characteristic and, therefore, is directly the result of, and is influenced

7

by selection. It is obvious that in order to lay for a long time and at a high rate a hen must have the capacity and ability to utilize large amounts of feed rapidly and efficiently. This means, among other things, that there must be ample room in the body cavity for the functioning of the vital organs. Further than this, there does not seem to be any reasonable basis for assuming a causal relationship between body type and egg production.

A   B

Fig. 41.—*A*, The head of a high producer, 281 eggs in one year; and *B*, of a low producer, 106 eggs in one year. Note the contrast in appearance of the eye, and in fleshing of the face. (*Courtesy of Kansas Agricultural Experiment Station.*)

Body Changes.—When laying, a hen has a large, moist vent, showing a dilated, pliable condition in contrast to the puckered hardness of the vent of a non-laying hen. The abdominal region is enlarged in the layer, as compared with the non-layer. The pelvic bones move apart and become comparatively elastic and pliable.

In an individual that is not laying these bones almost come together just below the vent. The same individual when in full laying may show a distance of three or even four fingers' between them. The distance from the pelvic bone to the point of the keel (breast bone) is increased at the same time. These changes provide room for the passage of the egg, the enormous increase in the size of the ovary, with its several rapidly growing ova, and for the distention of the alimentary tract to accommodate large amounts of feed.

The rate of egg production is indicated in a measure by the relative softness and pliability of the skin and the thinness and elasticity of the pelvic bones. The subcutaneous fat of the abdomen is used up by laying, so that the abdominal skin of the heavy producer becomes velvety and the whole abdomen soft and flexible.

The pelvic bones feel thin, tapering and elastic. In the non-layer they are likely to feel thick, blunt and stiff, while the whole abdomen is surrounded under the skin with a layer of hard fat if the bird is on full feed.

Among the most valuable indications of the heavy layer are the refinement of the head and the closeness and dryness of feathering. The wattles and earlobes fit close to the beak and are not loose and flabby. The face is clean cut and rather thin. Puffiness in the face indicates meat rather than eggs. The eye is full, round and prominent as viewed across the tip of the beak. The high layer is trimmer in feathering than the poor layer, but after prolonged heavy production the oil does not keep the plumage so sleek and glossy. It becomes worn and frayed.

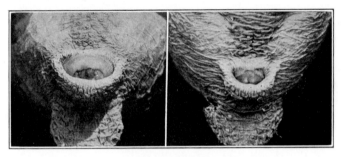

FIG. 42.—*A*, The vent of a laying hen, and *B*, of a non-laying hen. (*Courtesy of Kansas Agricultural Experiment Station.*)

There is a close correlation between the relative size of the comb and wattles and ovarian activity. If they are comparatively large, full, smooth, hard and waxy, the hen is probably laying heavily; if the comb is limp the bird may be laying slowly; but if it is dried, shrunken and cold, she is not laying at all. When the comb is expanding in advance of another period of production it often feels warm to the touch.

Pigmentation.—In those varieties showing yellow pigment in the subcutaneous fat, shanks (and earlobes in Mediterranean and Continental breeds), the pigment tends to disappear as laying progresses. The presence or absence of this pigment in the fowl or its eggs is directly correlated with the presence or absence in the feed of a carotenoid pigment called xanthophyll. For this reason a hen fed on a ration devoid of such feeds as yellow corn and green forage, which carry it in considerable amounts, might have the appearance of laying so far as pigment is concerned, though she had never produced an egg. The character of the feed the hen has been receiving should, therefore, always be considered in relation to her condition with reference to pigment.

When hens have feeds carrying an abundance of pigment, and the skin, shanks and beak are not normally pale as in the English breeds, the beginning of laying diverts all the pigment received in the feed to the ovary, where it finds its way into the developing yolks. The pigment of other parts gradually disappears as a result of the natural physiological change in the structure of the skin. It is not replaced as long as the individual continues to lay.

The vent loses its pigment very quickly so that a white or pink vent in a yellow-skinned variety usually indicates that the bird is laying, while a yellow vent indicates that she is not laying.

The eyering formed by the inner edges of the eyelids loses its pigment a trifle more slowly than the vent. The earlobes of the Mediterranean breeds bleach out somewhat more slowly than the eyering, so that in these breeds a white earlobe on a vigorous bird usually means a longer period of continuous laying than does a bleached vent or eyelid.

The color disappears from the beak next, beginning at the base and remaining longest at the tip. The lower part loses color more rapidly than the upper. With the average yellow-skinned bird a bleached beak means that laying has been in progress for from four to six weeks.

The shanks are the last to lose their color. Bleached shanks, therefore, indicate a much longer period of production than does the bleaching of the other parts. The pigment disappears from the front of the shank first and finally from the back. A bleached shank usually indicates continued egg production for at least fifteen to twenty weeks.

When laying stops, the pigment reappears in the several regions in the same order in which it disappeared. The relative rapidity of loss and regain in the various parts is probably correlated with the thickness of the skin, the pigment change being slowest where the epidermal covering is thickest. The fact that a given hen stopped laying two or three weeks back sometimes may be determined by the fact that the tip of the beak is colorless while the base is yellow.

Molting.—The shedding and renewal of feathers normally occurs once a year, though it may occur in certain individuals twice in one year and, more rarely, only once in a period of two years. In the wild fowl it would have no relation whatever to egg production. Under the influence of domestication, however, the laying period has been gradually lengthened until it often overlaps the natural molting season.

Under the influence of the genes for high production, and particularly of those related to persistency and the length of the laying period, the natural tendency is for a good hen to continue to lay as late in the fall as she possibly can. The result is that she either molts late, i. e., after her long laying period is over, or molts and lays at the same time. The low-producing hen, on the other hand, stops laying in July or August well in advance of the time that growth of a new feather coat must begin in order to put the hen in condition to resist the cold weather of winter.

Observation of the conditions that most commonly occur in laying flocks has led many persons into two faulty conclusions with regard to molt. One is that the onset of molt is a cause of the cessation of laying, and the other is that hens never lay and molt at the same time. The facts seem to be, rather, that a hen molts

Fig. 43.—A wing showing four new primary feathers partly grown. Note the axial feather. (*Courtesy of Kansas Agricultural Experiment Station.*)

late because she lays late, and that hens bred for continuous production at a high rate not only may, but often do, lay and molt at the same time. This latter condition probably does not occur except when a hen is increasing, or at least maintaining, her body weight.

The order in which the different sections of the fowl lose their feathers is fairly definite. The usual order is head, neck, body (including breast, back, and abdomen), wing and tail. Not only this, but there is a high degree of regularity about the order of molt within the several sections. The wing primaries, for example, begin to drop before the secondaries. The first primary to be shed is the inside one, next to the axial feather, and the remainder are shed in succession until the last one to be dropped is the outermost primary near the tip of the wing.

The order of molt of the secondary feathers is not so regular as that of the primaries, but the most common order, when the secondaries are numbered from the axial feather toward the body, has been reported as 11, 12, 13, 14, 10, 2, 3, 4, 5, 6, 7, 8, 9, 1. The axial feather is dropped at the same time as the secondary next to it.

In addition to being a late molter, the high-producing hen is also likely to be a rapid molter. Extensive observations have shown that there is no difference in the rate at which high-producing and low-producing hens grow new feathers, but that there is a decided difference in the rate at which the old feathers are shed. In no instance did an individual primary feather become completely grown in less than six weeks, and some feathers required seven weeks to complete their growth. The feathers made about 20 per cent of their growth in each of the first three weeks, and from 12 to 15 per cent during each of the second three weeks.

The rate of laying is not materially affected by the molt, in the case of hens that lay and molt at the same time, but the rate of molt is slowed up by production. The net result is that the advantage gained by the late molter, as measured by length of the period of non-production, is due, not to differences in the number of feathers dropped or to the rate of growth of an individual feather, but to the fact that two jobs are performed at one and the same time.

It should be remembered also that time and rate of molt are influenced to a considerable extent by weight and physical condition of the hens, and by environmental conditions including feeding and management.

Temperament.—A good layer is more active, more alert, and yet at the same time more easily handled than a poor layer. She is among the first off the perch in the morning and among the last on it at night. When not on the nest she is busy and business-like, scratching or ranging in an eager search for feed. The great layer is a bird of a seldom satisfied appetite.

Applying the Theory in Practice.—From what has preceded, it should be fairly obvious that any method which will identify the hens that (1) begin to lay at an early age, (2) lay at a high rate without pauses of any sort, and (3) continue to lay late into the fall at the end of their laying year, will automatically select the most productive hens in the flock. One method of accomplishing this objective is to use trap-nests all through the year. It is only by this means that we have been able to find out the things that are known about selecting hens for egg production.

In practice, however, it is usually not feasible to run trap-nests throughout the year, and the flock owner is compelled to depend upon judgments that, in turn, are based upon his observation of the external physical characteristics that have just been discussed. If he is interested merely in getting rid of the poorer individuals in order that they may be replaced with pullets, a single sorting of the flock in the month of September may be all that is required. If, on the other hand, he is interested in making as accurate a selection as possible in order to save the best of the flock for breeding purposes, he will find it necessary to do much more than this. Several observations, distributed throughout the year, will enable him to sort the flock into various production groups with a fairly high degree of accuracy.

A Banding Scheme May be Used.—If the pullets are not given numbered bands, colored celluloid bands may be used as markers. Blue, red and white bands may be placed on the left leg to indicate

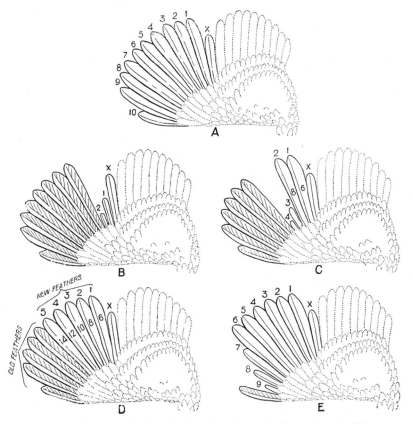

Fig. 44.—*A*, a normal wing showing the primary feathers, *1* to *10*. They are separated from the secondaries (shown in dotted outline) by the short axial feather, *x*. *B*, the beginning of a wing molt. *1* and *2* are new feathers growing in. *C*. an eight-week molt. Elapsed time in weeks is indicated on each feather. *D*, an unusual instance in which only five primaries were molted. *E*, a wing as it appears near the completion of a normal molt. (*Courtesy of Kansas Agricultural Experiment Station.*)

successive differences in time of starting to lay. Green bands may be used to mark those individuals that show a winter pause and molt. A black band may be put on every hen that goes broody, and the blue, red and white bands may be used again in reverse order, on the right leg, to indicate successive differences in time of stopping to lay in the fall. With this scheme, the entire flock will be handled some six or seven times during the year, and a very reliable index of the laying ability of each individual will be secured. It will lack only the quantitative character of a trap-nest record.

A Substitute for the Trap-nest.—In discussing the formation of the egg it was pointed out that if hens are examined early in the morning, those which are going to lay on that day can be detected by feeling the egg in the uterus. If one cares to go through this procedure on three successive days each month, keeping a record of each individual hen handled, he will have, at the end of the year, a highly accurate record of the relative laying ability of the hens that make up the flock and also a basis upon which to estimate the actual number of eggs laid by each hen. The correlation between the number of eggs laid in a period of thirty-six days made up of the first three days in each of twelve months, and the total number of eggs laid during the year, is very high. The actual correlation coefficients obtained in analyzing one series of records were:

White Leghorns	+0.897	±0.007
White Wyandottes	+0.939	±0.007
Rhode Island Reds	+0.874	±0.011
Barred Plymouth Rocks	+0.858	±0.017

Disturbing Factors.—No matter what method is used in attempting to apply the theory of production judging to practical use, it should be remembered that even under the most favorable conditions some mistakes will be made. The inevitable biological error is considerable and, though there is much of practical value in the whole plan of selecting laying hens on the basis of external physical characters, it is futile to attempt to accomplish worthwhile results by the use of some one or two characteristics alone.

THE NATIONAL POULTRY IMPROVEMENT PLAN

The National Poultry Improvement Plan became operative July 1, 1935. It is administered in each State by an Official State Agency cooperating with the U. S. Department of Agriculture. Authority for an official state agency to administer the plan within the state is a memorandum of agreement between it and the U. S. Department of Agriculture. The Department of Agriculture is responsible for coordinating the program among the cooperating states.

The objectives of the plan are to improve the production and market qualities of chickens and to reduce losses from hatchery-

TABLE 19.—HATCHERY PARTICIPATION IN THE NATIONAL POULTRY IMPROVE-
MENT PLAN, 1958–59. NUMBER AND EGG CAPACITY BY REGIONS, WITH DATA
FOR SELECTED STATES. AS REPORTED BY THE U.S. DEPARTMENT OF AGRICUL-
TURE.

Region or State	Number	Egg Capacity Total (Million eggs)	Egg Capacity Average (Thousand eggs)
North Atlantic	380	54.6	144
Maine	25	7.7	308
New Jersey	58	10.6	183
Pennsylvania	78	13.7	176
East North Central	575	68.4	119
Indiana	189	26.2	138
Illinois	150	18.0	120
West North Central	736	83.1	113
Iowa	125	15.6	125
Missouri	122	23.4	192
South Atlantic	506	109.0	215
Delaware	19	10.4	548
Georgia	158	39.3	249
South Central	361	67.9	188
Alabama	68	15.8	232
Mississippi	61	15.4	252
Western	159	18.7	118
Washington	29	4.1	141
California	32	6.4	200
United States	2,717	401.6	148

TABLE 20.—FLOCK PARTICIPATION IN THE NATIONAL POULTRY IMPROVE-
MENT PLAN, 1958–59. NUMBER AND SIZE OF FLOCKS BY REGIONS, WITH DATA
FOR SELECTED STATES. AS REPORTED BY THE U.S. DEPARTMENT OF AGRICUL-
TURE.

Region or State	Number of flocks	Total Birds (Millions)	Av. number per flock
North Atlantic	2,915	7.6	2,603
Maine	859	2.2	2,599
New Hampshire	158	1.0	6,368
Pennsylvania	1,058	1.5	1,383
East North Central	14,130	5.9	416
Indiana	5,726	2.5	436
Illinois	4,150	1.4	328
West North Central	18,219	7.0	386
Minnesota	2,884	1.8	630
Missouri	7,173	2.2	305
South Atlantic	7,580	11.5	1,516
North Carolina	2,891	3.8	1,320
Georgia	1,574	4.7	3,017
South Central	6,066	6.0	992
Alabama	590	1.4	2,384
Mississippi	600	1.3	2,147
Western	1,423	1.9	1,359
Washington	241	0.5	1,914
California	140	0.6	4,400
United States	50,333	39.9	793

(105)

disseminated diseases.   The National Turkey Improvement Plan is operated on a very similar basis.

The provisions of the plans are changed from time to time to conform with the development of the industry and with new information as it becomes available.   These changes are based upon recommendations made at the biennial National Plans Conferences by official delegates representing participating flockowners, breeders, and hatcherymen from all cooperating states.

Complete details regarding the plans are available in Miscellaneous Publication No. 739, issued by the U. S. Department of Agriculture.   The latest revision is dated February, 1959.

Chapter 5

Incubation

WITH the rapid growth of the hatchery business, fewer and fewer chicks have been hatched on the farms where they are grown until about 96 per cent of all chicks raised, either as farm chickens or as commercial broilers, are now bought as baby chicks. The breeding flocks which supply the hatching eggs are nevertheless widely distributed on farms, and it is therefore important for any student of poultry production and management to know something of the factors which influence hatchability, especially those which operate before the eggs are placed in incubators.

SELECTING EGGS FOR HATCHING

There are certain characteristics of individual eggs which are known to interfere with hatchability. Selection against these conditions will be effective in terms of the immediate hatching percentage, without regard to any considerations of heredity.

Workers at the Beltsville Agricultural Research Center selected from 47,950 eggs, by candling, those which had any one, but only one, of eight different defects. These eggs were incubated weekly over a period of one year, and the hatching results compared with those for control eggs which showed none of the defects and were therefore considered normal. Eggs showing two or more defects were excluded from the study.

The percentage hatch of fertile eggs was 80 for small eggs (45 grams or less), 72 for eggs containing large blood spots, 71 for extra large eggs (65 grams or more), 68 for eggs with air cells located in positions other than the blunt end, 53 for slightly cracked eggs, 49 for misshapen eggs, 47 for eggs with rough or thin shells, and 32 for eggs with loose air cells. These figures are to be compared with a percentage hatch of 87 for the control eggs, which ranged in size from 50 to 59 grams and had none of the specified defects.

Hereditary differences in egg shell quality are responsible for wide variation in the loss of weight by evaporation of moisture from eggs during incubation. This is important from the standpoint of both hatchability and the keeping quality of eggs for market purposes.

There is some evidence to support the opinion that dark brown and medium brown eggs hatch better than light brown eggs from the same flocks, but this may be due in part to the tendency for eggs of light color (among brown eggs) to have rough, thin or porous shells.

Breeders who want to hatch as many eggs as possible from hens with known records, rather than from pullets, are usually faced with the problem of large eggs and their known lower hatchability when incubated along with medium or small eggs. If enough large eggs are being used to make it worth while, they can be set twelve hours ahead of the pullet eggs. It is still better, from the standpoint of

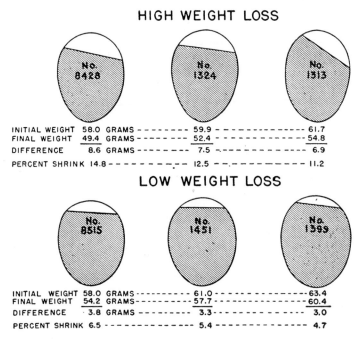

FIG. 45.—There is a wide variation among hens in weight loss of their eggs during incubation, because of hereditary differences in egg shell quality. (*After Quinn, Gordon, and Godfrey.*)

hatchability, to set them in separate machines so that they can be given slightly lower relative humidity during the incubation period. This will insure maximum hatchability of the large eggs and will bring all chicks out at about the same time.

Predetermining Fertility and Sex.—The manifest advantage of being able to ascertain, by external examination, which eggs are fertile before setting them, and which are males or females, is so great that it has led to much speculation.

The claim has been made that an egg with high specific gravity is fertile, and that one with relatively low specific gravity is likely to be infertile. The truth is that differences in specific gravity may be observed in both fertile and infertile eggs.

Egg shape is likewise of no value as an indicator of the sex of the future chick. Both long narrow eggs, sometimes credited with hatching only males, and short round eggs, supposed to produce mostly females, will produce about equal numbers of both sexes.

The position of the air cell in the egg, for which a similar claim has sometimes been made, is equally unreliable as a means of determining which eggs are destined to produce chicks of the desired sex.

CARE OF HATCHING EGGS

At the time of laying, the fertile egg is usually in a fairly advanced stage of development from an early embryological standpoint, having been incubated within the body of the hen for approximately twenty hours. It would seem that the ideal method of caring for hatching eggs would be to allow development to proceed without being checked, by setting the eggs at once. Poultrymen, however, usually are under the necessity of holding them for a longer or shorter period. During this period development is suspended, or at least is very slow, and the very practical question of how to handle eggs with the least possible damage to their vitality and hatching power presents itself.

Length of Holding Period.—It is the modern view that holding eggs for hatching is a necessary evil, to be practiced as little as possible, even under the best conditions. Although there are a few records of chicks having hatched from eggs held as long as thirty-five days, all available data are in agreement in showing that hatchability decreases as the time of holding is increased. Commercial hatchery practice is to set twice a week, and many operators will not accept eggs more than one week old. Individual breeders may find it advisable to hold eggs for incubation as long as ten days if correct holding conditions are provided.

Curiously enough, the time required for incubation seems to be directly related to the age of the eggs set. Observations at the Missouri Station were that eggs which were from fourteen to twenty-one days old required from fourteen to eighteen hours longer for incubation than did eggs which were less than eight days old when set. Other studies have shown similar results.

Holding Temperature.—It is the general belief that the sooner the embryonic development under way at the time of laying is checked, the better are the chances of holding eggs successfully for hatching. This belief has led to the widespread adoption of the practice of gathering eggs frequently during the incubating season, and putting them in a cool place immediately.

Repeated tests have shown that eggs held at 50° to 55° F. hatch better than those held at 30° to 40° or at 60° to 75° F. The upper and lower limits are not specific because the time of holding is also involved, but holding for prolonged periods at either the high or the low temperatures causes many of the embryos to die during the first few days of incubation.

When it is necessary or desirable to hold hatching eggs for more than seven days, the percentage hatch can be significantly increased by warming the eggs at 100° F. for one to five hours early in the holding period. Similar improvement has resulted from holding over night at room temperatures of about 70° F. The reason why such treatment is effective is not known.

Position.—If eggs for incubation are to be held not more than a week, their position is not of great importance. They may be held in ordinary egg cases, preferably being packed large end up, or they may be laid in trays in the natural horizontal position.

Turning.—As already pointed out, the yolk, with the germ spot uppermost, tends to float near the shell. It is prevented from coming in actual contact with the shell membrane by the dense layer of white which surrounds it. When left in the same position for a considerable time a constant though gentle tendency upward parts the dense white and allows the germinal disc to come in contact with the shell membrane. With evaporation constantly taking place, the tiny embryo may adhere to the membrane and be destroyed. When the eggs are not allowed to remain in the same position, but are turned fairly frequently, a new point of contact is given, and more white brought between the germ and the shell membrane. Turning is of no practical importance if eggs are to be held no longer than one week. If they are to be held for a longer period, there is a distinct advantage in turning them daily.

DEVELOPMENT OF THE CHICK

It is a matter of common observation that the reproductive cycle of birds differs from that of domestic mammals in at least two particulars. First, the fertilized ovum never forms an organic connection with the mother, and second, embryonic development, for the most part, takes place outside the body of the mother.

The normal incubation period of chicken eggs is twenty-one days, though there is some variation in each direction. The eggs of Leghorns and other light breeds commonly hatch a few hours earlier than those of the heavier breeds. For a general statement it is well to remember that for each species of birds the incubation period is of definite duration; that under conditions of artificial incubation it can be lengthened somewhat with ease, but that it can be shortened only with extreme difficulty.

In general, the smaller the bird, the smaller is the egg, the higher is the body temperature and the shorter is the incubation period, though there are numerous exceptions.

It should also be remembered that in its embryonic development the bird is much more rapid than the mammal, and that this is very likely an adaptation to life within the egg.

Structural Development.—Structural development begins shortly after fertilization by division of the single female germ cell on the surface of the yolk into two daughter cells. These cells in turn divide, and a continuous proliferation of cells is inaugurated which (except for the period after laying until the egg is set), continues actively, not only during incubation but throughout subsequent growth until maturity.

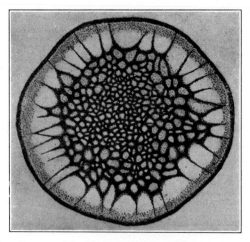

Fig. 46.—Appearance of the blastoderm (magnified) of a hen's egg after eight hours in the oviduct. It shows 346 cells, 34 marginal and 312 central. (*After Patterson.*)

The first division or cleavage of the germ cell occurs about the time the egg enters the isthmus, and the second follows in about 20 minutes. The third division, to form the 8-cell stage, also takes place in the isthmus, and by the time the egg is well within the uterus it has advanced to the 16-cell stage. Within the next four hours it advances by continued cell division to approximately the 256-cell stage.

As a result of this process of cell division while the egg is still in the oviduct, a disc-shaped layer of cells is formed. It is first a single layer of cells, but later on is several layers thick. This layer of cells, in intimate contact with the underlying yolk, constitutes the undifferentiated blastoderm as shown in magnified form in Figure 46.

Eventually the cells in the center of the blastoderm become detached from the surface of the yolk to form a cavity called the blastocoele. Because these cells are no longer attached to the yolk, this central area is transparent—the *area pellucida*, while the outer portion which remains in contact with the yolk is opaque—the *area opaca*. It is in the center of the area pellucida that the development of the embryo proper takes place.

Before laying, or very soon thereafter, the blastoderm becomes differentiated into two layers of cells by a process referred to as gastrulation (gut formation). This involves the rapid proliferation of

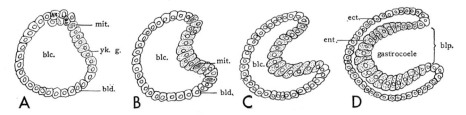

GASTRULATION IN FORM WITH ISOLECITHAL EGG HAVING ALMOST NO YOLK—AMPHIOXUS.

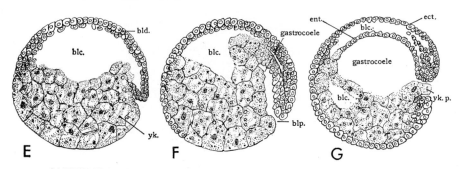

GASTRULATION IN FORM WITH TELOLECITHAL EGG CONTAINING MODERATE
AMOUNT OF YOLK—AMPHIBIA.

Fig. 47.—Schematic diagrams to show the effect of yolk on gastrulation. (*From Patten, "Early Embryology of the Chick" 4th edition. By permission of The Blakiston Company, publishers.*) In the case of the chick, the still greater amount of yolk effectively prevents the formation of an open blastopore.

Abbreviations: (blc.) blastocoele; (bld.) blastoderm; (blp.) blastopore; (ect.) ectoderm; (ent.) entoderm; (mit.) cell undergoing mitosis; (yk.) yolk; (yk. g.) yolk granules; (yk. p.) yolk plug.

cells along one portion of the margin of the blastoderm, to form a second layer of cells. This second layer of cells, by its inward growth eventually divides the cavity (blastocoele) into two. The lower cavity is the gut or gastrocoele. It is in this manner that the blastoderm becomes differentiated into two of the three germ layers—the the ectoderm above, and the layer of entoderm below growing into the blastocoele. (See Figures 47 and 48.)

Shortly after incubation begins, the third germ layer, or mesoderm, originates or becomes differentiated by growing into the blastocoele between the ectoderm and the entoderm in much the same way that the entoderm earlier pushed into the blastocoele. Thus the blastoderm at this stage consists of three distinct layers of cells resting on the surface of the yolk, *i.e.*, ectoderm, mesoderm and entoderm. These three layers constitute the materials out of which the various organs and systems of the body are to be developed.

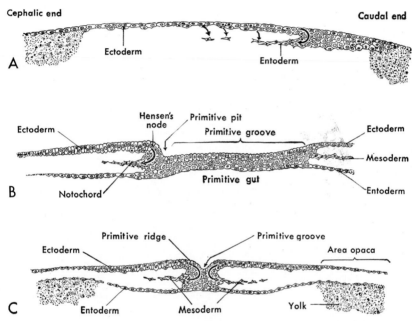

Fig. 48.—Schematic diagrams indicating the cell movements involved in the gastrulation of chick embryos. (*From Patten, "Early Embryology of the Chick" 4th edition. By permission of The Blakiston Company, publishers.*) (A) Longitudinal section of the blastoderm from a pre-primitive streak chick during entoderm formation. (B) Longitudinal plan of embryo of approximately 17 hours of incubation to show the relations of the various parts. (C) Cross section of an embryo in the primitive streak stage to show the turning in of cells at the primitive groove to enter the mesodermal layers.

From the ectoderm, the skin, feathers, beak, claws, nervous system, lens and retina of the eye and the linings of the mouth and vent are developed. The bones, muscles, blood, reproductive and excretory organs develop from the mesoderm, while the entoderm produces the linings of the digestive tract and the respiratory and secretory organs.

Gastrulation is usually, though by no means always, complete by the time the egg is laid. It seems to have been shown conclusively that the period of the gastrulation process is an exceedingly critical

8

one, while the early postgastrula stage, during which most eggs are laid, is comparatively non-critical.

The stage of embryonic development in fresh-laid fertile eggs tends to be characteristic of individual hens, and appears to be correlated with hatching power.   At the Massachusetts Station, pre-gastrula and early gastrula were the most common stages of development in eggs from low-hatching hens.   Early gastrula stages were characteristic of hens with medium hatching power, and well-advanced gastrula was most commonly found in eggs from hens which gave a high percentage hatch.

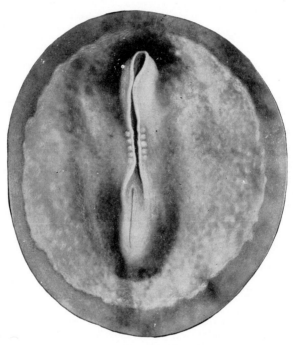

Fig. 49.—Chick embryo of 25–26 hours photographed by reflected light to show its external configuration. (*From Patten, "Early Embryology of the Chick" 4th edition. By permission of The Blakiston Company, publishers.*)

Too much development at the time of laying may be as detrimental as too little. Observations made by workers in the U. S. Department of Agriculture indicate that maximum hatchability occurs when the interval between successive eggs is twenty-seven hours, and that there is a marked decrease when the interval is in excess of twenty-eight hours.

One of the first marked changes in structure after the egg has begun to incubate is the appearance of the primitive streak. Simultaneously with the differentiation of the mesoderm, the primitive streak arises as two thickenings in the ectoderm, starting near the point of origin of the entoderm. The primitive streak eventually disappears completely, but it serves to mark out the future longitudinal axis of the body of the embryo and its posterior extremity. Although the embryonic axis is fairly uniform, it is not absolutely fixed. It usually lies approximately at right angles to the long axis of the egg, being directed away from the observer when the small end of the egg is to the right.

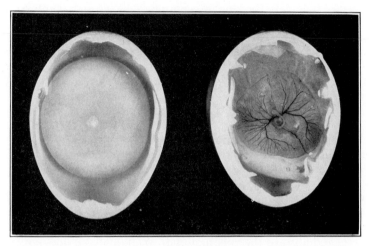

Fig. 50.—An infertile (left) and a fertile egg after being held for 72 hours at a temperature of 102° F. (*Courtesy of Illinois Agricultural Experiment Station.*)

The growth and development of the embryo from the cells in the area pellucida soon shows a more rapid growth of cells in certain regions than in others. This uneven growth gives rise to a series of folds in which the various germ layers are involved. It is these folds which mark off the embryo proper from the rest of the blastoderm. The first of these, the head fold, lifts the anterior end of the embryo above the remainder of the blastoderm. Later the tail fold undercuts the posterior extremity of the embryo to elevate it. Both of these join with the lateral folds which mark out the sides of the embryo. Eventually this undercutting or folding lifts the embryo well above the yolk, leaving only a narrow stalk to serve as a connection between them.

During the first twenty-four hours the head of the embryo becomes clearly defined and in it may be observed the beginnings of the central nervous system as well as the foregut, the forerunner of the alimentary tract. Blood islands appear in the area opaca outside the body of the embryo. The blastoderm enlarges considerably, embarking on the process of growth in which it ultimately surrounds the yolk.

The second day sees the embryo beginning to turn on its left side, the formation of the heart which may be observed to beat at about the thirtieth hour, the primary divisions of the brain, the beginning of the formation of the eyes, the ear pits and the formation of the tail bud.

The Extra-Embryonic Membranes.—There are four extra-embryonic membranes which are essential to the normal growth of the embryo. They are the amnion, chorion, yolk sac and allantois.

The amnion and the chorion originate together from a fold of the extra-embryonic tissue which first appears in the head region, but which eventually encircles the entire embryo. This fold, consisting of ectoderm and a layer of mesoderm, grows upward and over the embryo to fuse eventually at the top. The outer portion, with ectoderm above and mesoderm beneath, is the chorion, while the inner part of the fold with the position of the germ layers reversed is the amnion.

The amnion is a transparent membranous sac filled with a colorless fluid which serves as a protection from mechanical shock and allows the embryo to move about rather freely as it develops.

A third extra-embryonic membrane, the yolk sac, consists of a layer of entoderm and mesoderm growing over the surface of the yolk, with the entoderm next to the yolk. The walls of the yolk sac become lined with a special glandular and absorbing epithelium which digests and absorbs the yolk material. Yolk material does not pass through the yolk stalk to the embryo even though a narrow opening or lumen in the stalk is still in evidence at the end of the incubation period.

At approximately 96 hours of incubation there is an outgrowth of the entoderm from the hind gut which pushes a layer of mesoderm ahead of it into the extra-embryonic cavity, to form the allantois. This fourth extra-embryonic membrane continues to enlarge until it eventually fills the entire extra-embryonic cavity and thus occupies the space between the amnion and the chorion. It is a highly vascular sac which fuses with the chorion, thus bringing its capillaries in direct contact with the shell membrane.

The allantois has four functions. It serves as an embryonic respiratory organ, it receives the excretions of the embryonic kidneys, it absorbs albumen which serves as nutriment for the embryo, and it absorbs calcium from the shell for the structural needs of the embryo.

The growth of the amnion constricts the opening from the intestine to the yolk sac, thereby forming what is called the yolk stalk. It also brings the yolk stalk into close contact with the allantoic stalk. These with their blood vessels are included in an extension of the embryonic body wall to form the umbilical cord.

Up to the sixth or seventh day there is nothing about the chick embryo which would help one to distinguish it from the embryo of other familiar animals. On the sixth day the main divisions of the legs and wings can be observed. The body, which has been very small in proportion to the head, begins to develop more rapidly. What appears to be voluntary movement may be noticed if the egg is opened.

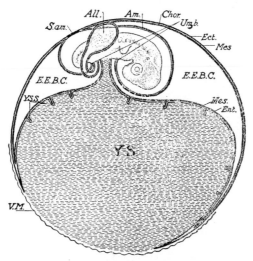

FIG. 51.—Diagram of the chick and its embryonic membranes during the fourth day of incubation. The abbreviations used in this and also in Figure 52 are as follows: *Alb.* albumen; *Alb.S.*, albumen sac; *All.*, allantois; *All.C.*, cavity of allantois; *All.I.*, inner wall of allantois; *All.S.*, stalk of allantois; *Am.*, amnion; *Am.C.*, amniotic cavity; *Chor.*, chorion; *C.T.R.*, connective tissue ring; *Ect.*, ectoderm; *E.E.B.C.*, extra-embryonic body cavity; *Ent.*, entoderm., *Mes.*, mesoderm; *S.-Am.*, sero-amniotic connection; *S.Y.S.U.*, sac of yok sac umbilicus; *Umb.*, umbilicus; *V.M.*, vitelline membrane; *Y.S.*, yolk sac; *Y.S.S.*, yolk sac septa. (*After Lillie.*)

During the eighth day the feather germs appear in definite tracts and on the ninth the contour of the embryo becomes quite birdlike. There is a chalky deposit about the mouth opening which is the beginning of the horny beak. By this time the allantois nearly surrounds the embryo, amnion and yolk. By the thirteenth day the down is distributed over the body and its color may be seen through the thin walls of the sacs which still enclose the individual down feathers. On this day the scales and nails appear on the legs and feet. By the sixteenth day they are quite firm and horny, as is also the beak.

By the fourteenth day the embryo has accommodated itself to the form of the egg, so as to lie parallel to the long axis. By the sixteenth the albumen is nearly gone and the yolk becomes increasingly the main source of nutriment.

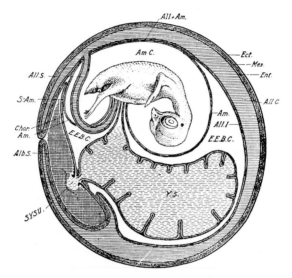

Fig. 52.—Diagram of the chick and its membranes during the twelfth day of incubation. For the designation of parts see legend of Figure 51. (*After Lillie.*)

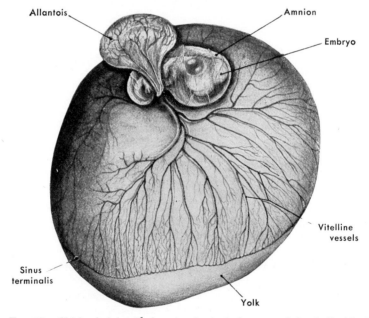

Fig. 53.—Chick of about $5\frac{1}{2}$ days incubation taken out of the shell with the yolk intact. (Modified from Kerr.) The chorion and the white of the egg have been removed to expose the embryo lying within the amnion, and the allantois has been displaced upward in order to show the allantoic stalk. (*From Patten, "Early Embryology of the Chick" 4th edition. By permission of The Blakiston Company, publishers.*)

On the seventeenth day the amniotic fluid begins to decrease. On the nineteenth the yolk sac begins to enter the body through the umbilicus, apparently forced by the muscular tension of the amnion. The beak usually pierces the air cell and the lungs begin to function, though it is not until the shell is pipped, generally on the twentieth day, that full pulmonary respiration becomes a fact, and the allantoic circulation and respiration cease.

When fully formed, the chick is normally placed with the fore-part of the body toward the large end of the egg, its head bent forward beneath the right wing and the legs brought up toward the head. The end of the upper mandible of the beak is equipped with a horny cap which bears a sharp point. By means of this, while slowly revolving in the shell, a circular path is chipped around the large end of the egg, the shell membranes being cut at the same time. When the shell is nearly cut around a final convulsion finishes the break, and the chick can emerge.

Physiological Development.—The physiological changes that occur during the development of the embryo are as full of interest to the inquiring student as are the structural changes that have just been described.

The metabolism of the developing embryo is a matter of special importance and some of the facts concerning it should be understood by the student of poultry husbandry.

With the exception of oxygen, the materials out of which the embryo is formed are all found in the various parts of the egg. They are protein, carbohydrates, fats and minerals. Of the minerals, calcium is to be noted especially because it is found largely in the shell rather than in the egg contents.

Though protein, carbohydrates and fat are all used as sources of energy, each of these serves in turn as the most important source of energy during three successive stages of development. Up to and including the fourth day it appears reasonable to believe that the carbohydrate in the egg contents is the main source. After the fourth day, and before the ninth, the production of urea is very intense, which suggests that protein is being rapidly broken down, and is therefore available as a source of energy. During the latter part of incubation fat is quite evidently the source.

It should not be inferred that any one of the three materials is the sole source of energy at a particular time. Analyses of the allantoic and amniotic fluids during development show that uric acid accumulates in the allantoic cavity beginning at some time during the fifth day of incubation, or not long after the embryonic kidney has entered into communication with the allantois. Uric acid continues to accumulate up to the time of hatching, the period of its most intense production being from the seventh to the eleventh days. This, of course, means a continued oxidation of protein. Similarly, carbohydrate is utilized, insofar as it is available, throughout the period of incubation, although it is of special importance at the beginning. Fat, on the other hand, is not used directly until rather late in the incubation period, though the possibility of a transference of fat into carbohydrate during the early stages of development has been suggested.

Of the mineral elements involved in the metabolism of the embryo, calcium is by far the most important, if for no other reason than that for about one hundred years it was a subject of keen controversy, particularly with respect to whether calcium is actually transferred from the shell to the embryo. Concerning the essential facts there is now no important difference of opinion. They may be stated briefly as follows:

The calcium content of the inside of the egg, including the embryo, rises markedly during incubation, the rise beginning about the twelfth day.

The calcium content of the embryo increases in a parallel fashion, *i. e.*, at the same rate and during the same time, but remains always quantitatively below that of the whole egg.

The calcium content of the yolk rises slightly during the incubation period.

The calcium content of the shell membranes increases from the beginning of incubation, and rises very sharply from about the seventh day to the time of hatching.

Infertile eggs, when incubated along with fertile ones, never contain any more calcium than do unincubated eggs.

These results can be explained only on the basis of a distinct transfer of calcium from the shell to the embryo. It is further evident that the transfer is due to the presence of the embryo, for infertile eggs are not affected. Of particular interest is the fact that the embryo seems to draw on the shell exclusively for its supply of calcium without making use of what is in the yolk until after hatching.

Critical Periods.—Embryo mortality is not uniformly distributed over the twenty-one days of incubation. Instead, there are definite peaks in the mortality curve. About half of the total mortality normally occurs during the last three or four days, with the nineteenth day representing the maximum. Another significant peak, though it is quantitatively less important, is during the second, third, and fourth days. A third, though usually lower, peak occurs between the tenth and fourteenth days.

This general pattern of embryo mortality is seen under all normal incubation conditions, whether total hatchability is high or low. Some causes of death are, however, more important at one peak than at another. Low-hatching hens tend to have an exaggerated early embryo mortality, indicating the difficulty of certain physiological adjustments in the early development of the embryo. Nutritional deficiencies in the ration of breeding hens—riboflavin, for example—

usually cause an exaggerated mortality at the 10- to 12-day point. Similarly, the late peak of mortality is likely to be increased materially, in relation to the other two, if incubating conditions are faulty. Unsuitable holding conditions for eggs prior to incubation may show up at either the early or the late peak periods.

OPTIMUM CONDITIONS FOR INCUBATION

Many of the investigations that have had as their object the study of optimum conditions for the developing egg rather than embryological development itself, have been based for the most part on a comparison of the conditions of eggs and their surroundings under natural incubation, and in commercial incubators.

There is some danger, however, in assuming that the hen and her nest furnish optimum conditions. The attitude that Nature may not be improved upon in some particulars, or stating it differently, may not be assisted to better serve man's needs, is a mistaken one. If it were not, there would be no hens laying 300 eggs in a year. In nature no such number of eggs is needed to secure the survival and increase the numbers of the race. The same may be said of the hatchability of eggs. Nature's needs and man's wants do not necessarily coincide.

Position of Eggs.—It is generally understood among poultrymen that the position of the egg during the period of incubation has a profound influence upon its development. It is a matter of common knowledge that the head of the chick normally develops at the large end of the egg. Usually, both in the nest and in the incubator, the large end of the egg is higher than the small end. This is due to the shape of the egg, and to the lessening of the specific gravity of the large end as incubation proceeds, because of the increasing size of the air cell.

When eggs are incubated large-end-up, about 2 per cent of the embryos develop with their heads in the small end of the egg. In eggs incubated in a horizontal position the percentage is about 3.5, but in eggs incubated small-end-up it is about 60. When expressed as a percentage of the dead-in-shell eggs, the corresponding figures are 7, 23, and 67.

By reversing the position of eggs which were incubated either large-end-up or small-end-up for different lengths of time, it was found that the malposition head-in-small-end-of-egg is usually determined during the second week of incubation.

Changing Position.—The hen turns the eggs she is incubating in two ways. The first is by peculiar lateral movements of the body with which she settles on the nest after feeding and which she continues from time to time throughout the day, and probably throughout the night. The purpose of these lateral movements is presumably to seek a more comfortable position. The practical results are to bring the body in closer contact with the eggs and so closer to the developing germ, and also, to turn the eggs. The second is by reaching under her body and moving the eggs with her beak. Observations of hens in glass nests have shown that the eggs were turned at least every hour both day and night, and in one instance as many as ten times in two hours.

Such observations as have been reported, show that in artificial incubation, fairly frequent turnings increase the hatching power of eggs. The usual commercial practice is to turn eggs three or four times daily, but there is ample experimental evidence to indicate that increased turning, up to eight times daily, will increase the percentage of eggs which hatch. Additional turnings cannot be justified in practice, though eggs may be turned as often as ninety-six times daily, *i. e.*, once every fifteen minutes, without detrimental results, provided they are turned back and forth about their long axes. If turned in only one direction, there is high embryonic mortality caused by ruptured blood-vessels and broken yolk sacs.

Temperature.—In reviewing the papers concerned with incubation temperatures, one cannot but be impressed with the fact that both the interest and the point of view of the avian embryologist differs greatly from that of the student of incubation problems. Embryologists have confined their careful work mostly to the early stages, lost in an admiration-compelling endeavor to understand the mysteries of that development. Needham, in his comprehensive review of "The Metabolism of the Developing Egg," speaking from the viewpoint of the biochemist interested in the bewildering series of chemical changes taking place within the limits defined by the shell of the egg, was led to make the remark that "the data of classical embryology are not very useful for our purpose because the majority of embryologists have been histologists, and for them the major interest has been in the first few hours of development. The primitive streak, the neural groove; these were the kind of phenomena they preferred to study—after the tenth day the embryo ceased to interest them, it became anatomical."

Some of the more recent experimental studies have been aimed at the effect of incubation temperatures on hatching results, and these are much more helpful to both the practical poultryman and the student of incubation.

Temperatures of Eggs under Natural Incubation.—The temperature at which eggs are naturally incubated depends primarily upon the temperature of the hen. This is quite variable, both among hens on the same day and for the same hen from day to day, though the variation appears to be much less among broody hens than among non-broodies.

There is a popular supposition that the temperature of a broody hen is relatively high, and that one of the characteristics of broodiness is the so-called "broody fever." The facts are that the temperatures reported for broody hens average about 2° F. below those for non-broody hens, being comparable to the temperatures of non-broody hens at times of minimum activity.

Observations made at the Montana Station showed that the temperature at the top of eggs containing live embryos remained fairly constant, averaging 102.3° F. The temperature at the bottom of the egg, however, increased several degrees as incubation progressed. During the first few days it was from 15° to 18° lower than the temperature at the top of the egg, but during the last few days it was only 10° or 12° lower. These readings were made with eggs in a horizontal position.

Temperatures of Eggs during Artificial Incubation.—Just how to apply these findings to the problem of artificial incubation is none too clear when the several different types of incubators are taken into account. Presumably there is an optimum temperature condition for each type of incubator, and occasionally for an individual machine. Not only this, but optimum temperature must always be a relative matter in that it is partially dependent upon humidity and air movement, as well as upon the exact location of the thermometer.

With the advent of mammoth incubators of the forced-draft type it soon became apparent that actual optimum incubating temperatures were lower than had commonly been supposed. Instead of 102° to 103° F., as measured by a thermometer with its bulb at the same level as the top of the eggs, either under the hen or in a still-air machine, the actual egg temperature was about 100° F. or a little less.

Extensive tests at the National Agricultural Research Center, Beltsville, Maryland, have shown an optimum incubation temperature of 100° F. when the relative humidity was kept at 60 per cent, the concentration of oxygen at 21 per cent, the carbon dioxide below 0.5 per cent, and the air movement past the eggs approximately 12 cm. (5 inches) per minute. In these tests the percentage hatch decreased at temperatures above and below 100° F., until at 96° and at 103.5° F. nearly all the embryos died.

Effects of High Temperature.—The permissible temperature range above normal is much more limited than the range below. This is not altogether surprising perhaps, since in natural incubation the opportunities for overheating appear to be very much less than for underheating.

Three principal effects of high temperatures are (1) marked speeding up in the rate of development, with an accompanying increase in carbon dioxide output; (2) the production of abnormal embryos in the early stages; and (3) the lowering of the per cent of fertile eggs which hatch.

The speeding up of development as the result of abnormally high temperatures with an accompanying increase in CO_2 output has been observed by a number of workers. During the greater part of the incubation period the developing chick reacts to increases in temperature as a cold-blooded animal, by increasing the discharge of CO_2. From about the nineteenth day until hatching it is neutral in this respect, and raising the external temperature does not seem to affect the CO_2 production. The day after hatching the chick responds to rises in external temperature as a warm-blooded animal, by decreasing the output of CO_2.

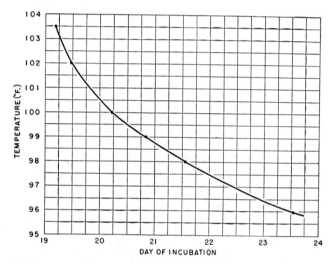

Fig. 54.—Effect of temperature on total incubation time. As the incubation temperature is decreased from 103.5° to 96° F., the number of days from the beginning of incubation to hatching increases from slightly more than 19 to $23\frac{1}{2}$. (*Courtesy of U. S. Department of Agriculture.*)

The effect of temperature on the length of the incubation period is shown in Figure 54.

High lethal internal egg temperatures have been determined as ranging from 106° to 110° F. during the first five days of incubation, and from 114° to 118° thereafter.

An accompaniment of high, though not necessarily lethal temperatures, is the production of abnormalities of various sorts, including crooked toes, crooked necks, and sprawling legs which prevent the chick from standing on its feet.

Effects of Low Temperatures.—Harvey, in 1651, observed that as the three-day embryo was cooled, the heart beat slower and slower until it ceased. The pulsations would resume when the temperature was raised. This is perhaps the first direct observation of the effect of abnormally low incubating temperature upon the embryo. Since then a large number of investigators have studied its effects.

In general, these effects may be placed in three classes which are undoubtedly closely related. These are: (1) the slowing down of the developmental processes accompanied by a diminution of the CO_2 output; (2) the production of abnormal embryos in early stages; and (3) the reduction of the per cent of fertile eggs which hatch.

Fig. 55.—A row of incubators in the Townsend Hatchery, Millsboro, Delaware. (*USDA Photo.*)

Certain contingencies may arise which necessitate holding eggs at subnormal temperatures for a few hours while incubation is in progress, and it is well to know something about how much cooling eggs will stand.

Workers studying this problem at the Storrs Station in 1916-1917 found that after the first twenty-four hours of incubation chick embryos from certain hens would stand from four to five hours' exposure at a temperature of 50° F. From this point on, the time limit

increased up to fifteen hours for eggs which had been incubated for
ten to twelve days, but after the seventeenth day continued exposure
to a temperature of 50° F. for more than six hours usually caused
the death of the embryos so treated.

FIG. 56.—Cut-away view of a room-type mammoth incubator showing fans for air circulation and setting trays in racks for easy tilting. (*Courtesy of Buckeye Incubator Company.*)

Recent studies at the Maryland Station have shown that at internal egg temperatures of 29° to 30° F. it was necessary to use an
exposure time of 95 minutes in order to kill half the embryos during
the first week of incubation, and from 70 to 80 minutes at later
stages. This does not mean, however, that half the eggs so treated
will hatch.

At the California Station it was found that twelve hours of current interruption in electric incubators, under room temperatures

approximating 70° F., produced an average decrease of 3.4 per cent in the number of chicks hatched.

Cooling Eggs.—The once nearly universal custom of cooling eggs during the incubation period probably arose from a desire to imitate Nature. When a hen leaves her nest to feed, the eggs become more or less cool. Because this happens in Nature, it has been assumed that better hatches will result if the eggs are cooled when artificially incubated. There appears to be little evidence that this supposition is well founded.

Fig. 57.—The separate hatcher is standard equipment in many hatcheries. (*Courtesy of Buckeye Incubator Company.*)

With the increased popularity of the forced-draft type of incubator, in which no cooling is practised, it came to be more generally recognized that cooling is unnecessary. The result is that whereas in times past nearly all eggs were cooled regularly, now very few are so treated, regardless of the type of incubator used.

Respiration.—In animal organisms, respiration refers to the interchange of gases between the organism and the surrounding medium.

With land-dwelling animals the surrounding medium is the air, and the gases exchanged are chiefly oxygen (O_2), carbon dioxide (CO_2) and water vapor (H_2O).

Several investigators have studied the effects upon the developing embryo of sealing the pores of egg shells and thus stopping the gas exchange. Various materials including varnish, shellac and water-glass were used. The net results of these studies, insofar as they have a bearing on incubation problems, seem to be (1) that the air cell normally performs an important function in embryonic respiration and (2) that the developing embryo is somewhat adaptable and may survive and even develop without the aid of the air cell, absorbing oxygen and discharging carbon dioxide through the shell at other places than the large end.

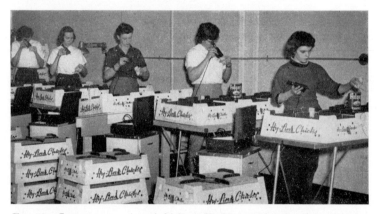

Fig. 58.—Instrument sexing of chicks at Hy-Line production plant, Johnston, Iowa. A trained operator can handle 500 to 600 chicks an hour. (*Courtesy of Hatchery and Feed.*)

Oxygen Requirements.—Air contains about 21 per cent of oxygen and it is therefore impossible in incubation to have an excess above this amount unless it is artificially supplied. Without adequate ventilation it is very easy to have a deficiency, because the carbon dioxide produced is at the expense of oxygen.

From tests at the National Agricultural Research Center it is apparent that it is very important for normal embryonic development that the oxygen concentration not be allowed to decrease below the amount in normal air. An excess of oxygen is not nearly so detrimental as a deficiency. A deficiency of 5 per cent of oxygen reduced the hatch about one-third, or from 81 to 55 per cent, but it took an excess of 25 per cent to reduce the hatch that much.

Carbon Dioxide Toleration.—That the amount of carbon dioxide in the air immediately surrounding incubating eggs might have some effect upon their development, was recognized by the early students of incubation problems.

Lamson and Edmond, at the Storrs Station, spent some five years studying this problem, and as the result of a great many individual trials and determinations they showed "that if the carbon dioxide in the air of the incubator goes above 150 parts in 10,000 there will be a high mortality of the chick embryos and that this dying will be greatly increased when the carbon dioxide rises above 200 parts" (or 2 per cent).

Fig. 59.—An electric debeaker is use. Many thousands of chicks are debeaked when only one day old. (*Curtesy of Hatchery and Feed.*)

More recent tests have shown that when the percentage of oxygen is held constant at 21, along with constant temperature, humidity and air movement, the decrease in percentage hatch is proportional to the increase in CO_2. All results are in agreement in suggesting a maximum CO_2 content of 0.5 per cent if optimum hatching results are to be secured.

9

Relative Humidity.—The capacity of air to absorb and hold moisture increases rapidly as its temperature rises, and the drier the air in an incubator, the more moisture it will take up from the eggs. Control of relative humidity is therefore important in artificial incubation.

There is a relationship between relative humidity and temperature, at least in forced-draft incubators. With three machines operating at the same dry bulb temperature (99° F.) there was a spread of forty-eight hours in time of hatching when they were operated at wet bulb temperatures of 75°, 85° and 90° F., respectively. These correspond to relative humidities of 33 per cent,

Fig. 60—The shipping room of a modern hatchery is a busy place. (*Courtesy of Hatchery and Feed.*)

56 per cent and 70 per cent. When the temperature in the low humidity machine was adjusted to 100° F., and that in the high humidity machine to 98° F., all three machines hatched together in the normal period of twenty-one days. The inference seems clear that, at least in the forced-draft type of incubator, as the humidity is increased, the temperature requirement is decreased.

Barott, at the Beltsville Research Center, found that with the temperature held constant at 100° F., the oxygen content kept at 21 per cent, the CO_2 content kept below 0.5 per cent, and the rate of air movement at 12 cm. per minute, the best hatches were obtained at a relative humidity of 61 per cent. The true optimum might easily be slightly above or below this figure, and a variation of five, or even ten points either way would not be seriously detrimental to hatching results.

That high humidity may be important in other ways than its effect on the hatching percentage is well illustrated by experiments conducted at the Kansas Station which showed that the maintenance of a wet bulb reading of 95° F. in a forced-draft incubator at hatching time practically eliminated the spread of pullorum disease from infected to non-infected chicks hatching in the same machine.

The mortality to two weeks of age among chicks hatched from eggs laid by non-reactor hens, and hatched in the same machine with eggs from reactor hens, was 29 per cent, 15 per cent and 6 per cent when the wet bulb readings at hatching time were 75°, 85° and 95° F., respectively. At the same time the mortality among healthy control chicks was 5 per cent.

Testing.—It was formerly customary to test eggs by candling one or more times during the incubation period in order to remove any that were not developing normally. If fertility was poor, the eggs from two trays might be combined in one. Under present-day conditions very little such testing is done, partly because of the labor involved and partly because improved methods of feeding and management have so increased the normal percentage hatch that there will be very few eggs to remove.

Two classes of eggs can be removed on the basis of an early test— "infertiles" and "dead germs." In a technical sense the term infertile refers to an egg that has never been fertilized, but practically it includes those that have started to develop but that have died at such an early age that they cannot readily be distinguished by candling. A dead germ is a fertile egg in which the embryo has died after developing to a point such that it is easily identified by candling.

The so-called infertile egg appears to be clear save for a floating shadow, which is easily distinguished as the yolk.

The live germ is spider-like in appearance during the first few days, the body of the embryo representing the body of the spider and the radiating blood-vessels its legs. The live germ floats about freely in the contents of the egg when the egg is rotated before the candling lamp.

The dead germ may be recognized by the absence of the blood-vessels, by its adhering to the shell, or by the quite typical pink ring surrounding it which is called a blood ring.

A second test may be made after fourteen to sixteen days of incubation. If the first has been accurately done there will be only dead germs to test out. The live embryo at this time appears nearly to fill the egg. In the one or two light spaces which are usually present, blood-vessels will be noticed and the embryo chick will frequently be seen to move when the egg is rotated.

The dead germs may vary in appearance from typical blood rings to embryo chicks of nearly normal size. The latter will usually be readily recognized by the absence of blood-vessels, a general indefiniteness of outline, and a quite different color from that of eggs containing live embryos.

If suitable equipment is used, infertile eggs may be detected with a high degree of accuracy after fifteen to eighteen hours of incubation. A 75-watt blue bulb is used. In each fertile egg there can be seen on the surface of the yolk a small spot about the size of a dime. This is the tiny embryo. No such spot can be seen in an infertile egg.

Even fifteen hours of incubation will cause a marked deterioration in the market quality of infertile eggs. Eggs of AA quality, after fifteen hours at incubation temperature, may grade no better than B quality.

SUMMARY OF FACTORS INFLUENCING HATCHABILITY

Through research and observation by many investigators there has been accumulated a large amount of information concerning various factors which influence the hatchability of eggs. The following summary gives some idea of the variety of conditions which must be taken into account in explaining high or low hatching results.

High summer temperatures are detrimental to hatchability and thereby increase the cost of producing chicks.

Severe cold spells during the winter are detrimental to the hatchability of eggs laid immediately following such cold spells.

Eggs laid by pullets usually hatch better than eggs laid by hens kept under the same sort of conditions.

High egg production is not in itself detrimental to hatchability. Eggs from hens with medium high records usually hatch better than eggs from hens with low records.

Large eggs do not hatch as well as medium to small eggs. The frequency of certain malpositions is higher among embryos developing in the large eggs.

Eggs with tremulous air cells do not hatch as well as normal eggs.

Hens laying at a high rate will, in general, give better hatching results than hens laying at a low rate under the same conditions of feeding and management.

Inbreeding commonly results in decreased hatchability.

Crossing low-hatching strains of two different breeds or varieties will almost invariably improve the hatching results.

The hatchability of eggs held for no longer than one week is not improved by turning prior to incubation.

When eggs are held longer than one week, there is a marked decrease in hatchability which is directly proportional to the holding time.

The time required for incubation is related to the age of the eggs set, the older eggs requiring several hours longer to hatch than eggs held for only a few days.

Chilling eggs at temperatures as low as 38° F. has no apparent harmful effect on hatching results until the period of chilling exceeds forty-eight hours.

The optimum constant holding temperature seems to be in the range of 50° to 55° F.

On the basis of data now available, the optimum conditions for incubation appear to be (1) a temperature of 100° F. (or perhaps 99¾), (2) a relative humidity of 60 per cent, (3) oxygen content of the incubator air 21 per cent, (4) carbon dioxide content 0.5 per cent or below, (5) eggs to be held with the large end slightly raised, *i. e.*, at an angle of 30° above the horizontal, and (6) all eggs to be gently turned eight or more times during each twenty-four hours.

HATCHERY OPERATION

The hatching of chicks as a business has long been an important part of the poultry industry in the United States, but the type of operation being carried on today is very different from that of even ten years ago. Some of the changes are indicated by the following tabulation as reported by the U. S. Department of Agriculture.

Year	Number of hatcheries	Total egg capacity	Average egg capacity
1934	11,405	276,287,000	24,000
1943	10,112	504,640,000	50,000
1953	8,233	616,976,000	80,000
1959	4,939	575,601,000	116,000

Many small community hatcheries have gone out of business, and the larger operators have tended to concentrate on producing either broiler-type or egg-type chicks. In addition to this type of specialization, many hatcheries are under franchise to produce only chicks that come from eggs produced on farms owned and operated by a single breeder organization.

Hatchery operation is a year-round business, especially for those operators producing broiler-type chicks. In 1939, before broiler chicks represented a very significant part of the total, 65 per cent of all commercial chicks were hatched in the three months of March, April and May. In 1949 the corresponding figure was 55 per cent. Since 1950, hatchings of egg-type and broiler-type chicks have been reported separately. In 1959, 62 per cent of the egg-type chicks—which made up only about one-fourth of the total production—were hatched in March, April and May, but only 29 per cent of all broiler-type chicks were hatched in those three months.

These changes have altered the former position of the hatcheryman, who was in effect a manufacturer who bought his raw materials from and sold his finished product to the same class of people. He

is still rendering an essential service, but often as a part of a large
integrated organization instead of as an independent operator. His
supply flocks are much larger, and fewer in number than before,
just as his customers may be fewer and individual chick orders very
much larger than in the early days of the hatchery business.

TABLE 21.—COMMERCIAL CHICK PRODUCTION, BY MONTHS, FOR SELECTED
YEARS, AS REPORTED BY THE U.S. DEPARTMENT OF AGRICULTURE.

	1959		1949	1939
	Broiler-type	*Egg-type* *Millions*		
January	154	36	80	34
February	150	62	140	83
March	183	118	264	171
April	180	130	302	230
May	175	86	258	192
June	169	27	117	75
July	166	14	59	31
August	150	13	52	24
September	122	14	55	21
October	122	14	64	20
November	130	13	59	19
December	142	14	55	16
Total	1,843	541	1,505	916

Chapter 6

Brooding and Rearing

BROODING and rearing deal with the growth of the chick after hatching, and more specifically with those factors affecting growth that are more or less completely under the control of the poultryman. The growth attained by an individual will depend upon its inherited ability to grow, its food supply, and such environmental factors as temperature, air supply and protection from parasites and diseases. Reference has already been made to the marked influence of heredity. Nutrient requirements and their importance are given special consideration in a later chapter.

Aside from their nutritional needs, there is little basic information concerning the requirements of chicks during the brooding period. Yet in many ways this is the most critical and difficult period in the management of domestic birds. No poultry business can long succeed without a practical and efficient chick-rearing department. Chickens must be well grown before they can yield a monetary return to their owner, regardless of the nature of the particular poultry product he is selling.

Successful brooding is still largely an art, though information is gradually being accumulated which may eventually put artificial brooding on a scientific basis.

Commercial installations of large capacity have been developed through the application of principles which have proved successful in smaller units. It is not uncommon to find 5000 or 6000 chicks being brooded together as a unit, or to find houses and equipment so arranged that one caretaker is responsible for as many as 25,000 or 30,000 chicks.

BROODING REQUIREMENTS

The requirements of brooding appear to be essentially those of housing, with the addition of temperature regulation. A complete brooder is simply a special form of house designed for the purpose of keeping chicks comfortable. To be commercially practical, brooding equipment must also be reasonably low in cost.

Temperature.—There is no general agreement among poultrymen as to what constitutes exactly the proper hover temperature for chicks just out of the incubator or at succeeding ages. There is no cumulative experimental evidence determining definitely what these temperatures should be.

Ideal temperature conditions probably exist when there is a range in temperature always available to the chicks, from a maximum of not less than 100° F. to a minimum of 60° or 70° F. When they have opportunity for a choice, chicks soon learn to find the temperature that is most comfortable to them. Trouble comes not so much from temporary exposure to low or to variable temperatures, as from continuous exposure to temperatures that are too high or too low, with no opportunity for the chicks to move at will to more comfortable temperatures.

Careful tests have shown that, with the temperature taken $2\frac{1}{2}$ inches above the litter, baby chicks are apparently comfortable at all temperatures in the range from 80° to 110° F. Not until the air temperature is some five degrees above or below this range is there definite indication of discomfort and of a tendency to avoid such areas. On the other hand, extensive tests at the Beltsville Agricultural Research Center involving 72 experiments with 30 chicks each, showed a maximum growth response during the first nine days after hatching when the average temperature was 91° F., dropping from 94° on the first day to 88° on the ninth. In a later series of 53 similar experiments, best results were obtained when the temperature was reduced uniformly from 94° on the first day to 80° on the eighteenth. Variation in controlled relative humidity from 35 per cent to 75 per cent made no appreciable difference in growth to 18 days of age.

It is unsafe to lay down absolute rules for all breeds and conditions. First and always the chicks must be comfortable. In quite cold weather it is likely to take a higher temperature to accomplish this than in more moderate weather. The temperature should in all cases be reduced as the chicks grow older, as rapidly as is compatible with their comfort, and artificial heat taken away altogether as soon as they are well feathered out.

Even after all artificial heat has been done away with, and the chicks are well feathered, the brooding apparatus should be held in readiness against unusually cool nights, which are likely to produce crowding if a little heat is not supplied.

An experienced poultryman depends almost entirely upon the action of the chicks in regulating the brooding temperature, but a beginner will find a thermometer helpful.

The thermometers used should be carefully tested at the beginning of each season, if they are to be relied upon, just as in the case of incubator thermometers.

Effects of Chilling.—A little chick, compelled to remain in the cold after he begins to feel chilly, soon becomes helpless. This is apparently caused by the paralysis of the breathing apparatus. The lungs are located on either side of the median line of the back at the circumference of the body cavity. Lobes of the lungs extend between the ribs and are protected from the outside temperature only by a thin membrane, the skin, and a coat of down. It is not surprising that when the chick is chilled the lungs are quickly affected.

In natural brooding, the back and lungs are the best protected portions of the body. When a chick becomes uncomfortably cold under conditions of artificial brooding, and is unable to locate heat enough to warm him quickly, he seems to obey that instinct which tells him to get his back up against the mother hen. The result is that he tries to crawl under the other chicks. This, taken up by more and more chicks, results in bunching and crowding with the accompanying evils of smothered chicks and a diminution of thrift on the part of the entire flock.

Diarrhea can be produced experimentally in baby chicks by exposing them to moderate changes in temperature. A sudden increase in temperature is just as detrimental as a decrease. Chicks kept under observation for a period of ten weeks showed that though the exposure to a change in temperature was not always fatal, there was a serious disturbance in metabolism which resulted in abnormal development.

The low lethal internal body temperature has been studied by several workers, and ranges from 62° F. on the day of hatch to about 67° at two weeks of age, with a gradual increase to about 73° at maturity. Maryland workers found that 2-day-old chicks could stand 35 minutes exposure at $-10°$ F., and that at twenty days of age they could stand 75 minutes before half of them succumbed.

Effects of Overheating.—Overheating occurs comparatively seldom, because chicks instinctively move away from the source of heat when too warm. If confined under a hover when the temperature runs up, they die rather quickly.

The high lethal body temperature for the chick is the same as that for older fowls, 117° F. This body temperature is reached in about ten minutes when chicks are exposed to an air temperature of 160° F. At room temperatures of 100° F., death losses among day-old chicks in sealed summer-size fibre-board chick boxes were found by Wilson at the California Station to range from 20 to 50 per cent. New Hampshire chicks were more susceptible to overheating than were White Leghorns.

Fresh Air.—When hovers are used, they should be so arranged that there will be a constantly changing supply of fresh air. With coal-stove brooders in which the hover acts largely as a deflector, there is usually good circulation of air. If a fringe or curtain is used, it should be short enough to clear the surface of the litter by at least two inches so as to permit free air movement.

With electric brooders having the heating element under the hover, particular care should be taken to see that there is a good flow of air. Not infrequently it will be discovered that even with open ventilators which appear ample, hardly any change of air is taking place. The inevitable result of such a condition is dampness.

Modern electric brooders are made with small circulating fans to help keep the hover area dry.

Dougherty and Moses at the California Station studied the relation of ventilation in electric brooders to the health and growth of chicks, and concluded that the development of dampness precedes serious vitiation of the air by a considerable margin. They found that a rate of circulation of air through the hover of 1 cu. ft. of air per 100 chicks per minute was insufficient to prevent excessive condensation or to meet the needs of the chicks to six weeks of age.

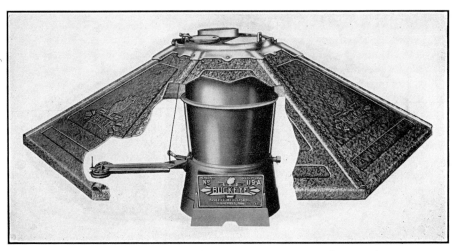

Fig. 61.—A common type of coal heated brooder. Picture shows the hover cut away to expose the thermostatic control and lower damper. (*Courtesy of Buckeye Incubator Company.*)

A flow of 2 cu. ft. of air per 100 chicks per minute was found to meet the needs fully as well as larger amounts, but it would not keep the hover dry after the chicks were three weeks old. As much as 4 cu. ft. of air per 100 chicks per minute (equal to an entire air change every 1.125 minutes in the brooders used) would not keep the hover entirely dry.

Such regulation of the ventilation of an electric brooder as will keep the interior reasonably dry will assure the chicks an ample supply of fresh air. Ventilation in excess of that needed to keep the hover reasonably dry and free from bad odors will not benefit the chicks, will cause an undue dissipation of heat, and will unnecessarily increase the electricity consumed.

Gas brooders are commonly installed without being vented to the outside. In a small brooder house this can aggravate the moisture and ventilation problem because of moisture formed and condensed during gas combustion.

Hover and Floor Space.—Commercial brooders are often overrated as to their capacity. In some brooders nearly one-half the floor space under the hover is occupied by the heater.

Well-fed chicks grow rapidly, often doubling their weight four successive times in the first six weeks, and it is apparent that a brooder which is filled to capacity with day-old chicks will be badly overcrowded within a very short time.

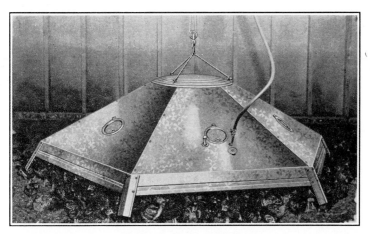

Fig. 62.—Gas heated brooders are popular in some parts of the country. (*Courtesy of H. D. Hudson Company.*)

Floor area requirements vary with the size, and therefore with the age of the chickens. As with many other management factors on which poultrymen have to make decisions, the optimum floor area for greatest biological efficiency may not be the same as the optimum for greatest economic efficiency. It is considered sound practice to provide ½ square foot of total brooder area per chick at the start. From 15 to 20 per cent of the total area will be hover space if hovers are used. If optimum growing conditions are to be provided, the floor area per chick must be increased by about ½ square foot at four weeks, and again at 8, 12 and 16 weeks so that after 16 weeks there will be not less than 2½ square feet of floor area for each chicken.

Just how many chicks to brood in one flock is a matter that must always be finally decided by the poultryman in each individual case. Large flocks effect a considerable saving in labor and avoid some duplication of equipment. On the other hand, optimum results with respect to rapid growth and low mortality can be obtained only when the number of chicks in a single flock is limited. The beginner will do well to put not more than 200 chicks under a single hover. Some experienced poultrymen, after trying the plan of brooding in flocks of 500 to 1000, have returned to the practice of putting not more than 200 to 250 chicks under one brooder, especially if the chickens are to be raised to maturity. Commercial broiler growers, on the other hand, very commonly start 600 to 1000 chicks to each brooder stove.

BROODING EQUIPMENT

A complete discussion of the many sorts and kinds of brooders that have from time to time been used in the commercial rearing of chicks might well be of interest, but it would be out of place in this book. Instead, there are included illustrations of many of the common types that are in use today, with some comment on the conditions to which they are best adapted and some of the limitations which must be kept in mind.

Fig. 63.—A drum-type oil-burning brooder. When temperature conditions are right the chicks distribute themselves over the "comfort zone" when settling down for the night. (*Courtesy of The Simplex Brooder Stove Company.*)

Portable brooders with individual heating units are made in many styles and sizes. They may be heated by coal, oil, gas or electricity. They vary in size from small lamp-heated or electric brooders of 50-chick capacity to large coal burners producing sufficient heat to warm a room for 1500 to 2000 chicks.

Battery brooders are a special type designed to accommodate large numbers of chicks in a limited space for short periods of time. They are most useful in carrying chicks from hatching time to about four weeks of age, and are never entirely satisfactory for raising chickens to maturity. They are very helpful as a means of avoiding most of the accidental mortality that is often experienced during the early weeks of colony brooding.

To the poultryman who is mechanically minded, the construction of home-made equipment is always a challenge, and brooding equipment has offered many opportunities for the display of all the skill and ingenuity of which such an individual is capable. Hot-water systems, battery brooders, heated-floor brooders, wood-burning brooders, and others have been built at home and used successfully.

Commercial broiler growers use all of the foregoing plus a variety of systems which depend upon the circulation of hot air or hot water from a central heating plant.

TABLE 22.—PERCENTAGE OF ALL CHICKENS RAISED, 1949, THAT WERE BROODED WITH HEAT FROM EACH OF SEVERAL SOURCES. (FROM A SURVEY OF 20,000 FARMS BY THE U. S. DEPARTMENT OF AGRICULTURE.)

			Source of heat			
Section	Electricity	Oil	Coal	Gas	Wood	Hens
Northeast (New England, N. Y., N. J., Pa., Del., Md.)	22	10	57	8	2	1
Corn Belt (Ohio, Ind., Ill., Iowa, Mo.)	44	31	9	6	4	6
Lake States and Great Plains (Mich., Wis., Minn., N. D., S. D., Nebr., Kans.)	32	48	5	6	1	8
Appalachian (W. Va., Ky., Tenn., Va., N. C.)	22	18	20	4	21	15
Southeast (S. C., Ga., Fla., Ala.)	19	41	16	10	6	8
South (Miss., La., Ark., Okla., Texas)	18	32	2	29	6	13
Mountain (Mont., Ida., Wyo., Colo., N. Mex., Ariz., Utah, Nev.)	36	37	8	5	1	13
Pacific (Wash., Oreg., Calif.)	61	22	3	11	1	2
United States	29	27	21	10	6	7

In a series of Delaware tests in which more than 35,000 broilers were used, gas-heated brooders gave production results equal to individual coal-heated brooders, but at a 27 per cent greater fuel cost. Oil-burning brooders took less labor than coal stoves. A central hot air system equalled individual coal stoves in production results and saved a great deal of labor. Infrared bulbs were much more costly as a source of heat than were the other types of brooders. The final rating was (1) central hot air; (2) oil; (3) individual coal stoves; (4) gas, and (5) infrared bulbs.

As suggested by the data in Table 22, based on a survey of 20,000 farms by the U. S. Department of Agriculture, the source of heat used is determined partly by climate, and partly by what is conveniently and economically available.

Other Equipment.—In addition to the brooder proper, it will be necessary to have various other items of equipment if brooding and rearing results are to be wholly satisfactory. There must be feeding and watering devices, and they must be changed from time to time as the chicks grow. A feeder that is suitable for chicks under one week of age will not give good results with a flock of six-weeks-old

Fig. 64.—A hot water brooding system in California. During the first 10 to 14 days chicks are kept close to the hover area by a corrugated paper guard. Some poultrymen use aluminum guards. (*Courtesy of Pacific Poultryman.*)

TABLE 23.—Manufacturers' Domestic Shipments of Brooders, by Type for Selected Years. (Data from the Bureau of the Census.)

Year	Floor type						Battery type (heated)
	Electric	Oil	Coal	Gas (thousands)	Wood	Total	
1940	91	115	33	4	—	243	9
1943	144	197	92	10	25	468	23
1946	141	172	36	30	6	385	76
1949	84	66	35	90	—	275	60
1953	102	28	8	95	—	233	36
1957	70	22	3	89	—	184	10

chicks. Both sanitary feeding and the avoidance of waste require that there be a suitable adjustment between the size and style of feeders used and the age and weight of the chicks.

Wind produces a problem with coal-stove brooders which should not be overlooked. The fireboxes usually have capacity enough to meet ordinary conditions, but few are large enough to hold an adequate supply of coal for a cold, windy night. All too often it is found in the morning that the fire has burned out completely and the chicks are chilled. A properly constructed, automatic, wind-damper set in the brooder stovepipe will be of great help in preventing this trouble. It is simply a check damper which opens with the increasing draft that is caused by a brisk wind, so that the fire continues to burn at a nearly constant rate.

Fig. 65.—Fins help to radiate heat from hot water pipes in this installation (*Courtesy of Poultry Tribune.*)

Fig. 66.—This central hot air heating system can be adjusted by raising or lowering the hovers. (*Courtesy of Broiler Business.*)

Early roosting is most easily accomplished if low roosts are installed while the chicks are quite small. Many devices have been tried to get chicks to take to the roosts at an early age, but none seems to be better than the sloping roosting platform that provides low roosts near the edge of the hover and higher ones that are easily reached from the low ones in front. The frame supporting these roosts should be covered with poultry netting or hardware cloth.

Fig. 67.—White Leghorn pullets in brooder house at Creighton Brothers, Warsaw, Indiana. (*J. C. Allen and Son Photo.*)

Fig. 68.—A 30' × 370' Pennsylvania brooder house with adjustable plastic screens. Pullets are transferred to range shelters at six to twelve weeks of age, depending on the season of year. Hot water heat is used in this building. (*Courtesy of Poultry Tribune.*)

Fig. 69.—Battery brooders make an ideal place in which to start baby chicks. (*Courtesy of Poultry Tribune.*)

Strains of chickens vary greatly in the tendency to develop crooked keels. In a susceptible strain, the incidence of this deformity will be increased by early roosting. At the Kansas Station it was found that under normal roosting conditions a crooked-keeled strain showed an incidence of 60 to 80 per cent crooked keels while a straight-keeled strain showed less than 10 per cent.

Fig. 70.—White Plymouth Rocks on range. Arbor Acres Midwest Farm, Thorntown, Indiana. (*J. C. Allen and Son Photo.*)

Unless only pullet chicks are bought, the cockerels need to be separated from the pullets. The age at which this is done will naturally vary with the breed being kept, but whenever it is done it is the common practice to remove the cockerels from the flock and to leave the pullets on the range. This gives the pullets additional, usually much-needed room, but it has the distinct disadvantage that while the cockerels that are soon to be marketed as broilers are often taken to a new area, the pullets, on which the poultryman must depend for his main income, are left to grow up on the range that has been run over by all the chickens during the early part of the season. A more ideal arrangement would seem to be to limit the amount of range area used during the first part of the season to a reasonable minimum, and then at the time the sexes are separated, to remove the pullets to a clean range, leaving the cockerels in the old quarters until they are ready for market. In order to accomplish this objective in a practical way, more and more poultrymen are making use of roosting sheds or range shelters for the pullets. These are simply frame sheds provided with a tight roof and wire sides. The only interior equipment needed is roosts.

FIG. 71.—An all-purpose type of range shelter. The sides may be enclosed by the use of panels. (*Courtesy of Illinois Agricultural Experiment Station.*)

FIG. 72.—Inside view of a light weight range shelter. (*Courtesy of Poultry Tribune.*)

They may be provided with wire floors in order to keep the pullets from coming in contact with the night droppings.

Time of Hatching.—Several stations have studied the effect of out-of-season hatching on the growth and performance of White Leghorns—New York (1919–1921), Oklahoma (1923–1925), New Mexico (1924–1926) and New Jersey (1936–1940). Results were in agreement in that spring-hatched pullets made the best growth, laid the most eggs and, where egg weights were recorded, laid a lower percentage of small eggs, than did pullets hatched at other seasons. Conditions of feeding and management in those years were not the equal of those available now, but it seems clear that fall and winter-hatched pullets were at a disadvantage in the matter of egg size, primarily because they were subjected to the influence of increasing length of day before they reached adult size and consequently began to lay at a younger age. The result was a large number of small eggs.

A recent report from the Delaware station shows somewhat comparable results with New Hampshire pullets hatched each month in the years 1946 and 1948. The pullets hatched in November through February averaged more than 10 per cent of eggs, for the laying year, which weighed under 22 ounces to the dozen. The May hatch produced 46 per cent small eggs during the first month of laying, but by the third month they were down to 2 per cent. The December hatch, by contrast, produced 84 per cent small eggs in the first month and were still laying 20 per cent small eggs in their fourth month. The May hatch reached 25 per cent production by the time they were 189 days old, but the December group was laying at this rate at 147 days. Since small eggs are worth less on the market than large eggs, this difference in performance needs to be given careful consideration before deciding on extensive out-of-season hatching.

The effect of time of hatching on returns is shown for 100 Central Indiana poultry flocks in Table 24. It is important that pullets be hatched early enough so that they will be laying at a high rate during the season of favorable egg prices in late fall and early winter.

TABLE 24.—TIME OF STARTING CHICKS AS RELATED TO RETURNS—100 CENTRAL INDIANA POULTRY FLOCKS, 1945–46. (DATA OF JOHNSON, ROBERTSON AND SICER.)

	Time of hatch		
	Before April	April	After May 1
Number of flocks	70	20	10
Average number of hens	159	155	131
Eggs per hen	158	151	158
Per cent of hens culled during year	67	54	52
Average price of eggs (cents)	39	38	38
Labor returns per hour (cents)	45	32	−2
Labor returns per 100 hens (dollars)	94	74	−8

CAPON PRODUCTION

The purpose of caponizing is to improve the quality of poultry meat. Farmers regularly castrate calves, pigs and lambs, but usually consider caponizing a much more difficult operation because it involves opening of the abdominal cavity. Actually, the operation is very simple and the method can be learned quickly by almost anyone.

A small flock of capons could be raised to advantage on many farms, either for family use or for sale to local customers. Larger flocks often compete seriously with laying hens and pullets for house room, which is one important reason why they are not often found on general farms. Unless they can be kept for two to four months beyond the time at which the cockerels would normally be sold as roasters, it is not worth while to take the trouble to caponize.

Selection of Cockerels to Caponize.—The size and condition of the young cockerels to be caponized is more important than their age or variety. Leghorn cockerels make excellent small capons, and Plymouth Rocks, Orpingtons, Rhode Island Reds, and various crossbreds are all suitable for large capons. It is very important that the operation be performed before the cockerels become too large. This means choosing heavy breed cockerels weighing 1 to $1\frac{1}{2}$ pounds, or Leghorns weighing $\frac{3}{4}$ to 1 pound. In fact, with suitable equipment, it is entirely possible to caponize cockerels when they are no more than two or three weeks old. The most common error is to attempt the operation on larger cockerels, with consequent high mortality and more slips, or incompletely castrated individuals. Only rapidly growing, vigorous cockerels should be chosen.

Preparation for the Operation.—It is always desirable to withhold feed for 18 hours and water for the last 12 hours prior to the operation, in order that the intestines may become empty and thus permit better vision into the body cavity. There is also much less danger of puncturing the intestines during the operation.

Performing the Operation.—A first requirement for successful caponizing is good light. Bright daylight, preferably not in direct sunshine, is ideal. Artificial light may be used, if necessary.

Some means of restraining the birds in a convenient position must be provided. The usual procedure is to fasten the wings and legs by straps or cords so that sufficient tension can be applied to hold the bird well stretched out. If both testicles are to be removed through one incision, the bird should be placed on its left side.

The instruments needed are a sharp knife or scalpel, a small probe which has a tearing hook on one end, a spreader for holding the ribs apart after the incision has been made, and a remover for taking out the testicles. Several different types of removers are available, but a forceps type is preferred by most operators.

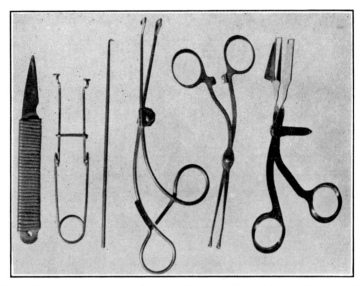

Fig. 73.—Instruments used for caponizing. Left to right: knife, spreader, tearing hook and probe, forceps for removal of the gonads, small forceps for operating on 2-week old cockerels, and an All-In-One instrument. (*Courtesy of Kansas Agricultural Experiment Station.*)

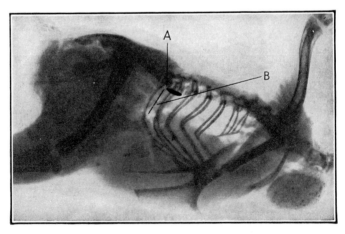

Fig. 74.—Radiograph of a living cockerel. The right testicle has been sketched in at *A*. The line of incision is indicated at *B*.

Making the Incision.—It is usually necessary to pluck a few feathers from the area through which the incision is to be made. A little cold water may be used to moisten the surrounding feathers so that they will lie down out of the way. Next, find the last two ribs with the fingers of the left hand; slide the skin upward and backward toward the thigh, making sure that the underlying thigh muscles are out of the way; force the knife through the skin and flesh between the last two ribs; lengthen the incision to about 1 inch, keeping it centered between the ribs and not too near the back; and insert the spreader so as to hold the ribs about $\frac{1}{2}$ inch apart. If the knife has not severed the peritoneal membranes, they should be torn with the hook so as to expose the testicles to the view of the operator.

Removing the Testicles.—The lower, or left testicle should be removed first. It is not visible, as a rule, and must be lifted into view by the forceps before it can be grasped. The entire organ and the connecting portion of the spermatic duct must be taken out in order to prevent the bird from becoming a "slip." Care must be taken, however, not to rupture any of the primary blood-vessels, or internal hemorrhage will result in death before the bird is removed from the operating table.

The remover is carefully worked over the testicle and so manipulated as to enclose the entire organ. It is then drawn out with a slight twisting motion. The same procedure is followed with the upper testicle. As soon as the spreader is removed, and the tension on the bird released, the skin and thigh muscles slip back over the incision, affording natural protection.

Because of the relatively high body temperature of chickens, it is possible to perform this sort of operation with little danger of infection. Ordinary cleanliness is all that is required.

Care After the Operation.—No special care of young capons is necessary, other than to give them a clean pen and range area where they do not have to compete with other chickens. Any good growing ration will be satisfactory.

Wind puffs often develop because air escapes from within the abdominal cavity before the incision between the ribs is healed, and becomes trapped beneath the skin. It is sometimes necessary to puncture these puffs four or five times on alternate days following the operation.

Slips result when some portion of the testicle is left in the body cavity. Occasionally a testicle is dropped inside the body after having been torn loose. If it is not removed, the bird will become a slip and will have all the external appearance of a normal cockerel. This is because the testicle, or in other cases a very small portion of it, becomes attached to the inner abdominal wall and continues to secrete the male sex hormone in sufficient quantity to cause

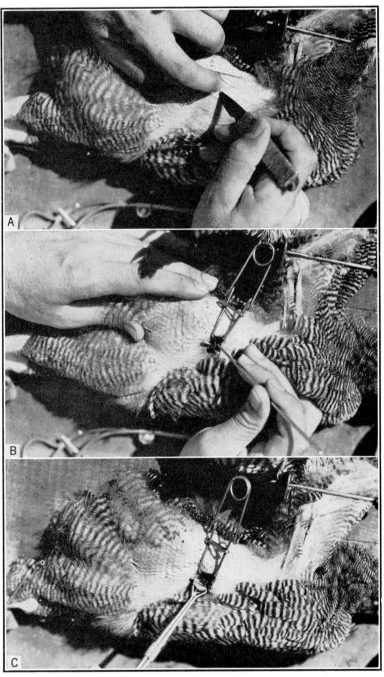

Fig. 75.—Performing the operation of caponizing. *A*, The skin and thigh muscle being drawn back preparatory to making the incision; *B*, tearing the peritoneal membranes after inserting a spreader to hold the ribs apart; *C*, removing the testicle. (*Courtesy of Kansas Agricultural Experiment Station.*)

enlargement of the comb and wattles and later toughening of the flesh.

Marketing Capons.—Persons who have once enjoyed roast capon of top quality are likely to be repeat customers year after year, and there is undoubtedly a potential market for capons which has never been explored. Common practice, however, has been to produce capons largely for local consumption. A few persons have developed a nice business in the sale of started capons, operated on at three weeks of age and sold at five or six weeks to customers who grow them to market age.

Chapter 7

Houses and Equipment

HOUSING of poultry for egg or meat production is important as a means of keeping many environmental conditions under the control of the operator. It also helps to insure maximum use of feed energy for productive purposes rather than in overcoming the effects of unfavorable weather.

With the right kind of stock, and a suitable food supply, production of eggs is likely to be in direct proportion to the comfort of the hens. The natural laying and breeding season is in the spring, and conditions then are those which provide comfort plus the stimulus of a gradually increasing length of day. A successful hen house will furnish its occupants with permanent protection from extremes of temperature and other unfavorable weather conditions. It will also enable the operator to provide the stimulus of artificial light when needed. In addition, it will be so arranged as to permit the necessary work of caring for the flock to be done with a minimum expenditure of time and effort.

THE HOUSING PROBLEM

Beginning about 1900 and continuing for more than twenty-five years, there was a period of much practical experimenting with different styles and types of poultry houses. The open scratching shed, the roosting closet, the "fresh-air" house, the muslin front, the straw loft, the half-monitor, and the warm tight house each had its staunch supporters. Gradually the cumulative results began to point to a few common recommendations on which nearly all could agree. But it was not until the poultry physiologist and the engineer began to give serious thought to the basic biological and weather problems involved that there was any accurate and dependable information on which to base recommendations for poultry house design and construction.

In mild climates the housing of poultry is very simple, but when winter temperatures average below 10° F., with average relative humidity above 80 per cent, and with sunshine amounting to less than 5 hours a day, the proper housing of highly productive flocks becomes a difficult problem. To understand the complicated nature of the problem, and the means by which it can be solved, it is necessary to look at poultry housing from three viewpoints: (1) As a problem in biology, (2) As a problem in engineering, and (3) As a problem in economics, as each is related to the matter of "weather" control in the hen house. This means that we need to know the ideal conditions of temperature, humidity, and air change for maximum egg production performance, the engineering design which will make it possible to control these conditions for a flock of given size, and the range or tolerance above and below the optimum which may be permitted for each factor without seriously interfering with production, so that we may decide what variations are permissible while still keeping construction costs within reasonable limits.

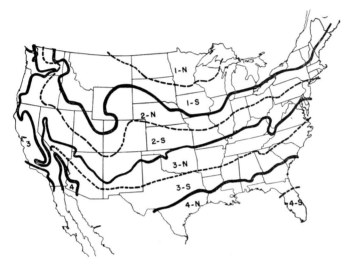

Fig. 76.—Temperature zones as related to poultry house construction. Average January temperature in Zone 1 below 20° F.; in Zone 2 20°–35°; in Zone 3 35°–50°; in Zone 4 above 50° F. Based on data from the U. S. Department of Agriculture.

Aside from such matters as light, floor space, litter materials, and the kind and amount of essential equipment, housing requirements for hens can be stated only in terms of temperature, relative humidity, and the number of air changes to maintain the necessary minimum amount of oxygen and the maximum permissible amount of carbon dioxide. This is easy to say but difficult to determine. It may be even more difficult to maintain any specified set of conditions.

TEMPERATURE

Chickens, like all other warm-blooded animals, produce heat, moisture and carbon dioxide as by-products of their biological activity. The entire process operates to maintain body temperature at about 106.5° F. (range from 104 to 109). Since this is nearly always above the air temperature in the poultry house by from 10 to as much as 100 degrees, the hen is constantly losing heat to her surroundings. This heat must as constantly be replaced or body temperature will fall and the hen can not long survive.

These facts might suggest that it would be desirable and perhaps practical to maintain laying house temperatures as high as 75° F. in

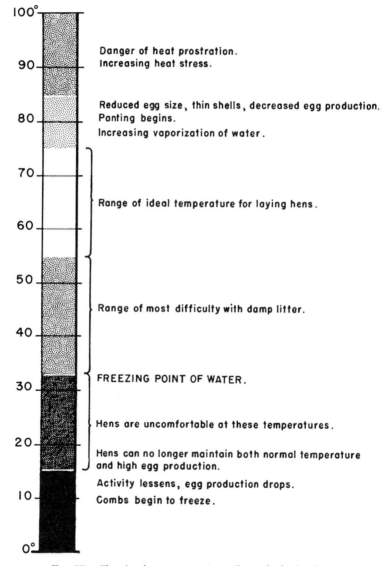

Fig. 77.—Showing how temperature affects the laying hen.

order to minimize heat loss to the air. But carefully controlled tests at the Beltsville Research Center indicate that a constant temperature of 55° F. is better than temperatures much above or below, at least for Rhode Island Reds. Hens kept at 55° F. laid at a rate of 75 per cent and consumed 3.5 pounds of feed for each pound of eggs. Those maintained at 85° F. laid at a rate of only 50 per cent and ate 4 pounds of feed for each pound of eggs, while

Heat loss *increased* by:	Heat production *increased* by:
Low air temperature	Physical activity
Increased air movement	Increased feed consumption
Low wall or floor temperature	Unbalanced rations
High humidity on cold days	"Chemical regulation" of body temperature when environmental temperature falls below the critical point
Loss of feathers (molting)	
"Physical regulation" of body temperature	

HEAT LOSS *In Balance With* HEAT PRODUCTION

Heat loss *decreased* by:	Heat production *decreased* by:
High air temperature	Decreased activity
Decreased air movement	Decreased feed intake
High wall or floor temperature	(No way of decreasing heat production when profitable egg yields are required. Feed a well-balanced ration to keep heat production at a minimum for the expected production and activity.)
Heavy feather coat	
Insulation of hen houses, with consequent increase in air and wall temperatures	

FIG. 78.—Factors influencing heat loss and heat production in the fowl.

those kept at 23° F., the lowest temperature tested, laid at a rate of only 26 per cent and consumed 12.3 pounds of feed for each pound of eggs. Temperatures no more than 10 degrees above or below 55° F. had only a slight effect on performance.

Heat Production vs. Heat Loss.—If the rate of heat loss is increased for any reason, as during a period of cold weather, heat production must be increased by a corresponding amount. Similarly, if heat production is increased, as by increased activity with no change in the surrounding air temperature, there must be a prompt increase in heat loss in order to prevent the body temperature from rising. Many different factors affect the rate of heat loss and the rate of heat production. The more important ones are shown in Figure 78.

Heat loss will be greater in winter than in summer because of the greater difference in temperature between the hen and her surroundings. If hens are exposed to wind, the increased volume of air moving past them, picking up heat as it goes, results in an increased rate of heat loss. Low wall or floor temperatures can result in greatly

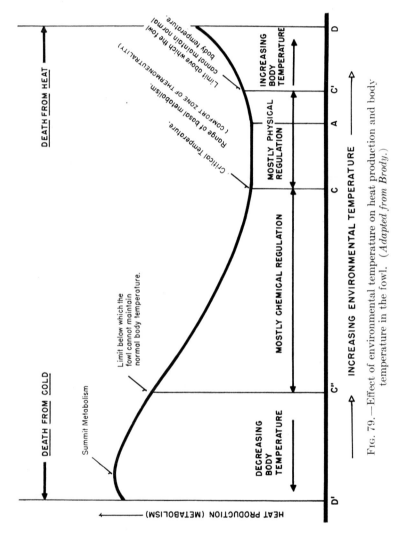

FIG. 79.—Effect of environmental temperature on heat production and body temperature in the fowl. (*Adapted from Brody.*)

increased heat loss so that hens may be uncomfortable in a building which has cold walls, even though the air temperature, as indicated by a thermometer, is not unreasonably low. High humidity makes air a better conductor, and moist air on a cold day will therefore absorb more heat from the hens than will dry air.

An increase in heat loss from any of the foregoing causes calls for increased heat production simply to maintain a balance and to keep the body temperature near normal. But heat production may vary independently of the demand caused by varying heat loss. Physical activity will increase heat production because energy is incompletely used in doing work and the wasted energy appears as heat. Increased feed consumption will increase heat production because the feed energy is not completely used, and heat is released in the process. The feeding of unbalanced rations, which leave excess nutrients to be oxidized and eliminated, will increase the total heat production. At environmental temperatures below the point at which physical regulation of body temperature is no longer effective, the so-called chemical regulation of heat production comes into play, causing an increase in heat production in order to maintain the normal body temperature as long as possible. (See Fig. 79.)

Conversely, heat loss from the body will be decreased by higher environmental temperatures, by decreased air movement, and by high wall and floor temperatures. As explained later, high humidity on hot days interferes with necessary heat loss.

Heat production will be lowered by decreased activity and by decreased feed intake, but since profitable egg yields are dependent on maximum feed consumption, there is no way to make practical use of this relationship except to feed rations that are reasonably well balanced, thereby keeping heat production at a minimum for the expected production and activity. The minimum heat production for hens at rest occurs at about 70° F.

MOISTURE

Of more practical concern to many poultrymen is the moisture given off by hens incidental to their use of feed. It often creates a real problem during cold weather. Unless it is removed by adequate ventilation or by the use of artificial heat, both the litter and the walls of the hen house may become soaking wet with condensed water vapor.

A complete water balance equation would have to take into account the fountain water consumed, free and hygroscopic water in the feed, the metabolic water released in connection with the digestion and metabolism of feed, as well as water removed in the eggs produced. In practice, however, the important components are the amount of water voided in the droppings and released to the air, the water vaporized by the hens, and the amount of water brought into the poultry house by incoming air on damp days. These will be considered in some detail.

Water Voided in Droppings. — Poultry feces, as voided, contain a high percentage of water. Reported figures range around 80 per cent, depending on whether they represent hourly or 24-hour samples. Not all of this moisture is lost to the air. Manure separated from poultry house litter under air dry conditions contains about 16 per cent moisture, equivalent to about 3 per cent of the original weight. But the moisture content of manure allowed to accumulate beneath the roosts seldom drops below 70 per cent. Under average winter conditions it is doubtful whether more than 30 per cent of the original weight of voided manure is actually released to the air as moisture. Forced ventilation or the use of artificial heat would of course raise this figure.

Data collected at the New Jersey station show that the weight of manure voided, because of its high moisture content, is about 90 per cent greater than the weight of feed consumed. The total feed intake of a flock of 100 4½-pound hens laying 80 eggs a day

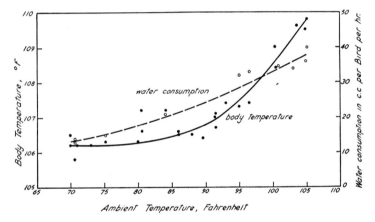

Fig. 80.—Effect of ambient temperature on body temperature and water consumption of White Leghorn pullets. (*After Wilson.*)

will be about 28 to 30 pounds. The corresponding amount of manure voided will therefore be 53 to 57 pounds. If 30 per cent of this is to become free water in the air of the hen house, there will be 16 to 17 pounds of water a day to produce wet litter unless it is removed by adequate ventilation. It is small wonder that litter gets wet during periods of high egg production.

This is one reason why more and more poultrymen are using mechanical cleaning systems for frequent removal of manure from poultry houses. Even twice-a-week removal will greatly reduce the moisture problem. Such a schedule will also help to keep flies at a minimum during warm weather. Some installations provide for daily removal of manure.

It should be clear that the moisture problem results from the presence of the hens and from their consumption of feed and water. In tests at the New Hampshire station it was found that litter samples taken from empty houses in January and February contained about 15 per cent of moisture, while those from pens filled with laying hens averaged about 35 per cent for insulated houses and ranged up to more than 60 per cent in uninsulated houses.

Vaporized Water and Heat Loss.—In addition to the water excreted in the droppings, there is a considerable amount of water which leaves the body by vaporization from the lungs. Since fowls have no sweat glands, there is very little opportunity for heat loss by evaporation from the skin. The amount vaporized from the lungs and air sacs varies widely with environmental temperature and humidity. It may also be influenced indirectly by the kind of feed. Substitution of corn for all of the oats and half of the wheat middlings in a standard low-energy ration reduced litter moisture significantly in tests at the Storrs Station.

Vaporization of water removes heat,* and variation in the quantity vaporized (indicated in the fowl by the rate of panting) is therefore an important means of varying the necessary heat loss from the body. At high air temperatures—approaching the normal body temperature—it is the only means by which the fowl can lose a substantial amount of heat. At low air temperatures, on the other hand, only a small fraction of the total heat loss is of this character—at 40° F. about 20 per cent and at 20° no more than 15 per cent.

Increased heat production, from whatever cause, increases the amount of heat lost as heat of vaporization. At high temperatures, especially when relative humidity is also high, fowls soon reach the limit of normal physical regulation and must resort to panting to facilitate vaporization of water as the only means of losing heat rapidly enough to keep the body temperature from rising. This condition exists whenever the surrounding air temperature equals or exceeds the skin temperature so that heat can no longer be dissipated by radiation. If the air temperature rises still higher, vaporization must also serve to rid the body of heat absorbed from the hot environment. This obviously cannot continue for long, and the fowl dies from heat exhaustion. Panting is nothing but a very marked increase in the respiration rate as the fowl attempts to get rid of more and more heat by this means. The amount of water vaporized increases slowly at temperatures of 75° to 80° F., and very rapidly thereafter, provided the humidity of the inspired air is low enough to permit. With inspired air at very low relative humidity but at temperatures of 105° F. or above, some records indicate a short-time evaporative moisture loss of 25 to 30 grams per hen per hour, along with very watery droppings. If the inspired air is both warm and

---

* Each quart of water vaporized at body temperature dissipates about 2150 B.t.u. of heat. B.t.u. means British thermal unit—the amount of heat required to raise the temperature of one pound of water one degree Fahrenheit. Water vapor is commonly measured in grains. One grain is equal to .0648 gram or 1/7000 of a pound.

11

saturated, the hen is completely unable to avoid collapse and death. The difficulty of eliminating excess heat, while maintaining other body processes, begins to show at air temperatures of about 85° F. Egg size decreases, egg shells become thinner, and production is reduced.

Death losses from heat prostration are often severe in the humid sections of the country, and they are also a serious problem in hot, dry areas where maximum daily temperatures range from 105° to 115° F. or higher. Survival under such conditions is closely related to the availability of drinking water and to the persistence with

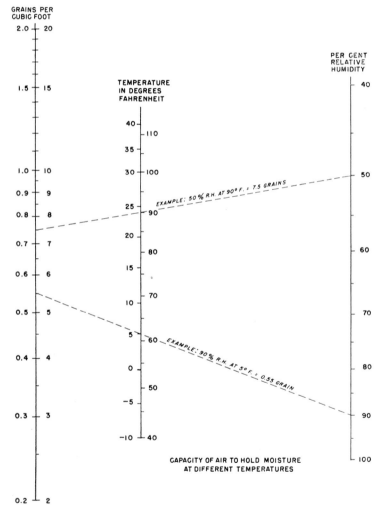

Fig. 81.—Chart for quick determination of the amount of moisture air can hold at different temperatures and relative humidities.

which fowls consume it. Losses can also be reduced by intermittent spraying of the fowls and the interior of the houses. Fine mist sprayers are especially helpful in dry areas. The amount of water used is low, about one gallon per hour for each nozzle, and the fine mist promotes evaporative cooling. When humidity is high, cold water can be used to lower the body temperature by contact. Tests at the Beltsville Research Center showed that when no method of cooling was provided, hens were able to survive a temperature of 90° F., provided the relative humidity did not exceed 75 per cent.

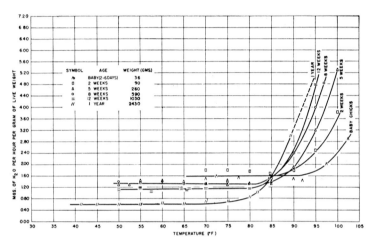

Fig. 82.—Relation of water of respiration to environmental temperature.
(*After Barott and Pringle.*)

At 95° they survived at humidities below 60 per cent, but at 100° F. they survived only if the humidity was 30 per cent or lower. Very fat hens succumbed first, perhaps because the air sacs were constricted and therefore unable to function efficiently in evaporating water from the body tissues.

At low temperatures, on the other hand, the heat loss due to vaporization of water shows little change from normal. Most of the heat loss is then in the form of sensible heat, by radiation and convection, and it is therefore available for warming the air in the hen house. When laying hens are on full feed, the excess heat available for maintaining the normal body temperature is adequate for air temperatures above 40° F. When such hens are active, as during the day, and are producing additional heat because of muscular activity, the critical temperature is lowered to about 20° or perhaps even to 15° F.

At temperatures below 15° or 20° F. hens must draw on stored or food nutrients for the heat energy necessary to maintain normal body temperature, and egg production will therefore be lowered.

Combs begin to freeze at about 6° above zero in dry air, and at 9° to 10° above zero in moist air.

It is clear that the compensatory range above the "comfort zone" of thermoneutrality (in which the animal feels neither hot nor cold) is much less than the range below and that fowls, like other farm animals, have more defenses against cold than against heat. They are, however, handicapped by their small size, because they have more body surface per unit of weight. The effects of a sudden drop in temperature are therefore more severe than with larger animals. In a 5-pound hen about 95 per cent of the total body tissue is within $\frac{3}{4}$-inch of the surface of the body. By contrast, in a 1000-pound steer only about 25 per cent of the total body tissue is so exposed.

VENTILATION

Ventilation is seldom a problem with average farm poultry flocks except during cold weather. At other times of the year the hens are permitted to run outside or the windows are open so that there is adequate and continuous change of air. Most commercial flocks, however, are housed continuously in buildings which require year-round ventilation of some kind. Ventilation systems in actual use include the following:

1. Open front, with no means of temperature control.

2. Adjustable windows or cloth-covered frames, or both, which may be opened according to weather conditions.

3. Baffled or louvered openings, usually with no provision for adjustment of air movement.

4. Rafter ventilation, *i. e.*, adjustable openings between rafters. Used most often with insulated houses.

5. Slot ventilation—consisting of two long, narrow openings in the front wall, one at the top of the wall and one at the bottom of the windows. Used only with insulated houses.

6. Flue ventilation. Flues may be in various parts of the house, but both inlets and outlets must be provided. Common in multi-story houses. Insulation is essential to best results.

7. Combination systems as, for example, outlet flues capped with revolving ventilators, combined with inlet openings which discharge air into the house after it has passed through an attic or plenum chamber to raise its temperature above that of outside air. Insulated walls and ceiling would be essential to best results with this type of ventilation.

8. Completely automatic systems with positive air circulation and thermostatic controls.

The total air breathed by fowls at rest in a comfortable environment is about 1 cubic foot per hen per hour—slightly less for small hens and slightly more for large ones. For 100 5-pound hens this would be about 2400 cubic feet every 24 hours. Measured by air

TABLE 25.—VENTILATION REQUIREMENTS UNDER VARIOUS ASSUMED CONDITIONS

Size of house (all 7 feet high)	10 × 10	20 × 20	40 × 40	36 × 100	30 × 200	30 × 200
Number of hens (4½ pounds each)	25	100	500	1200	2000	3000
Cubic feet per hen	28.0	28.0	22.4	21.0	21.0	14.0
Square feet of floor per hen	4.0	4.0	3.2	3.0	3.0	2.0
Square feet of exposed area per hen	15.60	10.00	5.76	4.89	4.91	3.27
Insulating value	4	8	10	16	8	8
Incoming air:						
Temperature	25° F.	15° F.	5° F.	-5° F.	10° F.	10° F.
Relative humidity	80%	90%	85%	85%	90%	90%
Outgoing air:						
Temperature	35° F.	40° F.	40° F.	40° F.	50° F.	50° F.
Relative humidity	80%	80%	75%	85%	85%	85%
Temperature difference	10° F.	25° F.	35° F.	45° F.	40° F.	40° F.
Pounds of feed eaten per 100 hens per day	24	21	25	27	28	28
B.t.u. of sensible heat per hen per hour	41	40	41	42	43	43
Manure per 100 hens per day (pounds)	46	40	47	51	53	53
Water lost to air in grains per hen per hour	40	35	41	45	46	46
Vaporized water in grains per hen per hour	19	19	19	19	19	19
Total water to be removed (grains)	59	54	60	64	65	65
Minimum air flow to remove moisture:						
Cu. ft./hen/hour	91	39	32	30	23	23
Changes per hour	3.2	1.4	1.4	1.4	1.1	1.1
Maximum air flow without lowering house tempesature:						
Cu. ft./hen/hour	10	17	30	31.5	23	33
Changes per hour	0.36	0.6	1.3	1.5	1.1	2.4

NOTE: Actual exposed area increased by an amount equal to 10 per cent of the floor area, to allow for increased heat loss through glass. Vaporized water calculated as 0.6 milligram per hour per gram of live weight. Weight of manure calculated as 1.9 times the weight of feed consumed. Water loss from manure assumed to be 30 per cent of the total weight of manure. Heat required to warm incoming air estimated as 1 B.t.u. per degree rise for each 50 cubic feet of air. The above calculations show that some of the assumed conditions are impossible to maintain.

change in the average hen house, built for the convenience of the caretaker and not simply to accommodate the hens, this is a very small requirement. It is entirely overshadowed by the rate of air change necessary to remove moisture from a tightly-built house. In most instances, if ventilation is adequate to keep the house dry, it will much more than meet the air requirements of the fowls. Under conditions of heat stress, that is when both air temperature and relative humidity are high, the respiration rate is very rapid and the total volume of air breathed may be eight or ten times normal.

The amount of air which must be moved through a poultry house to carry out excess moisture will depend upon the inside and outside temperatures and the difference between them, and on the relative humidity of the inside and outside air. Raising the temperature increases the capacity of air to hold moisture. In the range of 30° to 75° F., each rise of 1° in temperature means an increase of about 5 per cent in moisture-holding capacity of the air. The amount of water vapor in a pound of saturated air at 5° F. is doubled at 20°, and redoubled successively at about 36°, 55°, 76° and 99°. For every grain or gram or pound of water vapor which air can hold at 5° F., it can hold 32 times as much at 99°.

If, for example, the relative humidity of outside air at any given temperature is 70 per cent, while inside the poultry house at the same temperature it is 80 per cent, the outside air contains $12\frac{1}{2}$ per cent less moisture than the inside air, and forced ventilation of the outside air through the building will remove the excess moisture. But if the relative humidity of both the inside and the outside air is at 80 per cent, no amount of air change will do any good. Either the temperature of the outside air must rise so that it can hold more moisture, or its humidity must drop, if mere air circulation through the house is to remove any moisture. This state of near equilibrium between inside and outside humidity, often with an excess on the outside, is common in many poultry houses during mild winter weather, often for several days in succession. Since no change can be effected in the outside air, dampness in the house can be reduced only by (1) providing some means of absorbing moisture, such as built-up litter, (2) raising the inside air temperature by a small amount of artificial heat, or (3) providing sufficient insulation to retain the heat which the hens themselves produce.

Suppose, however, that the outside temperature is 15° F. with a relative humidity of 75 per cent, while the inside temperature is 35°, and that one wishes to keep the inside relative humidity from going above 75 per cent. If outside air is moved through the hen house at a not too rapid rate, it will be warmed to 35° and its capacity for carrying moisture will be more than doubled. At 15° and 75 per cent relative humidity, it would be carrying 0.75 grain of moisture per cubic foot. (See Fig. 81.) After being warmed to 35° it can carry 1.8 grains at the same relative humidity. Each cubic foot passed through the house can therefore pick up an extra grain of moisture, provided the rate of air movement is slow enough to prevent an appreciable drop in the temperature of the inside air. (If the incoming air is saturated, it will carry 1.0 grain per cubic foot at 15° F. It can then pick up but 0.8 grain more at 35° and 75 per cent relative humidity. But at a maximum of 85 per cent relative humidity, it could still pick up 1 grain per cubic foot.)

Assume that the foregoing conditions exist in a 40 × 40 foot pen or house 7 feet high and containing 500 $4\frac{1}{2}$-pound hens. The respiratory moisture given off by the flock, calculated at 0.6 milligram per hour per gram of live weight (see Fig. 82), will amount to 226,300 grains in 24 hours. If moisture released from the droppings is taken as 17 pounds per 100 hens per day, this will amount to an additional 595,000 grains each 24 hours, making a total of 821,300 grains of moisture to be removed. At one grain per cubic foot of air, it will take 34,200 cubic feet per hour, 69 cubic feet per hen per hour, or 3.1 changes of air per hour, to remove the water vapor. This is not an excessive rate of air movement, since leakage and infiltration will cause two or more changes per hour in most poultry houses even when all windows and doors are closed. In tightly constructed windowless houses which have pressurized ventilation systems, it is not unusual to provide as much as six or eight cubic feet of air change per hen per minute. The hens in such houses are usually in cages and the total air space per layer may be no more than eight or ten cubic feet. With pressurized ventilation there is no evidence of drafts inside the house.

INSULATION

The heat production of a fasting hen at rest is about 2.75 gram calories per hour per gram of live weight. For a $4\frac{1}{2}$-pound (2041-gram) hen this amounts to 5613 gram calories or 22 B.t.u. per hour. Normal activity will cause an increase in heat production, and feed consumption will cause an additional increase proportional to the amount of dry matter consumed. The activity increment is usually estimated at about half the basal heat production, though for hens in cages it may be no more than one-third. A 50 per cent increase would add 11 B.t.u. per hour in this example. For hens laying at a high rate, say 80 per cent, and therefore consuming about 30 pounds of total feed per 100 hens per day—as might be expected during cold weather—the increase in heat production due to feeding would be about 14 B.t.u. per hen per hour. This calculation assumes 91 per cent of dry matter in the feed and a heating effect of 68 Calories per 100 grams of dry matter consumed. Adding the three values (22 + 11 + 14) brings the total heat production of such hens to 47 B.t.u. per hour.

This is of necessity an approximation because of the variation in activity and feed consumption among individual hens, because of the regular diurnal variation in basal heat production with a minimum at about 8 P.M. and a maximum at 8 A.M., and because of reduced heat production during the variable roosting period. Furthermore, a reduction must be made to allow for the latent heat of vaporization, because of moisture in the expired air, which is not available for warming the air of the poultry house. At winter temperatures of 30° to 40° this is about 8 per cent of the total heat production. Deducting this amount leaves a figure of 43 B.t.u. per hen per hour, or 103,200 B.t.u. per 100 hens per day, which will be used in the examples to follow.

The lower total heat production of 4-pound hens is, in practice, partly offset by common procedure of keeping more such hens in a house or pen of given size. If hens are laying at a lower rate than is here assumed, the total feed consumption will be less, and the total heat production will therefore be lower. On the other hand, the amount of moisture to be removed by ventilation will also be lower.

Insulation Needed.—In a 20 × 20 foot house 7 feet high, the combined wall and roof area is about 960 square feet. Adding 40 square feet to allow for the extra heat loss through the usual window area gives 1000 square feet of exposed area, or 10 square feet per hen. The heat production just calculated amounts, then, to 4.3 B.t.u. per hour per square foot of combined wall and roof area. If walls and roof consist of a single layer of siding and roll roofing, the insulating value is about 2. By definition, this means that with a difference in temperature between inside and outside air of only 2° F., and with no direct ventilation, that is with the house tightly closed, the heat loss will be 1 B.t.u. per hour through each square foot of exposed area. A flock of 100 hens on full feed could therefore maintain the inside air temperature of such a house at (2 × 4.3 =) 8.6° above that of the outside air. With the necessary minimum amount of ventilation, the difference would be somewhat less, and at winter temperatures of 15° F. or below, the hens would be very uncomfortable.

If the outdoor temperature is likely to average around 5° for days at a time, and if the minimum inside temperature is to be held at 40°, it will be necessary to increase the insulating value from 2 to (35/4.3 =) 8.1 in order for the hens to be able to maintain this greater temperature difference without the aid of artificial heat. Furthermore, this assumes a tightly closed house, with no consideration of the problem of moisture removal.

It is well to remember that insulation alone sometimes creates a ventilation problem which did not previously exist, and that it is much easier to work out the practical relationships with large flocks than with small ones. If, for example, we apply the foregoing assumed conditions to a flock of 500 hens in a 40 × 40 house instead

of to 100 hens in a 20 × 20 house, we will have (500 × 43 =)
21,500 B.t.u. per hour for 2880 square feet of combined wall and
ceiling area, or 7.5 B.t.u. per square foot instead of 4.3. Conversely,
with a flock of 25 hens in a 10 × 10 house, the heat available would
be only 2.75 B.t.u. for each square foot of wall and ceiling area, thus
making the insulation problem very much more difficult.

POULTRY HOUSE DESIGN

To combine the data on heat production, moisture removal, and
insulation for the purpose of hen house design, it is necessary to include at least one other factor, namely, the amount of heat required
to warm the outside air used for ventilation. At temperatures in
the 35° to 40° range, it will take 1 B.t.u. per degree of rise for each
50 cubic feet of air. Hence, if the volume of air moved through a
hen house in one hour is 5000 cubic feet, and if the difference in
temperature between inside and outside air is 10° F., there must be
sufficient heat available to permit 1000 B.t.u. per hour to be used
in warming the outside air, or the inside air will soon drop to the
same temperature as the incoming air.

It is possible to combine all of the foregoing related factors into a
heat balance equation or formula as follows:

Let H = the heat available, in this case the B.t.u. of sensible heat
produced per hen per hour

D = the difference between inside and outside air temperature in degrees Fahrenheit

A = the combined wall and ceiling area exposed to heat loss,
in square feet per hen, with due allowance for glass area

I = the insulating value of the walls and ceiling (or roof)

V = the volume of air change in cubic feet her hen per hour

50 = the cubic feet of air warmed 1 degree F. by 1 B.t.u.

For balanced conditions, the sum of $VD/50$ and AD/I must not
exceed the value of H. Hence, $H = VD/50 + AD/I$, or $H/D =$
$V/50 + A/I$.

Since the unknown factor is often the amount of air change required or permissible for a given temperature difference, the formula
can be transformed to read $V = 50(H/D - A/I)$. In our example of
500 hens in a 40 × 40 foot house 7 feet high, assuming an insulating
value of 8 and a temperature difference of 25°, we would have
$V = 50(43/25 - 5.76/8)$, or 50 cubic feet of air per hen per hour.
Since the total volume of air in the house is 22.4 cubic feet per hen,
this would be 2.2 changes per hour. But we have previously found
that 3.1 changes, or 69 cubic feet per hen per hour, are required to
remove the calculated amount of moisture. Since the heat balance
equation shows that this is too high a rate of change to avoid a drop
in temperature, we must decide whether to (1) let the house cool
down to a difference of 21.3° between inside and outside, (2) let it

remain damp and be satisfied with reduced ventilation, or (3) improve the insulation so that the greater temperature difference can be maintained.

To find the minimum insulating value necessary for the existing conditions, we can substitute known values in the heat balance equation, or transform it to read $I = A/(H/D - V/50)$. We will then have, under the assumed conditions, $I = 5.76/(43/25 - 69/50)$, or 17.2. In the northern sections of the country where winter conditions are often more severe than those assumed in the foregoing example, experience has shown that an insulating value of 16 is usually sufficient.

To calculate the temperature difference which can be maintained by our flock of 500 hens when the insulating value is 16, we can restate the heat balance equation to read $D = H/(V/50 + A/I)$. Substituting the known or assumed values, we have $D = 43/(69/50 + 5.76/16)$. Solving this gives 24.7°, very close to the desired difference of 25° F. If the inside relative humidity is permitted to rise to 85 per cent, as is commonly done in practice, the difference in temperature can be somewhat greater. Furthermore, no account has been taken of the heat available during clear days from solar radiation. This is considerable. The use of doublewall insulating glass windows makes it possible to take advantage of still more of the sun's heat to raise inside temperatures during cold weather.

Under some conditions it may be practical to devise means for making use of artificial heat instead of building such well-insulated houses. This is apparent if one considers the fact that the sensible heat produced by a flock of 500 hens in 24 hours is no more than the calculated heat of combustion of 40 pounds of good coal. Such a comparison neglects the practical problem of heat distribution, and it makes no allowance for flue losses, but it helps to emphasize the fact that it is impossible for a flock of hens to keep a poorly insulated house warm and dry in severe winter weather.

The application of the foregoing discussion to practical conditions may be summed up in the following recommendations for procedures which will aid in keeping hens comfortable in cold weather, without the use of artificial heat. They are listed in their approximate order of importance.

1. Build large houses rather than small. Make them 30 or 40 feet deep instead of 20. Use long houses with several pens rather than several smaller houses, and thereby reduce total exposed area subject to heat loss. For large flocks, use 2-story or 3-story houses for the same reason.

2. Insulate the ceiling or roof in order to reduce heat loss in winter and lessen the absorption of solar heat in summer. In a large single-story house, the ceiling or roof represents a much higher percentage of the total area exposed to heat loss than it does in a small house.

3. Use deep or built-up litter as an aid in temporary absorption of moisture given off by the hens.

4. Control ventilation so that heat is conserved during the period of low night temperatures while the hens are relatively inactive. Humidity will rise, but it can be corrected during the daytime when the sun's heat will help dry out the house.

The aim of the foregoing procedures is to maintain hen house temperatures above freezing at all times, and to maintain a minimum difference between inside and outside temperatures of 20° F. A secondary consideration is to keep the relative humidity down to 80 or 75 per cent, and the moisture content of the litter down to 40 per cent. These latter conditions are more important from the standpoint of preventing dirty eggs than from their effect on egg production.

HOUSE CONSTRUCTION

The purpose in building a poultry house is to furnish the greatest possible comfort to the flock at the least possible cost per bird. Just where the law of diminishing returns comes in with reference to the grade of lumber and the class of skilled labor employed for the construction, is a matter of judgment in individual cases.

Fig. 83.—A two-story hen house with a 6-inch fill of wood shavings for insulation in side walls and roof. When outside temperatures ranged from 0° to 20° F., the inside temperature was maintained at 45° to 55°. (*Courtesy of Minnesota Agricultural Experiment Station.*)

It is, of course, possible to err in creating an unjustifiable overhead by building an expensive house, as is not infrequently done. Just as possible and as frequent is an overeagerness to save money on first costs by using poor material and unskilled labor which is usually followed by an undue depreciation and an unsatisfactory house.

Foundations.—A good foundation must be solid enough to support the building, deep enough to prevent heaving by frost, and high enough above grade to keep out surface water. In order to leave room for the opening and shutting of doors where a deep litter is used, the top of the foundation must be at least 6 inches above the floor level. This brings the tops of the door sills 8 or more inches above the floor. If for some reason it is necessary to locate the house where the texture of the ground is such that it tends to hold moisture, a tile placed even with the bottom and just at the outside of the foundation, and furnished with a suitable outlet is a necessary precaution if the house is to be dry.

Floors.—The hen-house floor must be moisture proof, free from cracks, and easily cleaned. It should be rat-proof and durable. A board floor, if properly laid, is free from cracks and is easily cleaned and disinfected. It is not a durable floor when compared with concrete, and it is not rat-proof unless raised well off the ground. While the air space below such a floor effectively stops capillary moisture, there are many times during the year when circulation of cold air beneath the house may make the floor so cold as to cause condensation of moisture from the warmer air inside the house. This "sweating" of the floor is a common cause of wet litter.

Concrete floors are dry if properly constructed. They are sanitary, durable and rat-proof. They are not cold when properly bedded with litter. In many parts of the country they have a valuable equalizing effect on the temperature inside the poultry house. The temperature of a wood floor remains within about 2° F. of the outside air temperature, for a temperature range of 25° to 95° F. A concrete floor, on the other hand, may be from 5° to 7° warmer than the air at low temperatures, and as much as 15° cooler than the air temperature when the latter is 90° to 95° F. This is a point of considerable importance in keeping fowls comfortable during hot weather.

Walls and Partitions.—The walls and partitions must be solid enough to support the roof and withstand heavy winds. Wide variation is possible in the use of construction materials, depending on availability, cost, and the insulating value desired. The recent trend has been to eliminate partitions in many of the larger houses, thereby making larger pens. This makes it necessary to give particular attention to strength of the overall structure in order to avoid danger of collapse from heavy snow loads or in windstorms.

Insulation.—It has become common practice to use some type of insulation in the construction of houses built for flocks of commercial size. Roof insulation helps in both summer and winter. Wall insulation is added in the colder parts of the country, the kind and amount depending on the length of the winter season and the expected minimum temperatures. Insulation values for various types of wall and roof construction are shown in Figures 88 and 89. The numerical values refer to the number of degrees difference in temperature which can exist between the warm and cold sides

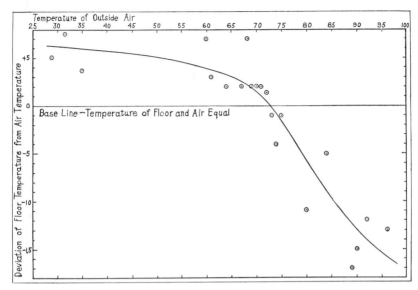

FIG. 84.—Curve showing difference between floor temperature and air temperature in a house with a concrete floor. (*Courtesy of Maryland Agricultural Experiment Station.*)

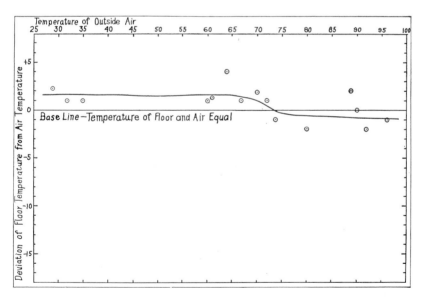

FIG. 85.—Curve showing difference between floor temperature and air temperature in a house with a board floor. The temperature of a wood floor tends to follow closely the temperature of the outside air. (*Courtesy of Maryland Agricultural Experiment Station.*)

of a wall while just permitting 1 B.t.u. of heat to pass through an area of 1 square foot of wall in one hour. Engineers commonly use what is known as the "U" value, or coefficient of heat transfer. It is the reciprocal of the insulating value. Insulating values of 2, 4 and 8 are equivalent to U values of .5, .25 and .125, respectively.

Vapor Barriers.—Condensation of moisture within an insulated wall greatly reduces the insulating value, and may permanently injure certain types of insulating material. It is therefore important

Fig. 86.—On a hot day—fowls snuggling down in the litter to make contact with the surface of the cool concrete floor. (*Courtesy of R. H. Waite.*)

Fig. 87.—Fowls from a house with a wood floor seeking relief from the heat in a shaded corner of the run. They were photographed at approximately the same time as those in Figure 86. (*Courtesy of R. H. Waite.*)

to use a vapor barrier of some sort on the inner or warm side of the insulation in order to prevent condensation at such times as the temperature falls below the dew point. This may consist of light-weight roll roofing, waterproof building paper, or two coats of aluminum-flake paint. Ordinary paint is not effective, nor is common building paper.

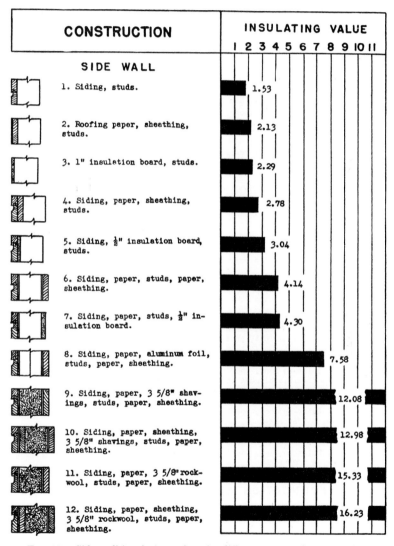

FIG. 88.—Side wall insulation values for different types of construction. (*Courtesy of Connecticut Agricultural Extension Service.*)

Windows and Ventilators.—It is customary to use windows in a poultry house for both light and ventilation. Cross ventilation is especially important during warm summer weather. Proper ventilation by means of windows alone is often very difficult in cold weather.

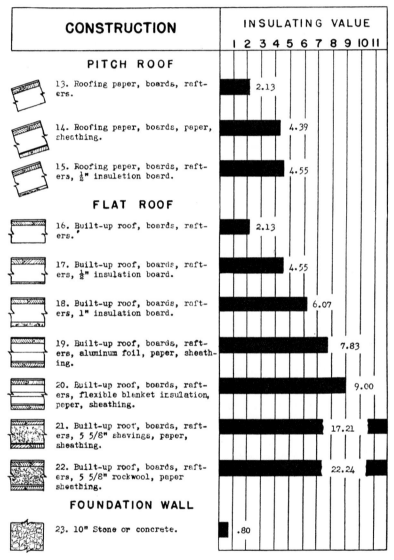

FIG. 89.—Roof insulation values for different types of construction. (*Courtesy of Connecticut Agricultural Extension Service.*)

In addition to the ventilating systems mentioned earlier in this chapter, it is becoming common practice to use ventilating fans to insure air circulation during warm weather, and to control the rate of air change in cold weather. The particular type and size of fan to use will vary with the size and style of house, and with the volume of air to be moved. It is easy to make the mistake of installing fans that are too small. A rule which can easily be applied to both hen houses and broiler houses is to provide a maximum fan capacity of not less than two cubic feet of air per minute for each five pounds of live weight of chicken. Smaller air movement can then be provided by reducing the speed of the fans or by operating only part of them at any one time. Outlets for cold weather use should take air from near the floor. In warm weather, on the other hand, they should take out warm air from near the roof or ceiling.

Fresh air intakes for cold weather use should, if possible, be arranged to discharge the incoming air near the ceiling rather than near the floor. The cold air from the outside then has a better chance to be warmed before coming in contact with the litter. For much the same reason, *i.e.*, prompt mixing of the incoming air with warm inside air, conditions inside the house in cold weather are usually better if the outside air is brought in through several small openings instead of through fewer large ones. On the other hand, since a positive movement of moist air to the outside is important, the outlets should be fairly large in cross-section and fewer in number than the inlets.

Roofs.—Composition roll roofing is the material most commonly used for poultry house roofs. It is draft and moisture proof, is easy to apply, and is relatively inexpensive. It must be properly laid, and it needs regular attention and occasional recoating, if it is to last more than a few years. It makes a house extremely hot in summer unless the roof is insulated or the roofing is coated with a reflecting type paint.

Aluminum roof coatings, including exterior type aluminum foil, are being successfully used to reduce interior summer temperatures. Differences of 5 or 6 degrees become important when exterior temperatures are high.

Built-up roofs, which consist of several layers of roofing paper cemented down with hot asphalt, are popular in some parts of the country, especially for roofs which have a very slight pitch.

Metal roofs are increasing in popularity because of their lasting quality. Less lumber is needed to support a metal roof than for composition roofing. It is advisable to use insulation under a metal roof in order to make the house cooler in summer, and to prevent moisture condensation in winter.

Styles of Houses.—There are numerous styles in poultry houses. Frequently the style chosen is merely a matter of personal taste, but under certain circumstances a particular style may be best suited to some unusual condition.

12

The style of roof most often seen is shed, gable, combination, or half-monitor. Brooder houses for farm use are usually portable, and small houses for laying hens may be. Commercial units may be square, up to 60 feet on a side, or rectangular. In some sections of the country multi-story houses have become very popular.

Illustrations of several different styles and types are shown in this chapter in order to give some idea of the wide variation in construction which is possible without sacrificing any important requirement of good housing.

Remodeling.—It is often more economical to remodel an existing barn or other building than to build a new hen house, and some of the most practical hen houses in use for both farm and commercial flocks are of this sort. If the remodeled building meets the requirements stated earlier in this chapter it may be just as satisfactory as a new house, and much less expensive.

POULTRY–HOUSE EQUIPMENT

Those pieces of equipment which are built in as a part of the house should be simple, few in number, adequate in size, removable for cleaning, and conveniently and systematically placed so that their care will take a minimum of labor.

Fig. 90.—One-story house for layers, with bulk feed tanks conveniently located. (*Courtesy of Creighton Brothers, Warsaw, Indiana.*)

Nests.—The desirable qualities of a nest are that it be roomy, easily cleaned and sprayed, dark, cool and well ventilated, and conveniently located.

Open Nests.—A convenient size of open nest is 10 × 14 inches, and 15 inches high. In high producing flocks there should be one nest for every 4 or 5 hens. Enough of the parts should be removable so that cleaning and thorough spraying are possible. Sections of nests should be so arranged that they can be taken out of the house for cleaning, spraying and sunning when it is desirable.

FIG. 91.—Interior of Creighton Brothers laying house, showing tiered roosts. (*J. C. Allen and Son Photo.*)

FIG. 92.—Nests are arranged along an alley in this Creighton Brothers house. (*J. C. Allen and Son Photo.*)

Dark nests are preferred because the hen likes seclusion for laying. Dark nests also reduce the likelihood of egg eating. Some arrangement for shutting the fowls out at night prevents them from roosting in the nests and fouling them. This they are prone to do, especially at molting time, in order to escape being crowded by other birds on the perch.

Fig. 93.—Slatted floor house on the farm of Franklin Steury, Berne, Indiana. (*J. C. Allen and Son Photo.*)

Some poultrymen like the "community" type of nest, which is really a covered box about 2 feet wide and 6 feet long. It has no partitions, and there is an opening at each end through which the hens may enter and leave. A sloping cover is hinged for convenience in gathering the eggs. Such nests are often built on legs so that the entire unit can be moved out from the wall for better ventilation during hot weather. Each community nest will replace 10 or 12 individual open nests.

Trap Nests.—These differ from open nests in that each one is provided with a trap door by means of which a bird shuts herself in when she enters. They are the accepted means of securing accurate individual egg records and are an essential part of the equipment for pedigree breeding where more than one female is continuously mated with one male.

They are of many different styles. First in importance is their dependability as to accuracy, though it is hardly less important that they be comfortable and attractive, if floor eggs are to be avoided.

Fig. 94.—Part litter and part slatted floor is another common arrangement. (*Courtesy of Automatic Poultry Feeder Company.*)

Fig. 95.—This three-story New Hampshire house is 48 × 216 feet, designed for 23,000 hens. Sectional construction and the use of fir plywood sheathing helped to keep the cost low. (*Courtesy of Poultry Tribune.*)

FIG. 96.—This low cost house in California, 50 × 400 feet, holds 20,000 fryers. Black plastic film on the roof and clear polyethylene film on the sides are protected above and below by wire netting. Lower view shows the method of framing. (*Courtesy of Pacific Poultryman.*)

FIG. 97.—This solar type laying house features double-wall insulating glass for winter warmth and a roof overhang to shade out summer sun. (*Courtesy of Libbey-Owens-Ford Glass Company.*)

(182)

No trap nest is a comfortable place in extremely hot weather unless every effort has been made to have it abundantly ventilated. This may even require nest floors of hardware cloth and the discarding of the use of nest bedding for a time, allowing the birds to lay on the bare wire. There should be one trap nest for every 3 hens.

Perches.—In order to insure comfort the perches should allow from 8 to 10 inches of room for each bird and be 15 to 18 inches apart. Good rest is as essential to chickens as to any other class of livestock. The most common material used for perches is 2 by 3 or 2 by 4 inch lumber. This may be laid on the side or placed on edge. In either case it is well to round the upper edges.

FIG. 98.—Double-wall insulating glass permits better lighting and reduces condensation on the inside surface to a minimum. (*Courtesy of Libbey-Owens-Ford Glass Company.*)

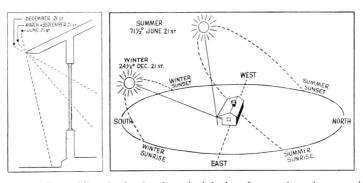

FIG. 99.—Dotted lines in the sketch at the left show how roof overhang can be used to shade out the sun's rays on June 21, yet permit them to strike the windows in winter. Diagram at the right shows the position of the sun at noon on June 21 and December 21 at Ames, Iowa. (*After Sprague and Eakin.*)

Fig. 100.—Automatic feeders are almost a necessity for large commercial egg farm operations. (*Courtesy of Chore-Time Equipment, Inc.*)

Fig. 101.—Mechanical removal of droppings helps to reduce moisture in a large hen house. Creighton Brothers Poultry Farm, Warsaw, Indiana. (*J. C. Allen and Son Photo.*)

Roosting Racks.—In order to eliminate the daily chore of cleaning droppings boards, many poultrymen have installed low roosting racks, or so-called droppings pits. The droppings accumulate on the floor, within a screened enclosure, and are removed only one to four times a year. Although there is a real saving in labor, the racks are not a substitute for good management. Unless some suitable fly repellent is used regularly, the accumulated droppings make an excellent breeding place for flies. This can be a serious

Fig. 102.—This long bin is used with an electric stirrer for drying poultry manure on a California farm. (*Courtesy of Pacific Poultryman.*)

handicap to adequate control of diseases and parasites. If the racks are built against a wall, it is difficult to prevent rotting of the lower part of the wall with consequent expensive repairs.

Feeding Equipment.—The design of feeding equipment varies considerably on different farms and in different parts of the country. No matter what style of construction is used, the feeding devices should be easy to fill, easy to clean, built to avoid waste, so arranged that the fowls cannot roost on them, and constructed in such a manner that so long as they contain any feed at all the fowls will be able to reach it. From the standpoint of practical results it is

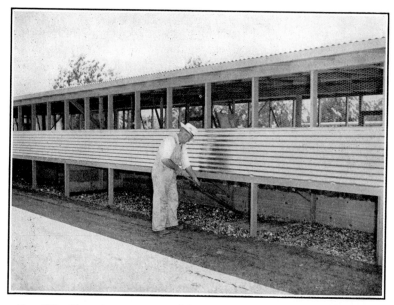

Fig. 103.—Droppings are removed from the rear in this 460' × 24' trap nest house for 3200 pullets on the Dryden Poultry Breeding Farm, Modesto, California. (*Courtesy of Horace Dryden.*)

Fig. 104.—Adjustable slot ventilation is widely used in New England poultry houses. (*Courtesy of Poultry Tribune.*)

essential that ample feeding space be provided. A safe rule to follow is to have 1 foot of hopper feeding space for every 5 hens.

Automatic or mechanical feeders have become popular in recent years. This is partly because they save a great deal of labor when they are working properly, partly because they can be adjusted for intermittent operation, with some resulting increase in total feed consumption, and partly because they appeal to many poultrymen simply as a mechanical gadget. They obviously are not economical for flocks of fewer than 400 hens, and they probably should not be

Fig. 105.—The community type of nest is preferred by many poultrymen. (*Courtesy of Poultry Tribune.*)

used by anyone who does not have the necessary mechanical aptitude for keeping such equipment in working order. If something goes wrong with the automatic equipment, the chickens are very soon without feed, and there is no convenient way of turning back to hand feeding during the emergency.

Watering Devices.—A perfect watering device should keep the water clean and cool in warm weather, and be of such construction that it may be easily cleaned and that freezing will not destroy its usefulness. To keep water clean the watering equipment should be high enough so that litter will not be scratched into it, and so located that the fowls can not contaminate it with droppings.

In houses which lack sufficient insulation to prevent freezing, soil heating cable may be used to protect water pipes. A thermostat should be used to shut off the current at some pre-determined point, say 35° F., to prevent needless use of electric current. Proper installation, with suitable ground connections, is highly important from a safety standpoint.

Automatic watering devices are important from the standpoint of saving labor. Shallow V-shaped troughs running the entire length of the hen house and carrying a constant flow of water are very satisfactory for large flocks.

Fig. 106.—Many poultrymen in southern California keep hens in outdoor laying cages. Practice varies from one or two layers per cage to units like those shown here with 25 layers in a 5′ × 5′ cage. (*Courtesy of Heisdorf and Nelson Farms.*)

Laying Cages.—In recent years many persons have become interested in the practice of keeping laying hens in individual cages or hen batteries. This has come about partly from the hope of reducing the mortality which has so often been a serious problem in commercial flocks, partly because laying cages make it possible to keep fowls in buildings which could not otherwise be used for laying hens; partly because of hoped-for economies in establishing a poultry business; and partly because of the mere novelty of the idea.

Fig. 107.—Shade is provided by a lattice connecting the eaves of two 34 × 228 foot cage houses in California. (*Courtesy of Pacific Poultryman.*)

Fig. 108.—Pipe with foggers rests on gravel between two cage houses in California. Such equipment is very important for keeping layers comfortable during very hot weather. (*Courtesy of Pacific Poultryman.*)

Laying batteries are ideally adapted to certain kinds of experimental work, and they are being used commercially with considerable success by persons who have taken time to study the details of poultry management before embarking on such a venture, but they are by no means a universal substitute for the more common and generally used houses and equipment.

Fig. 109.—Caged layers in the poultry house of Charles B. Collins, Princeton Indiana. (*J. C. Allen and Son Photo.*)

In some parts of southern California, where freezing temperatures are the exception and little protection from cold is needed, outdoor laying cages have become popular. As many as one-fourth of all layers in some areas are housed in this manner.

All that is necessary in the way of construction is a roof over the cages and some kind of framework to hold the cages off the ground. Many variations in watering and feeding arrangements are possible, but most are aimed at making it possible to do the necessary labor of caring for the hens and gathering the eggs in a minimum amount of time. Some operators have been able to keep labor time down to 0.7 hour per hen per year, but the average is nearer one hour, which compares favorably with the time required under conventional methods of housing.

Certain management problems, such as cannibalism, damp litter and trapnesting are completely solved by the use of laying cages. On the other hand, there are certain new problems to meet. The percentage of cracked eggs is sometimes rather high. There will be few very dirty eggs, but a large number may be slightly soiled.

Fig. 110.—Some automatic feeders are designed especially for use with caged layers. (*Courtesy of Oakes Manufacturing Company.*)

Regular cleaning and removal of droppings becomes of great importance in order to keep down odors in the battery room. The fly problem may be serious in the outdoor cage installations. Some hens develop the habit of wasting much of their feed, and others do not eat normally as compared with hens running loose on the floor. This means that special attention must be given to rations which are to prove suitable for caged layers.

Protection from excessive heat is often a problem where the outdoor cages are used, and rather elaborate sprinkling systems are sometimes necessary to prevent serious death losses when summer temperatures often range from 95° to 105° in the middle of the day.

It is important that laying cage equipment be used to as near 100 per cent capacity as possible at all times. For this reason it is customary to hatch or buy baby chicks throughout the year at intervals of two or four weeks, and to make continual replacements of birds which have died, have ceased to lay, or have been removed because of poor physical condition. On some plants this replacement runs as high as 7 per cent a month, or a turnover of 84 per cent a year. Reasonably high egg production and good egg prices are essential to profits under such conditions.

One of the interesting and important practical findings in the management of caged layers is that there are marked differences between strains of fowls in their adaptability to close confinement in laying batteries. Without doubt this is a limiting factor in the profitable operation of such plants. Numerous engineering problems in connection with lighting, ventilation, heating and humidity have also been met and not all of them have as yet been completely solved.

CARE OF THE HOUSE

A successful poultry house must be clean, reasonably dry, well ventilated and, above all, comfortable for the hens. Good management aimed at maintaining these conditions will pay dividends in sustained production.

Types of Litter.—An important point in maintaining comfortable conditions in the poultry house is having the right kind of litter. Many different materials are used for this purpose, depending largely on what is locally available. Among the materials in common use in different sections of the country are straw, shavings, ground corn cobs, cottonseed hulls, peat moss, shredded corn stalks, shredded sugar cane, oat hulls, and sawdust. Ground corn cobs head the list of desirable farm-produced litters.

In a series of tests at the Delaware station, in which more than 66,000 broilers were used, sawdust was consistently lowest in cost per 1000 broilers, of the twelve litter materials tested. It was readily available in the area—an important practical consideration—but its moisture content frequently was too high at the time of purchase to make it wholly satisfactory. Peanut shells, ground corn cobs, peat moss and sugar cane fiber were all ranked above sawdust except for cost. Pens containing mineral type litters were often dusty.

Built-up Litter.—When all grain is hopper-fed it is important to have a litter which does not pack readily. Ground or crushed cobs, shavings, and sawdust meet this requirement, and are well adapted to use as deep or built-up litter. Built-up litter provides a warm floor. For this reason it is especially well adapted for use in the northern sections of the country. If kept in good condition, it will absorb considerable moisture on days when the humidity is high, and release it on following dry days. Maintaining deep litter takes much less labor, in spite of necessary stirring, than is required to renew shallow litter at frequent intervals in order to keep it reasonably dry. Finally, there is some advantage to be gained by the fact that fowls can pick up from the litter some products of intestinal synthesis which may simplify the feeding problem. Such built-up litter need not be cleaned out oftener than once a year, and some poultrymen continue to use it for two years or longer.

The usual procedure with deep litter is to start in the fall with two to four inches of dry litter, and add to this gradually until the floor is covered eight to ten inches deep by about the first of December. After that no more litter is added, but the old litter is stirred occasionally to keep it in good condition. It may be removed and replaced with clean, shallow litter in the late spring, or it may be left in until the regular fall cleaning.

Adding hydrated lime to deep litter will help to keep it in workable condition so that it is less likely to pack down. The amount of lime used varies from 15 to 25 pounds for each 100 square feet of floor area. It should be distributed evenly and then worked into the litter by stirring. Additional applications can be made from time to time as necessary.

Old built-up litter, whether limed or unlimed, contains fewer yeasts, molds and bacteria than comparatively new litter. This is probably because of its increased alkalinity, pH of 8.0 or more.

Value and Preservation of Poultry Manure.—Since poultry manure contains not only the feces but also the excretion of the kidneys, it is much richer in nitrogen than that of other domestic animals. Analyses of the urine obtained from catheterized fowls show that about 64 per cent of the urinary nitrogen is present as uric acid, and therefore very readily available to growing plants. By putrefaction it is very readily changed to ammonium carbonate. This means that as poultry manure is ordinarily handled, much of its nitrogen is liberated as ammonia and consequently lost as far as fertilizing value is concerned. Since the night droppings from 1000 hens may easily amount to 20 tons a year, substantial savings can be made by proper treatment.

Workers at the New Jersey Station found that fresh manure produced by laying hens contained about 78 per cent moisture, 1 per cent nitrogen, 0.8 per cent phosphoric acid, and 0.5 per cent potash.

Untreated poultry manure lost a large percentage of its nitrogen as ammonia, especially in warm weather.

Superphosphate was the most effective material used to prevent loss of nitrogen, and the recommended rate of application was 100 pounds per ton of fresh manure.

Hydrated lime was the most effective deodorizer. It also had a marked effect in reducing nitrogen losses and in improving the handling qualities of the product. The recommended application is 100 to 200 pounds per ton of manure, or about $1\frac{1}{2}$ pounds per 100 hens per day if scattered over the droppings boards or in the space under roosting racks.

The Minnesota Extension Service recommends that approximately 250 pounds of 20 per cent superphosphate and 20 to 25 pounds of muriate of potash be mixed with each ton of manure in order to balance it for use on crop land. For spreading over the droppings beneath the roosts, it is recommended that $\frac{1}{2}$ pound of a similar mixture be used daily for each 100 hens. Labor can be saved by spreading a little less than 2 pounds of this mixture twice a week.

Because of its high moisture content, artificial drying of poultry manure is expensive, and therefore not often practical for individual poultrymen. The cost, as reported by the New Jersey Station, would be at least $15 per ton of dried product if reduced to a moisture content of 10 per cent. If deodorizing equipment is used, the cost would be still higher.

Chapter 8

The Principles of Poultry Nutrition

THE primary reason for keeping poultry is to accomplish the trans-
formation of vegetable, animal and mineral matter in forms not
usually eaten by man, into human food in the form of eggs and
meat. In order to understand how to do this most efficiently it is
necessary to know something of the food nutrients and their digestion and use by the fowl.

The Maintenance of Life.—The first use of all feed is to support
life. Unless life is maintained it is obvious that growth, reproduction, and gains in body weight cannot occur. The continuation of
life and normal functioning of the animal organism depend upon
(1) the maintenance of normal body temperature; (2) a certain
minimum amount of muscular activity; (3) the renewal of tissues;
(4) the periodic renewal of the feather coat; and (5) the elaboration
of secretions.

In order for the various functions of the body, such as digestion,
metabolism, fertilization and incubation, to be performed at their
best it is necessary that there be maintained that degree of heat
which is recognized as the normal temperature of the individual.
For the common fowl this has been found to be about 107° F. This
is several degrees higher than that maintained by man or by the
common farm animals.

A considerable amount of muscular work must be done if the
bird is to live. It must at least make the motions necessary for
eating, and most individuals find it necessary to move about in
search of feed. This is done of the fowl's own volition, and such
movements are termed voluntary. At the same time there is
considerable muscular activity within the body of the fowl over
which it has no control, and which is termed involuntary. Such
motion, for instance, is found in the beating of the heart and in the
contractions of the gizzard and intestines. Energy must be furnished for both voluntary and involuntary motion, but the energy
set free for such purposes is never completely used. Some of it is
wasted so far as motion is concerned, but may be used for the maintenance of body temperature.

Nitrogen and minerals are continually being lost from the tissues
of the body and must be replaced. The exact nature of these
processes has not as yet been entirely explained. From the practical

(195)

viewpoint, however, it is perhaps sufficient to recognize the fact that the losses do occur and must be replaced.

There are numerous secretions that must be manufactured in the body of the fowl. Hormones, digestive enzymes, and mucus must be made. In order that the joints and muscles may move with little friction, and that the egg may slip down the oviduct to a successful expulsion, there must be secretions of the sort that may be referred to as lubricating material.

A certain part of the feed, therefore, must always be used for fuel, repairs and glandular secretions; that is to say, for the maintenance of life. The feed requirements for maintenance in domestic birds are about the same per unit of body surface area as for other farm animals. Per unit of body weight, however, the requirement is greater than for other farm animals because of the relatively small size of birds.

With hens in 50 per cent production, more than one-half of the food energy goes to meet the needs of maintenance alone, and more than three-fourths of it is used for the combined purposes of maintenance and muscular activity.

Growth.—Growth is the direct result of a specific growth impulse in the young animal, and consists primarily of an increase in bone, protein tissue and water. Bone furnishes the framework for the support of the reproductive and vital organs and the attachment of the muscles. The protein tissue furnishes the material out of which the muscles and bodily organs are very largely fashioned. Muscle, which is termed lean meat when used for food, is one of the ultimate objects of poultry production, and often, as in the case of broiler production, is the primary object. The development of the vital organs is necessary to the maintenance of life itself.

Since every cell of the body contains protein, growth is possible only when protein is furnished in the food material in excess of the amount needed for maintenance. Similarly, certain of the tissues cannot be increased unless there is an ample supply of mineral matter.

Reproduction.—Not until growth is complete, or is nearing completion, can reproduction occur. Because the egg is so highly prized for human food as to have great commercial value, man has sought for many years to increase the laying ability of the domestic hen. As a result of continued selection, the reproductive season has been increased from a short period in the spring to a matter of several months. In the case of highly developed strains it has become an almost continuous process. The whole philosophy of management and feeding for increased egg production is bound up in an effort to induce abundant reproduction. As with growth, reproduction can occur only when an excess of feed is furnished.

Fattening.—Feed consumed above that necessary for maintenance is either stored in the body as a reserve in the form of fat, or is dissipated as heat. The fact that certain individuals fatten readily while others, for the most part, merely transform excess food energy into heat has not as yet been completely explained.

THE NUTRIENTS

All feed ingredients are composed of one or more of the distinctly different groups of nutrients: (1) water, (2) minerals, (3) proteins, (4) carbohydrates, (5) fats, and (6) vitamins.

Of these, water alone is a definite chemical compound. Minerals, proteins, carbohydrates, fats and vitamins, which collectively form the dry matter, are classes or groups of compounds, each group having certain distinctive characteristics. Compounds of similar physical or chemical composition are placed within each group for convenience.

Both the fowl's body and the egg are composed of the same six groups of food substances. These are not, in most cases, transferred directly as such from the feed to the tissues, but are split up in the digestive tract, absorbed and rebuilt in the body.

There is, however, a close relation between the composition of the feed and its use in building tissue. The minerals in the body or in the egg can come only from the minerals in the feed. The protein of the body can not be built up nor the protein of the egg formed except when nitrogen carriers of the proper kinds are furnished from the outside. While fat may be manufactured from protein, it is normally built up from carbohydrates or made over from fats in the feed. The very small amount of carbohydrates in the fowl's body and the still smaller amount in the egg usually have the carbohydrates of the feed as their original source, but may also come from the proteins. The source of vitamins in the body of the fowl is the vitamins or provitamins of the feed, except as they may be supplemented by those which can be synthesized by the chicken or by organisms in its digestive tract.

Water.—Water plays a highly important part in the digestion and metabolism of the fowl. (1) It is a constituent part of the body and of the contents of the egg, comprising from 55 to 75 per cent of the former and more than 65 per cent of the latter; (2) it serves to soften the feed in the crop, preparing it for maceration in the gizzard; (3) it aids and takes a part (hydrolysis) in the processes of digestion and absorption; (4) as an important constituent of the blood and lymph it serves as a carrier, transporting the end-products of digestion from the digestive tract to all parts of the body, and waste products from all parts of the body to the points of elimination; (5) it serves to cool the body by evaporation through the air sacs, lungs and skin, and to equalize the temperature of the various regions and parts; (6) it is the main constituent of mucus which acts as a lubricant for the joints and muscles.

Water usually forms from 8 to 12 per cent of the air-dry weight of the common grains which generally make up the most of the poultry ration. Water is also formed in the body by oxidation of the hydrogen of the organic nutrients. These sources combined, however, furnish but a small fraction of that required, which points to the necessity of a liberal supply beyond that furnished in the feed.

Minerals.—Minerals, frequently referred to as ash, is a term used to designate collectively the mineral compounds found in feeds, the fowl's body and the egg. The proportion of ash varies from less than 1 per cent (wheat flour and polished rice) to as high as 70 per cent (steamed bone meal) of the weight of common poultry feeds. It forms between 3 and 4 per cent of the live weight of the bird, and approximately 10 per cent of the weight of the whole egg. While the common feeds of plant origin, such as the grains and legumes, would usually supply sufficient mineral matter to meet the needs of the hen for maintenance, they fall far short of furnishing the quantities needed by the laying hen or the rapidly growing chick.

The mineral elements required in poultry feeding are calcium, phosphorus, sodium, potassium, sulphur, chlorine, magnesium, iron, manganese, copper, cobalt, molybdenum, and zinc. Most of these can be used in inorganic form, but sulphur can be utilized only as a constituent part of the protein molecule, and cobalt only as it forms a part of the vitamin B_{12} molecule. Calcium, sodium and potassium salts are essential for muscular action. Calcium as a carbonate forms nearly the entire shell, or about 10 per cent of the new-laid egg. Calcium, phosphorus and magnesium, as inorganic salts, are important constituents of bone.

Phosphorus is essential in most metabolic processes, such as liberation of energy, enzyme activity, and the functioning of vitamins. It is also found in the egg, where it forms about 0.27 per cent of the edible portion. Iron, which is an essential constituent of the hemoglobin of the blood, and sulphur, which is a constituent of most body proteins, are also found in the egg. Chlorine is found in the hydrochloric acid of the gastric juice and in the blood serum. Manganese, though needed in very small amounts, is essential to normal development of the embryo and the growing chick. Copper, which, in the presence of iron, has a marked catalytic effect on the synthesis of hemoglobin, is therefore essential to normal health and well-being. Sodium and potassium phosphates and carbonates are among the most important buffering substances, and as such they assist in maintaining the acid-base balance of the tissues.

There is considerable silicon in the ash of feathers, but there is no evidence to show that it is an essential mineral for the chicken.

In common farm feeds, enough is ordinarily furnished of all the mineral elements with the exception of calcium, phosphorus, sodium, and sometimes manganese and zinc. The calcium may be furnished as calcium carbonate in the form of limestone or marine shells.

Phosphorus, if needed, may be supplied in the form of steamed bone meal, defluorinated rock phosphate, or in the bone portion of meat scrap or fish meal, while common salt (sodium chloride) supplies the sodium and chlorine. Manganese is perhaps most easily supplied as the sulphate or dioxide.

Proteins.—The term protein designates collectively a group of organic compounds containing carbon, hydrogen, oxygen and nitrogen. They may also contain sulphur, phosphorus and iron, but the presence of nitrogen is their most distinguishing characteristic. In routine chemical analysis the protein is estimated from the amount of total nitrogen by the use of a conventional factor, 6.25, on the assumption that all of the nitrogen is in protein form and that all proteins contain 16 per cent of nitrogen. Protein determined in this manner is often referred to as crude protein.

Analyses of chicken tissues show that the protein content of the entire body varies from about 15 per cent at hatching time to about 25 per cent in 5-pound Leghorn cockerels. In fat hens it may drop to 12 per cent or even less. Protein forms about 12 per cent of the entire weight of the new-laid egg, and about 50 per cent of the dry matter of the egg contents. The dry matter of the white of the egg is nearly 94 per cent protein, and the corresponding figure for the yolk is over 34 per cent.

While protein is the general term used to describe a large group of nitrogenous compounds, there are hundreds of individual proteins which have been isolated, purified and named. Each of these is made up of a number of simpler compounds known as amino acids, and it is the amino acids which determine the nutritional adequacy of any protein or protein-supplement for maintenance, growth or egg production.

Of the 21 or 22 amino acids which are important in nutrition, at least 17 have been determined in whole-egg protein in amounts ranging from 2 to 12 per cent of the total protein present. For those which have been determined in chicken muscle, the level is much the same as in egg protein except that chicken muscle contains significantly more lysine, but less cystine and methionine, than does whole-egg protein.

Amino acids are commonly grouped as essential and non-essential but, because of differences between animal species, and differences in the requirements for maintenance, growth, and the production of eggs, milk or wool, it is not possible to set up a single list of essential or indispensable amino acids. The distinction, when it is made for a specified set of conditions, depends upon whether a particular amino acid is a dietary essential and must therefore be furnished in the feed, or whether the animal can synthesize it from mixed feed proteins at a sufficiently rapid rate to promote the particular function being considered.

Quite obviously, all of the amino acids found in chicken tissues are physiologically essential. Some of them however, like histidine, are so widely distributed in feed proteins that an adequate supply is almost certain to be present in any practical ration. Others can be synthesized by the chicken in adequate amounts during normal metabolism. Some amino acids are more difficult than others for the body to synthesize. The lysine requirement in particular must apparently be supplied entirely through the feed. The relative rate

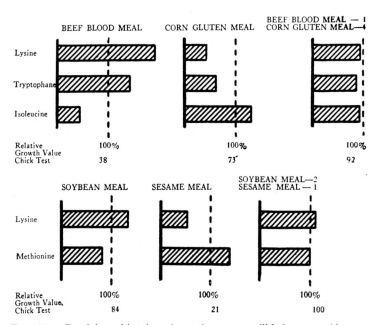

Fig. 111.—Careful combination of protein sources will help to provide proper amino acid balance. After Almquist. (*Courtesy of U.S. Industrial Chemicals, Inc.*)

of synthesis of non-essential amino acids undoubtedly varies with many nutritional and physiological conditions which, in turn, affect the specific reequirements as, for example, those for average and maximum rates of growth.

When the requirements of the chick, as measured by growth response, are compared with the amino acid makeup of the proteins in common feed ingredients, it quickly becomes apparent that careful attention must be paid to five of the amino acids when formulating practical chick rations. These are arginine, lysine, methionine, cystine and tryptophan, because they are the ones most likely to be deficient if rations are formulated with only the total protein content in mind. They may therefore be looked upon as the critical amino acids.

The relative importance of twenty amino acids is indicated in

Table 26, but some qualification is necessary. Glycine, for example, is placed in the essential list not because the chick is unable to synthesize it, but because it cannot do so rapidly enough to promote or sustain maximal rates of growth. Evidence is accumulating that proline may also become a limiting amino acid under conditions in which synthesis does not proceed at a sufficiently rapid rate.

The nutritive value of any given protein ingredient depends upon the extent to which it is able to furnish the critical amino acids, and occasionally others, in the proportions required by the chicken; or upon the extent to which it can supplement other protein ingredients in this respect. Two protein ingredients which supplement each other may give better results when fed in combination than a third which by itself is better than either of the first two.

TABLE 26.—AMINO ACIDS USED BY THE GROWING CHICK, AND THEIR RELATIVE IMPORTANCE AS DIETARY ESSENTIALS

Critical	Essential but not critical	Required under certain conditions	Not required
Arginine	Glutamic acid	Cystine*	Alanine
Cystine*	Glycine	Tyrosine	Aspartic acid
Lysine	Histidine		Hydroxyproline
Methionine	Isoleucine		Proline
Tryptophan	Leucine		Serine
	Phenylalanine		
	Threonine		
	Valine		

* Cystine is not required if there is sufficient methionine present to take its place, but since this does not often happen, it belongs in the critical list in terms of ration formulation.

Two examples of supplementary action between different proteins are shown in Figure 111. Beef blood meal is a rare example of a deficiency of isoleucine, although it contains all five of the critical amino acids in appreciable amounts. Corn gluten meal, on the other hand, contains a surplus of isoleucine, but a deficiency of both lysine and tryptophan. When the two are combined in the ratio of 1 part of blood meal to 4 parts of corn gluten meal, the mixture is nicely balanced with respect to all three amino acids, and in feeding tests it has proved to be much more effective in promoting chick growth than either blood meal or corn gluten meal alone. The second example involves lysine and methionine, as provided by soybean meal and sesame meal.

Presumably the most efficient utilization of feed occurs when all of the physiologically essential amino acids are supplied in amounts slightly above those needed by the chicken. This is neither feasible nor necessary when formulating practical poultry rations. It is sufficient to see that the critical amino acids are furnished in ample amounts, and that the total protein is high enough to enable the chicken to synthesize the necessary amounts of some 15 others which are non-critical. There are, however, certain interrelationships, not only among amino acids but between amino acids and vitamins, which must be taken into account.

Methionine can furnish part of the materials needed by the chicken for synthesizing the other sulphur-containing amino acid, cystine. If there is enough methionine present, cystine is not necessary, but surplus cystine will not replace methionine. It is therefore customary to provide a minimum of methionine and also a minimum amount of the two together. Similarly, tyrosine can be synthesized from excess phenylalanine, but is dispensable only when there is enough phenylalanine in the ration to meet the needs for both of these amino acids.

Another amino acid, tryptophan, can be used by the chicken to form niacin, one of the water-soluble vitamins. Here again, it is more practical to provide ample amounts of niacin than to depend upon the limited amounts of tryptophan present in most feeds. Similarly, methionine is an important methylating agent and can, if necessary, take the place of part of the choline (another water-soluble vitamin).

There is abundant evidence also that many of the vitamins are necessary for the retention and full utilization of the amino acids.

Carbohydrates.—Carbohydrates are compounds of carbon, hydrogen and oxygen in which the hydrogen and oxygen are almost always in the same mutual proportion as in water (H_2O). They are plentiful in plants, appearing usually in the form of sugars, starches, pentosans or cellulose. As protein predominates in the fowl's body, so carbohydrates predominate in the structure of the plant.

Starch is the form in which most plants store their reserve energy. The starches stored in the kernel of corn and the potato tuber are familiar examples.

The skeleton or framework of plants consists mostly of cellulose. In feeds it is called crude fiber, and it is actually a disadvantage in the formulation of rations for young chicks. Common seeds and grains vary from 2 to 11 per cent in their content of crude fiber.

Carbohydrates are important and valuable in poultry feeding because they furnish the chief source of energy for the growing chick or laying hen.

Fats.—In this group of nutrients are included not only the true fats but also certain fat-like substances such as cholesterol, ergosterol, waxes and lecithins. The true fats are organic compounds of carbon, hydrogen and oxygen, but they contain these elements in very different proportions than do the carbohydrates. Perhaps the most characteristic difference is that the fats contain a much lower percentage of oxygen. It is because of this and their higher content of hydrogen that the fats have such a high calorific value.

Certain fats, like tallow, are quite firm and hard because they contain rather large percentages of the higher molecular weight and saturated fatty acids. Others, like chicken fat, are quite oily because they contain considerable percentages of the lower molecular weight, and unsaturated fatty acids.

Fats (lipids) are present in all cereal grains, but in very small proportions as compared with the body of the fowl or even the egg. While they form less than 5 per cent of the air-dry weight of corn and oats, and less than 2 per cent of wheat, they constitute nearly 20 per cent of the live weight, and about 45 per cent of the dry-matter weight, of a 4-pound Leghorn pullet. Fat comprises 9.3 per cent of the weight of the new-laid egg, all but a trace being located in the yolk, of which it forms 33.3 per cent.

Fat is the reserve material of the animal body. The percentage of fat seldom falls below 6 in the very lean animal, while it may rise as high as 40 in the very fat animal. It serves as a store of energy to be drawn upon as the need arises. Since fat is a non-conductor of heat, the subcutaneous deposits constitute a very efficient protection against cold. This is more important in large animals than in poultry.

Fat-Soluble Vitamins.—Perhaps the most significant fact about vitamins as a group is that, although they are absolutely essential to the normal functioning of the animal body in certain respects, most of them are needed in but minute amounts in comparison with the other nutrients. It is worth noting that eggs, when laid by hens fed on rations which are nutritionally adequate, are prominent among the excellent animal sources of vitamins. No other substance except milk is so important a carrier of so many of the vitamins.

Although most of the known vitamins are unrelated chemically, they may conveniently be classified as fat-soluble and water-soluble. The first group includes vitamins A, D, E and K. All the rest are water-soluble. The functions of the individual vitamins in poultry nutrition will be indicated briefly in the following paragraphs, together with symptoms of deficiency. The requirements for those which need to be considered in the formulation of rations will be given in Chapter 10.

Vitamin A.—All animals, so far as known, require some dietary source of vitamin A or one of its precursors. Its function is closely related to the proper nourishment of epithelial tissues. In this way it helps to protect the chicken against various bacterial infections. Deficiency symptoms include deposits of urates in the ureters and kidneys, general unthriftiness, lessened egg production and, in extreme cases, nutritional roup. Potent sources are fish liver oils and vitamin A and D feeding oils. Chickens, like other animals, are able to transform the carotenes of plant tissues (fresh green forage, alfalfa meal, and the like) into vitamin A. They can also make similar use of the pigment cryptoxanthin in yellow corn.

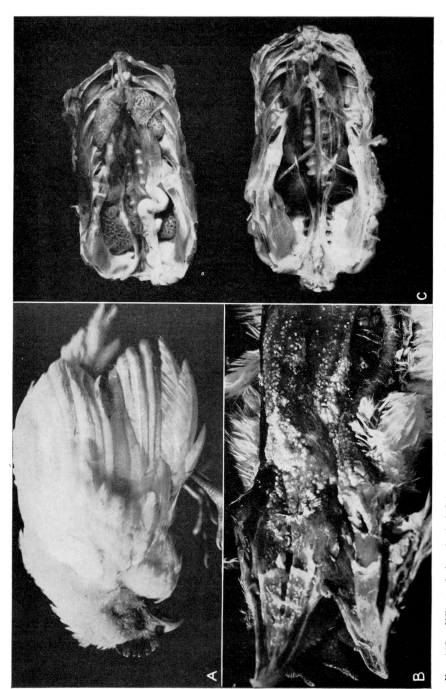

Fig. 112.—Effects of vitamin A deficiency. *A*, An advanced stage. Note the exudate from the eye and the general ruffled appearance. *B*, The pharynx and esophagus are studded with pustules. *C*, Whitish urate deposits in the kidneys and the enlarged ureter of the upper specimen are compared with the normal condition below. (*Courtesy of the National Research Council.*)

Fig. 113.—Effects of vitamin deficiencies. *A*, Ungainly manner of balancing the body which results from a deficiency of vitamin D. The beak is also soft and rubbery. *B*, Effect of a deficiency of alpha tocopherol. *C*, Generalized hemorrhage in a young chick caused by a deficiency of vitamin K. (*Courtesy of the National Research Council.*)

Vitamin D.—The primary function of vitamin D is to promote normal absorption, deposition, and retention of calcium and phosphorus in the young animal. If this vitamin is deficient or absent, young chicks will soon develop rickets, a condition in which the growing bones fail to calcify normally. The chicks are not only unthrifty, and retarded in growth, but they become lame and show a disinclination to walk.

The most important function of vitamin D in mature fowls is concerned with reproduction. Under conditions of vitamin D deficiency the shells of eggs being laid by hens on such a diet become progressively thinner until production finally ceases. Long before these conditions are apparent, however, there will be an unfavorable effect on the eggs from the standpoint of embryo development and hatching power. The low hatching power of eggs produced by hens fed a ration which is deficient in vitamin D is probably related to the low power of the developing embryos to transfer lime from the shell.

The ultra-violet rays in sunlight and in the light from quartz mercury vapor lamps have the power to serve the same practical function as vitamin D in relation to calcium and phosphorus metabolism. What happens is that one or more of the sterols present in the skin, when exposed to the action of ultra-violet irradiation, is changed to vitamin D.

Not over 0.1 per cent of the sun's radiant energy in many parts of the country has anti-rachitic value, but even this small amount need not be available to chicks for more than ten minutes daily in order to afford protection against rickets if the chicks are fed an otherwise complete ration which lacks the anti-rachitic factor.

The chemical nature of vitamin D is much more complicated than was thought a few years ago. It is known to occur in several different forms, and these are of varying potency for different species of animals. The most potent practical sources are fortified fish liver oils, vitamin A and D feeding oils, and irradiated animal sterols. The potency of these materials is expressed in International Chick Units.

It must be emphasized that vitamin D is not a substitute for the minerals required in bone formation. Calcium and phosphorus must be present in the proper amounts and in the right ratio. Vitamin D merely enables the body to make use of these substances in bone formation.

It has been amply demonstrated that the antirachitic potency of egg yolks can be greatly increased by irradiation of the hens or by the feeding of substances rich in vitamin D.

Vitamin E (Tocopherols).—A deficiency of vitamin E in the ration of breeding hens causes a marked reduction in hatchability, although egg production is not affected. Prolonged deficiency may cause sterility in males. When eggs laid by hens fed a ration devoid of vitamin E are incubated, the embryos rarely develop beyond the fourth day.

Since all whole grains and many green plants are good sources of this vitamin, it is practically impossible for hens to suffer from a deficiency if their ration consists largely of farm-grown feeds. Even when purchased feeds are fed to closely confined flocks, a deficiency of vitamin E is very unlikely unless the ration consists largely of degerminated grains and contains no dried or fresh green roughage.

In growing chicks the function of vitamin E is somewhat more complicated. A deficiency can result in (1) encephalomalacia or "crazy chick disease," (2) exudative diathesis, or (3) muscular dystrophy. The first of these conditions will not occur unless the ration being fed contains appreciable amounts of unsaturated fats. Exudative diathesis can be prevented not only by vitamin E but also by very low levels of selenium. The mechanism by which selenium functions is not yet understood. The third condition—muscular dystrophy—occurs in laboratory animals when the ration contains minimal amounts of selenium but is deficient in vitamin E. Chicks so fed do not show exudative diathesis but will develop symptoms of dystrophy. The condition seems to be aggravated when only minimal amounts of the sulphur-containing amino acids are present.

Chicks can make very good growth on rations completely lacking in vitamin E provided no appreciable amounts of unsaturated fats are included. This suggests that the primary, and perhaps the only, function of vitamin E in chick rations is to serve as an antioxidant. Some workers therefore question whether it should be considered a vitamin at all.

Vitamin K.—The function of vitamin K is intimately associated with normal clotting of blood. Chicks fed a ration deficient in this vitamin are likely to have severe hemorrhages following a bruise or injury to any part of the body, and may bleed to death from such minor injuries as those incidental to wingbanding. Mature fowls are not so easily affected, but when breeding hens are fed rations deficient in vitamin K, the chicks hatched from their eggs have very low reserves of the vitamin and are therefore susceptible to severe bleeding because of greatly prolonged blood-clotting time.

Poultry rations are not likely to be deficient in vitamin K because it is abundant in alfalfa meal, green pasture grasses, meat scrap, and fish meal. Only under certain stress conditions is a deficiency of vitamin K likely to become critical.

In addition to the recognized fat-soluble vitamins, certain unsaturated fatty acids, *i.e.*, arachidonic, linolenic and linoleic, have been found to be essential in the diet of the chick.

Water-Soluble Vitamins.—These include all of the vitamins of the B Complex and ascorbic acid (vitamin C). The original designation vitamin B was later shown to include two quite different fractions, and eventually some 10 compounds of different chemical nature and of varying importance in animal feeding. Each has been synthesized in pure form, and this has made possible the determination of requirements for several species of animals.

The B vitamins as a group are especially important in poultry nutrition because they are intimately concerned with the various enzyme systems, and with the regulating or controlling of processes involved in the liberation of energy and the utilization of organic food nutrients.

Thiamin.—This is the vitamin formerly designated as B or B_1. A ration deficient in thiamin is inadequate for growth, and brings on nervous disorders in both young and old birds, culminating in paralysis of the peripheral nerves (polyneuritis).

The chicken has a rather high and continuous requirement for this vitamin, but since it is found in abundance in the grains, in the fresh green leaves of many plants, and in skim milk and buttermilk, the effects of a deficiency are not often observed under practical conditions. Rarely is the poultryman concerned with the problem of an adequate supply of this vitamin.

Riboflavin.—Chicks need riboflavin for growth, both before and after hatching. Rations low in riboflavin have been a frequent cause of low hatchability. Among the best sources are liver, yeast, dried whey, dried skimmilk or buttermilk, and fermentation by-products. Other good sources are fresh green forage and alfalfa meal. Fish meal and meat scraps contain some riboflavin, cereal grains and mill feeds comparatively little. To meet the requirements of rapidly growing chicks and of breeding hens for this vitamin, some concentrated source of riboflavin is needed in the ration.

The manufacture of synthetic riboflavin has made it possible to market riboflavin mixtures containing known amounts (usually 1 gram per ounce) of this vitamin. Two ounces of such a mixture added to a ton of feed will increase the riboflavin content of the feed by one milligram per pound.

Niacin (Nicotinic Acid).—Niacin is essential for the normal growth and development of the chick. Since corn contains very little niacin, rations containing high percentages of corn will fail unless this vitamin is added. Corn is also low in tryptophan so that there is little opportunity for conversion of this amino acid into niacin. A deficiency of niacin results in a dark inflammation of the tongue and mouth cavity. There is loss of appetite, feathering is poor, and chicks become nervous and irritable. With lowered feed consumption, growth is greatly retarded.

Good sources of niacin include liver, yeast, wheat bran and middlings, fermentation by-products, and most cereal grasses. Niacin is also available commercially in crystalline form.

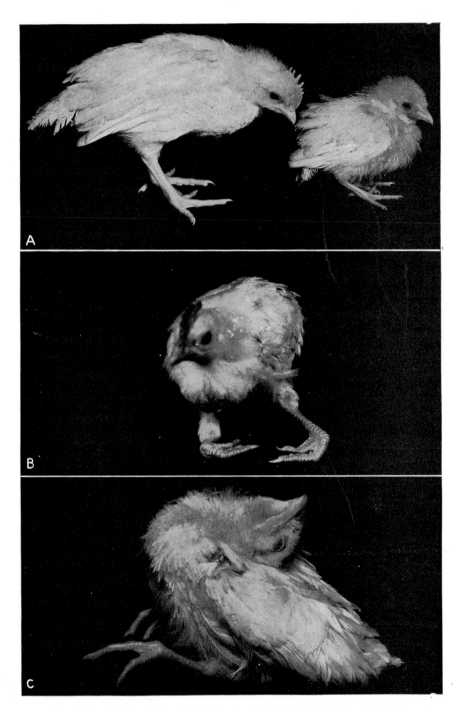

Fig. 114.—Effects of vitamin deficiencies. *A*, Effect of nicotinic acid deficiency on chick growth. *B*, Riboflavin deficiency in a young chick. Note the curled toes and the tendency to squat on the hocks. *C*, Head retraction caused by a deficiency of thiamin. (*Courtesy of the National Research Council.*)

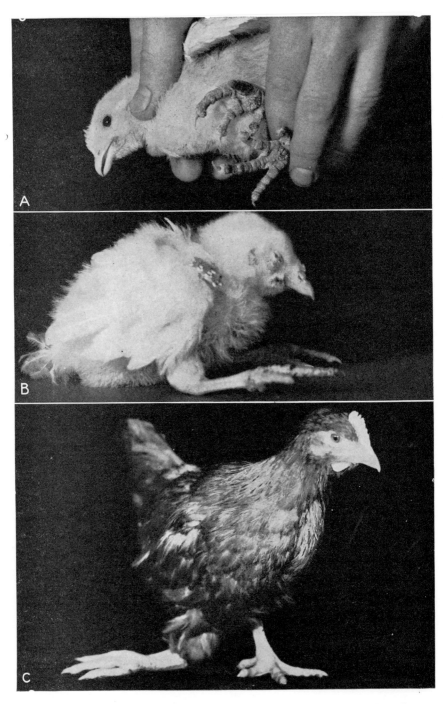

FIG. 115.—Effect of vitamin deficiencies. *A*, Biotin deficiency. Note the severe lesions on the bottom of the feet, and the lesions at the corner of the mouth. *B*, An advanced stage of pantothenic acid deficiency. Note the lesions at the corner of the mouth, and on the eyelids and feet. *C*, Perosis or slipped tendon resulting from a deficiency of manganese. This condition may also be caused by a deficiency of either choline or biotin. (*Courtesy of the National Research Council.*)

Pantothenic Acid.—Young chicks fed a ration deficient in pantothenic acid show slow growth and extremely ragged feathering. Scabby lesions appear at the corners of the mouth, on the edges of the eyelids, and around the vent. In severe cases they are also seen on the bottoms of the feet. A deficiency in the ration of breeding flocks results in lowered hatchability. Pantothenic acid was formerly called the filtrate factor or anti-dermatitis factor.

Among the best sources are brewers' yeast, alfalfa, cane molasses, fermentation residues, milk products, and green pasture grasses.

Vitamin B$_6$.—This term is now used to include pyridoxine, pyridoxal and pyridoxamine, all of which serve essentially the same function in metabolism. Continued deficiency results in jerky movements, aimless running about, followed by convulsions, complete exhaustion, and death. In mature fowls there is loss of appetite, followed by rapid loss of weight and death. Partial deficiency causes lowered egg production and poor hatchability.

Since grains, wheat and rice by-products, milk products, meat and fish products, alfalfa, and many other feeds contain appreciable quantities of pyridoxin, a deficiency in ordinary rations is very unlikely.

Biotin.—A deficiency of biotin in the ration of young chicks results in skin lesions quite similar to those observed in pantothenic acid deficiency. The bottoms of the feet become rough and calloused and later crack open and become hemorrhagic. Eventually, similar lesions appear at the corners of the mouth, and the eyelids may become granular.

When chicks are fed raw egg-white, they develop biotin deficiency because biotin is inactivated by avidin, one of the proteins in egg-white. An excess of biotin must be supplied under such conditions. Cooked egg-white has no such unfavorable effect.

Biotin is also involved in the prevention of perosis, and is essential for good hatchability of eggs. The amount needed for good health and egg production in mature hens is apparently very small.

Biotin is rather widely distributed, and deficiencies are not likely to occur under practical feeding conditions. Among the good sources are grains and their by-products, liver meal, dried yeast, alfalfa meal, milk products, and green pasture grasses.

Choline.—Choline, along with manganese, folic acid, niacin and biotin, is necessary for the prevention of perosis (slipped tendon) in growing chicks. It is required in much larger amounts than are the other vitamins, but it is present in many commonly used feed ingredients.

A lack of choline results in retarded growth, poor feed utilization and perosis. Choline seems also to be necessary for normal egg production, but hens are able to synthesize all that they require. Along with methionine, it serves as an important source of methyl groups which are necessary in metabolism.

Good sources of choline include liver meal, fish solubles and fish meal, soybean meal and distillers' solubles. It is also present in appreciable amounts in meat scrap and dried milk. Rations high in corn may easily be deficient in choline unless other ingredients which contain liberal amounts of this nutrient are included.

Vitamin B_{12}.—This newest of the B vitamins to be isolated is probably required in the ration of all young growing animals, including the chick. It is also very necessary in the ration of breeding hens. Many of the better rations have always contained adequate amounts of vitamin B_{12} because they have included liberal amounts of fish meal, meat scrap and milk products. On the other hand, some rations in which no animal protein concentrates were included have failed to promote good hatchability. This lack is easily corrected by the addition of no more than 5 per cent of fish meal or a few milligrams of pure vitamin B_{12} in a ton of feed (0.25 per cent of a B_{12}-antibiotic supplement).

Ruminants are able to produce their own B_{12} by fermentation in the rumen or paunch. Similarly, B_{12} is present in fermentation residues from the commercial production of antibiotics. These residues constitute one of the best practical sources of the vitamin.

Ascorbic Acid.—Since chickens, in common with other farm animals, are not susceptible to scurvy there is no need to supply ascorbic acid (vitamin C) in their rations. Chicken livers are rich in ascorbic acid, even though the ration may have contained no source of this factor—thus indicating clearly that the chicken is able to synthesize the vitamin. It seems also to be synthesized by the chick embryo. Some workers have suggested that added amounts of ascorbic acid are needed in the ration of high-producing hens to improve shell quality, but the general practice is to disregard it when formulating rations.

Folacin.—Folacin or folic acid must also be included in any complete list of vitamins needed by the chicken. When young chicks are deprived of it they show retarded growth and poor feathering. Colored plumage will be lacking in normal pigmentation. A characteristic anemia is also present. Practical rations are rarely, if ever, lacking in adequate amounts of folacin.

ANTIBIOTICS

Antibiotics are widely used in human medicine, as well as in the treatment of certain animal diseases, usually by intramuscular injection, but their routine use in livestock and poultry rations is a more recent development. The discovery of their value in this connection was made when certain fermentation residues left over from the commercial production of antibiotics were fed to animals. The effects were at first confused with those of B_{12} simply because the two substances occurred together in trace amounts in fermentation residues.

The antibiotics in most common use include aureomycin, bacitracin, procaine penicillin, streptomycin and terramycin. Others are continually being tested and it is probable that new ones will prove equally effective. The amounts fed are small, usually 0.25 per cent of an antibiotic supplement in the ration. This might well represent no more than 10 grams of the antibiotic in a ton of feed.

The growth response obtained from the use of antibiotics is directly related to the control of unidentified weak pathogenic bacteria, and the influence of the antibiotic is therefore referred to as a disease level effect. Since it is impractical to grow large numbers of chickens under absolutely disease-free or bacteriologically "clean" conditions, antibiotics are widely used and recommended. There is, however, much less evidence to support the routine use of antibiotics in the feeding of laying hens.

DIGESTION

Digestion is the process, accomplished by the alimentary system, of so dissolving and chemically changing the material taken into the alimentary canal that it can be absorbed by the blood and used by the body.

The Digestive Process and Assimilation.—The nutrients of the feed must undergo certain changes before they can be absorbed and used by the body. Something is known concerning these changes in regard to the proteins, carbohydrates and fat. Nothing is known regarding the changes, if any, in the case of the vitamins, and very little regarding the minerals.

Mechanical Processes.—The mechanical processes involved in digestion, some of which have been mentioned in discussing parts of the alimentary tract, include prehension of food, mechanical disintegration of the food, intimate mixing of the resulting particles with the digestive enzymes, exposure of the final products to a large absorptive surface, propelling of the food along the alimentary tract, and discharge of the digestive residues and other excretory products. All but the first and last of these processes are accomplished by smooth or involuntary muscles.

Enzymes and Enzyme Action.—The importance of enzymes in digestion is clear when it is realized that the changes in nutrients that take place in the animal body are brought about at ordinary temperatures, and in nearly neutral solutions that are extremely dilute. To hydrolyze proteins in the laboratory requires twenty-four to sixty hours of constant boiling with strong acids, and yet the digestive enzymes accomplish it easily in a very short time. The chemist cannot make fat from sugar in the laboratory, but the body does it easily.

The action of these digestive enzymes is chiefly hydrolytic. Very little heat is liberated by their action, hence little energy is lost by the animal. Certain *exogenous* enzymes, bacteria, yeasts and molds taken in with the food play a part in digestion. They cause a wide variety of reactions, in many of which there is loss of energy unless the body is in an environment such that it can make use of the heat liberated.

Proteins.—Feed proteins as such cannot be made use of by the cells of the body. In fact, if injected directly into the blood stream, they act as poisons. They have to be broken down into amino acids which can pass through the membranes of the intestine and be absorbed by the blood. The blood distributes the amino acids to all parts of the body where they are used for the construction of body tissues and their products.

Carbohydrates.—The starches and even the sugars, such as maltose, cannot pass through the intestinal membranes until they have been broken down into simple sugars referred to as the monosaccharides.

Carbohydrate digestion in the fowl consists chiefly in the hydrolysis of starch to maltose, and then to glucose, which is absorbed rapidly from the intestine. Glucose, fructose and galactose are the only monosaccharides to get into the liver through the portal system, and glucose is the only carbohydrate of the blood stream.

Fats.—The processes involved in fat absorption are still a subject of controversy among physiologists. Current theories suggest that it is not necessary for fats to be hydrolyzed before they can be absorbed. Whatever the process or processes involved in absorption, the fats found in the capillaries and in the lymphatic system are neutral fats. In the fowl it seems clear that a large part of the fatty acids of a high fat meal are absorbed by way of the portal system, rather than by way of the lymphatic system.

The fats of the lymphatic system approximate the composition of body fat much more nearly than do the ingested fats. The body does the best that it can to transform the ingested fats into fats that are characteristic of the species. Furthermore, for any given animal, the fat formed from excess carbohydrates is always the same.

Crude Fiber.—Food materials used in poultry feeding nearly all contain some crude fiber. As determined in the laboratory, this consists of cellulose, lignin, cutin and some pentosans. In the ruminant some of this material is broken down by the action of exogenous enzymes taken in with the food, as well as by bacterial action. With fowls, however, bacteria have little opportunity for action. As soon as the hard-coated grains become moist and soft enough for bacteria to work upon them, their chemical reaction is already acid. Very soon after passing from the gizzard to the intestine they are mixed with the bile, which inhibits bacterial development. The rectum is so short that there is no appreciable amount of bacterial action possible there. This leaves the ceca as the only place in which bacteria have an opportunity for effective action.

Because of the short time required for feeds to pass through the digestive tract of the fowl, very little digestion of crude fiber can occur even in the ceca. It has been shown that the ceca slowly fill with the fluid contents of the intestine, and then empty themselves at intervals ranging from eight to twenty-four hours, depending upon the nature of the food consumed. This would suggest ample time for bacterial action, but the amount of food material to find its way into the ceca is apparently not very large in proportion to the amount consumed.

While chickens consume over twice as much feed as is required by the same weight in cattle, they cannot make efficient use of the coarser kinds of feed, such as hay and fodder. They must be fed a concentrated ration made up quite largely of grains and their by-products.

Minerals and Vitamins.—Minerals are usually absorbed from the intestine without change in composition, and cannot be said to undergo digestion in the ordinary sense of the term. This same statement possibly applies to the vitamins as well.

The Final Nutritive Materials.—The usual diet of the fowl is made up of a great number of feeds of a very heterogeneous character. The proteins and carbohydrates in particular are extremely variable from time to time. Under the action of the digestive enzymes this great mixture of substances is broken down to a small number of comparatively simple chemical compounds that can be used by the cells of the body. This process, which we call digestion, and which in a technical sense really occurs outside the body, renders the animal more or less independent of the particular kinds of feed that happen to be available, and furnishes the cells with an essentially constant supply of uniform nutritive material.

METABOLISM

One of the properties of cells is the assimilation of the end products of digestion as these are carried to them by the blood and lymph. If digestion is looked upon as including all changes taking place from the time the food is consumed until it is in proper form and condition to be assimilated by the tissues of the body, metabolism may be considered as including all processes that the nutritive materials undergo from the time they enter the blood stream until the end products are eventually excreted from the body.

Carbohydrate Metabolism.—As has already been stated, the carbohydrate of the blood stream is all glucose. Glucose may be used to form the carbohydrates of the cells, it may be used as fuel, or it may be used in the formation of glycogen or fat. The total carbohydrates in the cells of the body can never be large, so that quantitatively the use of glucose for this purpose is relatively unimportant. Its oxidation for fuel is physiologically the most important use.

As soon as there is a surplus of glucose above the fuel needs it is used for the formation of glycogen. This occurs in the liver.

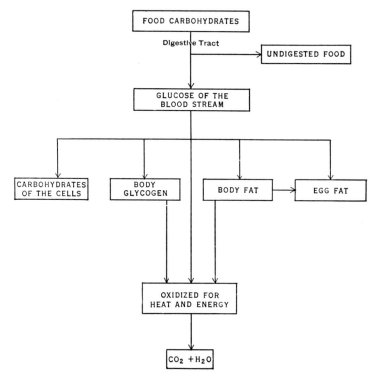

Fig. 116.—Diagram showing the normal uses which the body makes of carbohydrates.

Glycogen is animal starch, and is the proximate form of carbohydrate storage. It is stored in various parts of the body, particularly in the liver. When necessity arises, the liver glycogen is changed to glucose of the blood stream and is carried to various parts of the body for energy purposes. The concentration of glucose in the blood is maintained at a nearly constant percentage by certain endocrine glands, through their control over the synthesis and hydrolysis of glycogen.

Finally, if there is still a surplus of glucose, it may be used in the formation of fat. The process is not fully understood, but it is obvious that it can occur, for animals may be fattened readily on rations that contain but traces of fat and only minimal amounts of protein. Fat, then, is the ultimate form of carbohydrate storage.

The important uses that the body makes of carbohydrates are indicated diagrammatically in Figure 116.

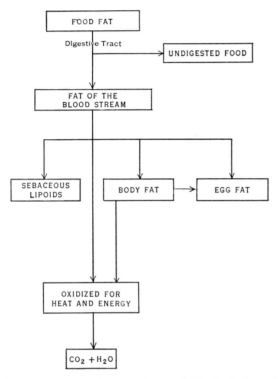

Fig. 117.—Diagram showing the normal uses which the body makes of fats.

Fat Metabolism.—The blood cells seem to have the ability to change the neutral fats of the lymph to phosphorized fats, chiefly lecithin. The phosphorized fats may be used either as an immediate source of energy or for storage. A certain amount must also be used for the formation of the lipoids of the cells and the sebaceous lipoids of the skin.

The sources of stored fat in the body are: (1) ingested fats which, after digestion and absorption, are found in a form that is more nearly like body fat than they were when eaten; and (2) carbohydrates that are used in the manner already described. The fat formed from carbohydrates is, for a given species, always the same. That formed from ingested fats is dependent to some extent on the character and amount of the ingested fat. The fact that the body is limited in its ability to transform ingested fats explains why, for example, the feeding of certain forms of fat to swine results in soft pork.

Fat once absorbed from the intestine is never excreted, except for the small amount of sebaceous lipoids in the skin. There is no physiological limit to the storage of fat, but there is a very definite

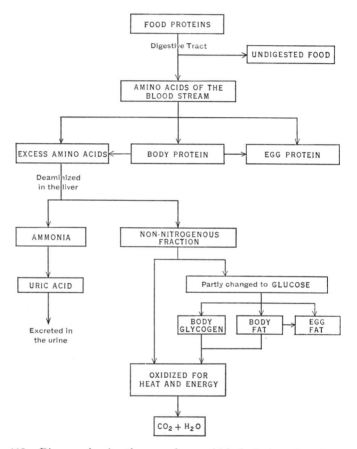

Fig. 118.—Diagram showing the normal uses which the body makes of proteins.

limit to the storage of carbohydrate as glycogen. When the glycogen stores are at a maximum, the excess carbohydrates are stored in the form of fat, as has already been explained. The important uses that the body makes of fats are indicated diagrammatically in Figure 117.

Protein Metabolism.—Proteins are not stored in the sense that the other nutrients are. Their chief function is structural, though an excess above the structural needs can be used for energy. Because of price, they are not so economically used for this purpose as are the carbohydrates, and hence, in practical feeding operations, it is usually desirable to reduce the level of feeding of the more costly protein feeds to a reasonable minimum as indicated by the requirements of the animals being fed.

Before the excess amino acids can be used for other than structural purposes they must be deaminized. The nitrogen that is thus split off is excreted by way of the kidneys, chiefly in the form of uric acid. The non-nitrogenous portion may be oxidized immediately to CO_2 and H_2O, or part of it may be stored in the form of glycogen or fat, if conditions make that necessary. The important uses that the body makes of proteins are indicated diagrammatically in Figure 118.

Minerals and Vitamins.—As to the metabolism of minerals and vitamins, very little is known. Since the minerals, at least, presumably are absorbed without change of composition, their utilization can be measured in terms of retention. About all that can be said in this connection is that there is nearly always a higher utilization with a low level of feeding, and that the mineral elements or ions are not degraded in metabolism. The release of calcium in metabolism does not require elimination. The calcium ions are in no sense worn out, but can be used over and over again as often as they are released. Their excretion may be simply incidental, due to leakage from the animal organism. Mineral elimination is both by way of the feces and the urine. Concerning vitamins, no quantitative information is available.

Chapter 9

The Feeds

In discussing the many ingredients which may be used in poultry rations, it seems logical to group them according to their chief uses on the basis of the nutrients which they contain.

The classification here used will be: (1) The cereal grains and by-products (energy-carrying feeds); (2) the protein supplements; (3) the mineral supplements; (4) the vitamin supplements; (5) water, and (6) miscellaneous feeds. The last named group includes a number of materials, some important, others not important, which are fed to poultry and which are not properly included in the other five groups.

THE CEREAL GRAINS AND BY-PRODUCTS

Grains are to be looked upon primarily as a source of energy. Except for the vitamin A potency of yellow corn, they are of substantially equal feeding value for poultry when compared pound for pound on a fiber-free basis. Some of the by-products, of course, differ significantly from the whole grains in gross composition.

All grains are deficient in protein, both as to amount and kind, since they uniformly lack one or more essential amino acids, including tryptophan, lysine and cystine. It is therefore necessary to supplement grains with suitable protein concentrates, which are usually included in the mash. They are also universally deficient in the required minerals, and must be supplemented in this regard.

The nutritive value of a grain is not changed by grinding it, nor can protein deficiencies resulting from the lack of essential amino acids be made up by the use of mill by-products from grain. The quality of protein in wheat bran or wheat middlings is no better than in wheat, and the protein in corn gluten meal is no better than in corn. These facts must be considered in formulating rations.

Certain other physical treatments will improve the nutritive value of cereal grains for poultry. Pelleting of corn, for example, enhances its growth-promoting value for chicks, presumably because of the effect of heat generated in the pelleting process.

Water soaking of coarsely ground grain significantly improves the nutritional value of barley, wheat and rye for growing chicks. The mechanism by which this improvement is brought about is unknown, but the effect seems to be increased availability of the energy of the

TABLE 27. — THE UNITED STATES FARM POULTRY RATION DURING JANUARY, 1944, AS REPORTED BY THE U. S. DEPARTMENT OF AGRICULTURE

Per cent of total ration

Geographic division	Commercial mash	Home-mixed mash	Commercial scratch	Corn	Wheat	Oats	Barley	Sorghum	Buckwheat
North Atlantic	50.4	3.7	19.4	10.7	9.3	4.9	1.0	..	0.6
South Atlantic	47.7	4.8	11.3	22.5	8.7	4.5	0.4	..	0.1
East North Central	23.3	23.7	2.5	29.0	8.7	12.2	0.4	0.1	0.1
West North Central	19.5	16.8	2.3	28.1	10.4	18.6	1.8	2.5	..
South Central	40.7	6.8	6.0	28.3	8.1	3.4	0.4	6.3	..
Western	44.1	7.3	5.4	5.4	27.0	3.8	5.1	1.9	..
United States	33.4	12.4	6.3	23.8	10.6	9.8	1.3	2.3	0.1

carbohydrate portion of the grain. Workers at the Washington Experiment Station reported an increase in the metabolizable energy of pearled barley from 1370 Calories per pound before water treatment to 1728 Calories per pound after treatment.

The most commonly used grains are corn, wheat and oats. According to a survey made by the U. S. Department of Agriculture in January, 1944, corn made up 24 per cent of the total poultry ration fed to laying flocks on farms in the United States, wheat 11 per cent, and oats 10 per cent. These percentages were in addition to what was fed in commercial scratch feed or in ground form in mash. No other grain amounted to as much as 3 per cent of the total ration.

Commercial scratch feed made up more than 20 per cent of the entire ration in each of the New England States and in New York, New Jersey and Florida. In most of the rest of the country it accounted for less than 10 per cent.

Corn fed as grain made up more than 33 per cent of the entire ration in Indiana, Illinois, Iowa, Missouri, Kentucky, Tennessee, Alabama and Mississippi, and over 20 per cent in fifteen other states.

Wheat fed as grain made up more than 33 per cent of the total ration in Montana, Idaho, Wyoming, Utah and Nevada, and over 20 per cent in six other western states.

Oats fed as grain made up over 20 per cent of the total ration in Minnesota, Iowa, and North and South Dakota. In only four other states did oats make up as much as 10 per cent of the ration.

Barley fed as grain made up more than 5 per cent of the ration in North and South Dakota, Montana, Idaho, Wyoming, Colorado, Utah and California.

Grain sorghums made up over 10 per cent of the ration in Kansas, Oklahoma, Texas and New Mexico. In only five other states did they amount to as much as 1 per cent.

Buckwheat was fed to the extent of 1 per cent in only two states, New York and West Virginia.

No comparable recent data are available, but some significant changes might be expected because of the shift in important areas of broiler production and the associated shifts in laying flocks.

Rice and rice by-products can be used with entire satisfaction in rations for both chicks and hens but, because rice is in such demand for human food, these feeds are not often available except in the sections of the country where rice is grown.

Rye has long been considered unsuitable for use in poultry rations because it is less readily eaten and because high levels of rye will cause sticky droppings. Recent Canadian studies have shown, however, that the mere process of pelleting broiler rations containing as much as 35 per cent of rye will make them equal to or better than similar rations containing the same level of wheat. The improvement of rye by water treatment has already been mentioned.

PROTEIN SUPPLEMENTS

Since all grains and grain by-products are deficient in both amount and quality of protein, it is necessary to supplement them with suitable proteins from other sources. The common ingredients for this purpose are the oilseed meals and certain animal protein concentrates. The relative importance of the various high-protein feeds is shown by the following figures for total consumption by all livestock, excluding work animals, for the years beginning October 1, 1949, 1954 and 1958.

	1949	1954	1958
		1,000 Tons	
Soybean cake and meal	4,514	5,428	8,938
Cottonseed cake and meal	2,375	2,405	2,198
Tankage and meat meal	842	1,339	1,484
Corn gluten feed and meal	926	1,034	1,044
Fish meal and solubles	261	395	512
Linseed cake and meal	670	488	417
Copra cake and meal	204	182	148
Dried milk products	100	165	110
Peanut cake and meal	93	18	75

Protein concentrates of animal origin have long been favored by poultrymen because of their special value in supplementing the cereal grains. With increased knowledge about amino acid and vitamin requirements, this distinction is no longer important. The question is not whether an animal protein or a plant protein is in itself a "good" protein, but whether the combination of proteins to be fed is adequate in its amino acid makeup.

Animal protein supplements often contain other nutrients, *e.g.* phosphorus, choline, riboflavin, vitamin B_{12}, in which the cereal grains are deficient.

Animal Protein Supplements.—The animal protein supplements commonly used in poultry feeding include milk and its products. packing-house by-products, and by-products of the fishing industry,

Fish Meal.—Fish meal has been used for many years in the feeding of poultry. Menhaden fish meal, made from the menhaden herring, accounts for about half the total production. Most meals today are made by the vacuum drying process and hence are of better quality than meals made by the former flame-drying process which exposed the product to high temperatures.

By official definition fish meal is "Clean, dried, ground tissues of undecomposed whole fish or fish cuttings, either or both, with or without the extraction of part of the oil. If it contains more than 3 per cent of salt (NaCl) the amount of salt must constitute a part of the brand name, provided that in no case shall the salt content of this product exceed 7 per cent." Most fish meals contain from 60 to 70 per cent of protein, and are good sources of riboflavin, niacin, pantothenic acid and choline.

Meat Scrap.—Meat meal or meat scrap is the "Finely ground, dry-rendered residue from animal tissues exclusive of hair, hoof, horn, hide trimmings, blood meal, manure and stomach contents, except in such traces as might occur unavoidably in good factory practice. When these products contain more than 4.4 per cent of phosphorus (P), they shall be designated either "Meat and Bone Meal" or "Meat and Bone Scrap." If the product bears a name descriptive of its kind, composition, or origin, it must correspond thereto. It must be designated according to its protein content."

Meat scrap is probably the most widely used of all animal protein supplements. Along with fish meal and milk products, it is a good source of vitamin B_{12}.

Milk Products.—Milk in its various forms is especially valuable as a constituent of the ration of young chicks, and of hens from which eggs are to be used for hatching. This is due not only to the high quality of milk protein but also to the riboflavin and other vitamins contained in milk, as well as to the presence of lactose which favors the assimilation of calcium. The official definition of dried buttermilk will serve as an example.

Dried buttermilk is the "Product resulting from the removal of water from clean, sound buttermilk derived from natural cream to which no foreign substances have been added, excepting such as are necessary and permitted in the manufacture of butter. It shall contain not more than 8 per cent of moisture, not more than 13 per cent of mineral matter (ash), and not less than 5 per cent of butterfat as determined by the Roese-Gottlieb method."

Poultry By-product Meal.—The official definition describes this product as the "Ground, dry-rendered, clean, wholesome parts of the carcass of slaughtered poultry, such as head, feet, undeveloped eggs, gizzard, and intestines, exclusive of feathers and gizzard and intestinal contents, except in such trace amounts as might occur unavoidably in good factory practice." Considerable quantities of this material are now available. It contains about 55 per cent of protein and, like other animal protein supplements, is a good source of riboflavin, niacin, pantothenic acid and choline. A new tentative definition would limit the ash content to 14 per cent, with not more than 4 per cent of acid-insoluble ash.

Tankage.—Tankage is a finely-ground product made from the residues from animal tissues as obtained in packing plants. Different tankages may consist of the products obtained by either the wet process or the dry-rendering process, or a mixture of these products, to which blood and stick may be added. Meat scraps, on the other hand, must consist only of dry-rendered residues to which no blood or stick has been added.

Tankages may be sold as digester tankage, meat meal tankage, or feeding tankage. If they contain more than 4.4 per cent of phosphorus (P), they must be designated "Digester Tankage with Bone," "Meat and Bone Meal Tankage," or "Feeding Tankage with Bone." Most tankage is manufactured to contain a minimum of 60 per cent protein.

Plant Protein Supplements.—The plant protein supplements available for poultry feeding are obtained chiefly from certain of the oil-bearing seeds such as cottonseed, flaxseed, peanuts, and soybeans.

Cottonseed Meal.—Properly processed cottonseed meal is a valuable protein concentrate for poultry feeding. Unless the pigment glands are removed during processing, or the gossypol which they contain is inactivated, the meal is not satisfactory for use in chick rations. A degossypolized product is now commercially available. By official definition it is "Cottonseed meal from which the gossypol has been deactivated, so as to contain not more than 0.04 per cent free gossypol." Commercial meals must contain at least 36 per cent of protein, and are usually available also with guarantees of 41 and 43 per cent. If made by the newer solvent process, the fat minimum is usually stated as 0.50 per cent.

Since cottonseed meal is relatively low in lysine, it should not be used as the only protein supplement in a ration. Small amounts of blood meal or fish meal will correct the deficiency.

Several investigators have noted the unfavorable effect of cottonseed meal on the storage quality of eggs, specifically the development of "cottonseed spots," and have indicated that deterioration begins as soon as four weeks after the eggs are placed in storage. The condition is not observed in the eggs when first laid.

The characteristic discoloration of yolks in eggs laid by hens fed cottonseed meal can be made to occur in a matter of minutes by placing the yolks in an atmosphere of ammonia. Iron is released from the yolk proteins, and combines with gossypol from the cottonseed meal to cause the discoloration.

If certain iron salts, such as ferric chloride or ferrous sulphate, are fed along with the cottonseed meal, they combine with the gossypol and prevent its absorption from the intestinal tract. About 0.5 per cent of the iron salt seems to be needed. Without this precaution, no more than 5 per cent of cottonseed meal may safely be fed to laying hens if yolk discoloration is to be avoided.

Linseed Meal.—In the extraction of linseed oil from flaxseed, the residue or cake is ground to make the linseed meal used in livestock feeding. Since the meal is laxative, and contains a substance which is toxic to chicks, it is not widely used in poultry feeding. The toxic material can be inactivated or destroyed by a simple treatment

15

which consists in letting the meal stand for 18 hours at about 100° F. after being mixed with about twice its weight of water.

Peanut Meal. — This is a by-product of the manufacture of peanut oil. It is not extensively used in poultry feeding.

Soybean Oil Meal. — This popular protein concentrate is made by crushing, cooking, and removing most of the oil from soybeans. It is a valuable protein feed and has come to be used more widely than any other such ingredient. It is sold under labeling which indicates the protein content and the method of manufacture.

Most of the commercial meal is now made by the solvent process so that it conforms to the following official definition. "Solvent Extracted Soybean Oil Meal is the product resulting from grinding Solvent Extracted Soybean Flakes. It shall be designated and sold according to its protein content." The flakes are obtained after extracting most of the oil from soybeans by cracking, heating, flaking and the use of solvents. After extraction of the oil the product is heated or toasted. Solvent meal contains about 45 per cent of protein. A dehulled product containing about 50 per cent of protein is also available.

MINERAL SUPPLEMENTS

About 10 per cent of the dry matter of the fowl's body and approximately 35 per cent of the dry matter of the whole egg are mineral matter. Therefore it can be seen readily that it is necessary to supply mineral matter in a form that may be assimilated by the fowl, for the rapid upbuilding of the bones in the growing chick and the formation of shell on eggs and even for maintenance or during the molt. It is also desirable that mineral matter in a hard form not easily assimilable be furnished for the purpose of crushing and grinding whole or cracked grains in the gizzard.

Seeds and seed by-products are particularly deficient in calcium, and very probably in sodium and chlorine. Whole grains are possibly somewhat deficient in phosphorus.

Feeds rich in calcium are meat scrap, fish meal and tankage, with milk products and legume roughage of secondary importance. Those rich in phosphorus include wheat bran, wheat middlings, soybean oil meal, cottonseed meal, linseed meal, milk products, meat scrap, fish meal, and tankage. Sodium and chlorine are best supplied in common salt.

The need for manganese in the rations of growing chicks and breeding hens has already been indicated.

Laying hens have an additional requirement for calcium for egg-shell formation, and should be given free access to oyster shell (or some other form of calcium carbonate) at all times.

Bone (Steamed). — The phosphate of lime is as desirable for the formation of bone in growing chicks as the carbonate of lime is in the ration of the laying hen for the formation of the egg shell. The customary form for furnishing it is steamed bone meal. This is a by-product of the packing house and consists of animal bones, from which the gristle, grease and moisture have been removed, ground to a meal.

Defluorinated Phosphate. — This product is made by heat treatment of superphosphate of fertilizer grade. To be so labeled, it must contain no more than 1 part of fluorine to each 100 parts of phosphorus. It is a satisfactory substitute for bone meal in poultry rations.

Grit. — The function of hard grit is presumably to aid in crushing and grinding feed and to prevent impaction in the gizzard. Most of the grit available commercially is made from granite, but crushed quartz, feldspar and phosphate rock have also been used. The size of particles must be regulated according to the size of the chickens to which it is fed. The extensive literature detailing experiments on the use and function of grit indicates (a) that chickens fed exclusively on ground feeds do not need grit, (b) that after having been deprived of either grit or a source of calcium, fowls will eat large quantities of any sort of grit which is offered to them, (c) that excess grit consumed by fowls passes out of the gizzard, and (d) that when the available supply of grit is restricted the gizzard will retain coarse particles for as long as one year or until they are completely pulverized.

Limestone. — The necessity for lime (calcium) in the ration as a raw material from which egg shells can be formed has long been recognized.

Limestone, which is calcium carbonate plus certain impurities, naturally forms a good source. It is not so popular with poultrymen as marine shells.

There is some evidence to show that dolomite, because of the magnesium that it contains, is not suitable as a mineral supplement for laying hens. At the Utah Station it was found that during a four-month feeding period with laying pullets, egg production decreased, the shells of the eggs became progressively thinner, and nearly every bird in the flock of 60 developed diarrhea. All of these conditions cleared up in a short time after substituting for the dolomite a limestone that was practically pure calcium carbonate. It was further found that calcite, oölite and high grade limestone, each of which contained 98 per cent or better of calcium carbonate, gave results equal to crushed oyster shell when measured by yearly egg yield, breaking strength of egg shells and mortality among the pullets.

Marine Shells. — Undoubtedly the most widely-fed source of calcium carbonate for laying hens is oyster shell, though other marine shells of similar composition are equally valuable. The reasons for their use are the same as for limestone.

The correlation between the number of eggs laid and the amount of oyster shell consumed is very high. In other words, the consumption of shell increases or decreases directly as egg production increases or decreases.

Oyster shell contains 96 per cent calcium carbonate. One pound of oyster shell contains lime enough for the shells of 7 to 8 dozen eggs. Like limestone, oyster shell is often fed in powdered form in the mash, with an excess supply crushed to a suitable size always available in hoppers.

Salt.—Salt in some quantity is considered necessary for all farm animals as a source of sodium and chlorine. It is most conveniently fed to poultry by mixing it in the mash at the rate of $\frac{1}{2}$ to 1 per cent of the total food intake.

That an excess of salt is toxic to chickens, and may easily result in death, has been well established, though the actual salt toleration of both chicks and older fowls is much higher than has commonly been supposed. At the Illinois Station it was found that chickens could be raised from nine to twenty-one weeks of age on rations containing as high as 8 per cent of salt with no apparent detrimental effects on their condition. A daily intake of salt *in the feed* of 6 to 8 grams per bird appeared to exert no harmful effect on birds nine weeks old, or older.

The minimum lethal single dose of salt for chickens weighing from 3 to 5 pounds each is close to 4 grams per kg. of body weight, that is 0.4 per cent of the body weight. The same relationship between body weight and the minimum lethal single dose holds for baby chicks. Workers at the Maryland Station found that young chicks were able to endure salt levels as high as 30 per cent for short periods of time, and that it was impossible to place enough salt in the all-mash ration of chicks to produce an appreciable amount of sudden mortality. The unpalatability of feeds containing dangerous levels of salt, plus the tendency to consume large quantities of water when fed a salty ration, appear to act as a protection against an overdose under natural conditions.

VITAMIN SUPPLEMENTS

Distillers' dried solubles, made by condensing the screened stillage obtained in the manufacture of alcohol from grain, is an excellent source of some of the water-soluble vitamins. Each pound of corn distillers' dried solubles, for example, contains about 2.5 milligrams of thiamin, 7.5 milligrams of riboflavin, 50 milligrams of niacin, 9 milligrams of pantothenic acid and 2,000 milligrams of choline.

Condensed fish solubles, made by evaporating the watery material pressed out of fish waste along with the oil, is an excellent vitamin concentrate. Each pound contains about 2.5 milligrams of thiamin, 6 of riboflavin, 70 of niacin, 16 of pantothenic acid and 1,800 of choline. This product is also an excellent source of vitamin B_{12} and probably contains a number of still unidentified factors which are of value in poultry nutrition.

Various fermentation by-products are available for feeding purposes. They may contain residual amounts of antibiotics or varying amounts of water-soluble vitamins. Certain primary fermentation products are also used as sources of some of the unidentified growth factors which are still being studied experimentally.

Other sources of the principal vitamins have been mentioned in connection with the discussion of the place of the individual vitamins in poultry rations.

WATER

This highly important part of all poultry rations has been discussed as a nutrient. It must be further emphasized that a suitable and constant supply of clean, cool water is essential to the best feeding practice. To provide water that is always clean and cool is a summer problem which must be met by the feeder's ingenuity if he is not so fortunate as to have running water available.

In the northern and central states a constantly available supply of water during the winter also presents its problems. This is particularly true in connection with feeding by means of artificial lights. It is fully as essential to have water available when the lights are turned on as it is to have feed. An increased consumption of both is one object in using lights. Water heaters of various styles are available. Many are so designed as to involve little or no fire hazard and have ample capacity for heating the water sufficiently to prevent its freezing in the coldest weather.

MISCELLANEOUS INGREDIENTS

The newer knowledge about nutritional requirements of poultry has eliminated the need for such formerly used materials as beets, cabbage, kale, potatoes and grass silage.

Certain other products that may be available locally for limited or occasional use would include dried stale bread, dried bakery waste, and dried apple or tomato pomace.

Cane or beet molasses, though most often used in ruminant feeding, are sometimes included in poultry rations. They are a good source of energy and may be used to replace cereal grains, pound for pound, up to 10 per cent of rations for either growing chicks or laying hens.

Dried yeast, available mostly as a by-product of the brewing and distilling industries, is often used in poultry rations. By official definition it must contain not less than 40 per cent protein. It is a good source of the water-soluble vitamins.

Chapter 10

The Nutrient Requirements of Poultry

WHAT A RATION IS

A RATION is often defined as the quantity of feed provided for a given animal during a day of twenty-four hours, whether it is fed all at one time, or in portions at several different times. In poultry practice, the amount fed from day to day is so often governed by the judgment of the poultryman, based on the changing needs of the fowls, that it is not customary to specify the amount to be fed in a given time. Instead, the feed formula, which is a statement of the kinds and proportions of the constituents to be fed, is more often referred to as a ration.

A Balanced Ration.—A balanced ration is a combination of feeds furnishing the several nutrients in such proportion, amount and form as will, without waste, properly nourish a given group of birds for a particular purpose.

A more specific definition proposed by Mitchell is that "A ration is balanced with reference to any animal if it contains all of the nutrients required in such proportions that the physiological functions occurring within the animal may proceed normally, or at rates that are maximal for the amounts of food consumed." He further states that the nutritive value of a balanced ration will not be enhanced by changing the percentage of any one of its nutritive constituents; and that in fact, the only method of demonstrating that a ration is properly balanced is to show that changing the percentage of any nutrient in it will not improve its efficiency in promoting the physiological function, or any one of a number of functions, with respect to which it has been balanced.

THE REQUIREMENTS FOR MAINTENANCE

According to common usage, a feeding standard is a statement of the exact quantities of all the digestible nutrients which it is believed should be provided in a ration that is to serve a particular purpose. It differs from a balanced ration in that it does not specify the amount or kinds of feed from which the nutrients shall be secured, and takes no account of form, physiological function, vitamins or water.

Since both chicks and laying hens are commonly fed in groups rather than as individuals, feeding standards are seldom used for poultry. The usual procedure is to specify minimum levels of the various nutrients which are needed in a ration to be used for a particular purpose. The level may be expressed as the percentage of protein in the total ration, the number of milligrams of a particular vitamin in each pound of feed, or the parts per million of some trace mineral. In any case, the recommendation must be based on a knowledge of the minimum nutritive requirements. The requirements for maintenance, for growth and for egg production will therefore be discussed separately in the following sections.

A very considerable part of the ration of laying hens is used for maintenance purposes, and this part of the cost of keeping them goes on day by day throughout the year, whether they are laying well or poorly or not at all. Hence the maintenance requirement is of practical as well as theoretical interest. It includes the requirements for both basal metabolism and normal activity. The combination is sometimes referred to as "economic maintenance."

By basal metabolism is meant the basal heat production, or the minimum energy expenditure of the individual. It is the heat production which occurs under conditions such that the influences of feed, of environmental temperature and of voluntary activity are removed. It results in a continuous demand for food energy and appears to be, for a given animal, one of the most constant of biological measurements.

Energy Requirements for Maintenance.—The amount of energy required for "economic maintenance" is affected by a number of different environmental factors, as well as by certain conditions which are inherent in the individual animal, such as size, age, sex, environmental temperature, and the degree of activity.

It is well known that basal heat production per unit of body weight varies with the size of the animal. The minimum heat production of day-old chicks, for example, is about 5.5 small calories per gram of live weight per hour, twice as much as the corresponding figure for adult hens. As an extreme example, the resting metabolism of a hummingbird can be expressed in terms of oxygen consumption as 15 cc. per gram of live weight per hour. The corresponding figure for an elephant is 0.15 cc.

The basal metabolic rate of males is usually higher than that of females by about 5 to 7 per cent. Castration lowers the basal heat production by as much as 13 per cent in 9-month-old-capons.

Effect of Temperature.—Because of the ability of warm-blooded animals to maintain a constant body temperature that is normally several degrees above the environmental temperature, the animal is constantly losing heat to its surroundings. This loss of heat means a loss of energy that must be supplied in the feed. Heat production must equal heat loss if the animal is to maintain its normal temperature, and this means that there is a rapid increase in the metabolic rate whenever the environmental temperature falls below the critical point. Unless sufficient excess energy for this purpose is liberated by increased voluntary or involuntary activity, additional food or stored energy must be oxidized.

The minimum rate of heat production in day-old chicks occurs at an environmental temperature of 95° F. Heat output is more than doubled at a temperature of 75° in order to compensate for increased heat loss. For the adult hen, the minimum basal heat production occurs over a range of about 10 degrees between 65° and 75° F. These values are for fasting chickens at rest.

Effect of Feeding.—Feeding an animal will increase its heat production, and the higher the level of feeding, the greater will be the heating effect. A flock of hens on full feed will be better able to withstand the effects of cold weather than will a flock which is for any reason on reduced rations. Liberal feeding of the energy-carrying feeds in cold weather is a thoroughly practical procedure for which there is a definite scientific basis.

Effect of Activity.—Physical activity requires the expenditure of energy. The hummingbird furnishes an excellent example. When "hovering," it consumes oxygen at the rate of 80 cc. per gram of live weight per hour, compared with the resting level of 15 cc. Normally active fowls have an energy requirement which is about 50 per cent above the basal requirement, when expressed as an average for a 24-hour day. The actual requirement will be higher during the day and lower when the fowls are roosting at night.

Protein Requirements for Maintenance.—The basal or minimal requirement for protein will be that resulting from the endogenous protein catabolism. It is measured by the amount of nitrogen in the urine of an animal that is fed a nitrogen-free diet so designed as to furnish all other nutrients in ample amounts. This requirement for nitrogen to cover the endogenous loss is often expressed in terms of milligrams per kilogram of body weight. It has been shown by Smuts, working at the Illinois Station, that for rats, mice, guinea-pigs, rabbits and swine, the endogenous nitrogen amounts to 2 mg. per Calorie[1] of basal heat production. This study was based on mature animals of each species, and it seems reasonable to suppose that the relationship might hold equally well for chickens.

The nitrogen requirement of young chickens is greater per unit of weight than that of older fowls. This is in line with the constant relationship to surface area found by Smuts, and means that the young animal has an exaggerated endogenous loss. As to the effect of sex, there is no information, though it seems reasonable to assume that the requirement per unit of weight will be higher in males than in females because of the higher basal metabolic rate of males.

---

[1] Unless otherwise stated, the term Calorie as used in this discussion means the large or kilogram calorie. It is the amount of heat required to raise the temperature of 1 kilogram of water by 1 degree Centigrade.

Generally speaking, no other factors affect the endogenous nitrogen loss under normal conditions. Hence the simplest method of estimating the basal nitrogen requirement is to apply Smuts' factor to the calculated basal heat production.

All available evidence indicates that muscular activity does not in any way affect the protein requirement, provided there is furnished an ample supply of food energy for the energy requirement of the activity.

Mineral Requirements for Maintenance.—The mineral requirements are more difficult to determine and evaluate, and but little definite information is available. There will be mineral losses under maintenance conditions, but the nature of mineral metabolism is such that in both the growing chick and the laying hen these losses are greatly overshadowed by the specific requirements for growth and egg production. Indirect evidence suggests a minimum requirement of 2 grams of calcium for each 100 grams of net protein. In terms of minerals fed, this amount would have to be doubled, as it has been shown by the use of radioactive Ca and P that only about half of the calcium and phosphorus fed is retained by the laying hen.

The other mineral requirements, like the vitamin requirements for maintenance, have little practical significance and are therefore not considered here.

HOW CHICKENS GROW

Standards of comparison are valuable in nearly every sort of work, and the measurement of chick growth is no exception. One must remember, however, that there is probably a normal rate of growth for each different breed and strain; that it will not be the same for males and females within a particular strain; that it may be affected by time of hatching and that whether or not a particular lot of chickens equals or exceeds the standard will depend on the kind and amount of feed supplied, as well as on many other environmental factors. Maximum rates of growth are usually obtained with crossbred males raised indoors with limited exercise, and fed rations that are nutritionally adequate in all known respects.

In Figure 119 are shown graphically the growth data for a group of crossbred males from hatching time to sixteen weeks of age. Three different measures of growth are included. The average weekly increases in body weight are shown as columns. The weekly increment (time-rate of growth) increases regularly till a maximum gain of 240 grams is reached during the eighth week. Thereafter the weekly increment becomes steadily less with each succeeding week. It should be said here that the weekly gains made by a flock of chickens, or by any individual in a flock, are often highly erratic, up well above the "standard" in one week, and down the next. This graph is intended to show average "expected" weekly increases rather than actual weights, although it was derived from several series of actual growth data.

The cumulative total, or attained weight, from week to week is shown as a solid line rising from left to right. A different scale is used here in order to get both measures on the same graph.

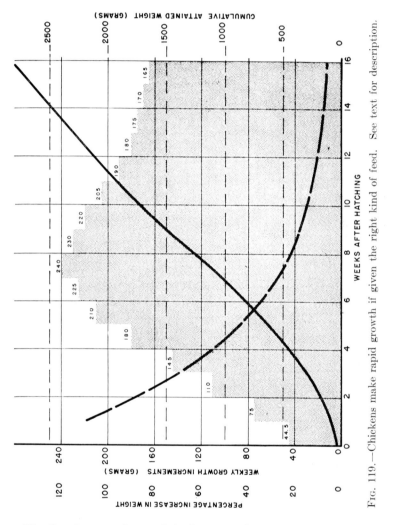

Fig. 119.—Chickens make rapid growth if given the right kind of feed. See text for description.

Finally, the rate of growth is shown as the percentage which each weekly gain is of the weight at the beginning of that week. Note that although the time-rate of growth increases from hatching to eight weeks of age, the percentage-rate of growth decreases from the very beginning.

TABLE 28.—DATA FOR THE GROWTH OF NEW HAMPSHIRE × BARRED PLY-
MOUTH ROCK CROSSBRED MALES SHOWN GRAPHICALLY IN FIGURE 119.

Age in weeks	Average weight grams	Weekly gain grams	Rate of gain per cent
0	40.5	—	—
1	85	44.5	110
2	160	75	88
3	270	110	69
4	415	145	54
5	595	180	43
6	805	210	35
7	1030	225	28
8	1270	240	23
9	1500	230	18
10	1720	220	14.5
11	1925	205	12
12	2115	190	10
13	2300	185	9
14	2480	180	8
15	2655	175	7
16	2825	170	6.4

THE REQUIREMENTS FOR GROWTH

Not until the maintenance requirements have been met can any surplus nutrients be used for other purposes such as growth or egg production. The requirements for these two functions will be considered separately. The nutritive needs for growth will be the specific requirements for tissue formation in the growing animal.

In theory, the requirements for energy, protein and minerals can best be measured by determining the daily deposition of these nutrients as they are added during growth. Detailed feeding standards can then be calculated after making allowance for the wastage in digestion and metabolism. In practice, however, it is much simpler to use the feeding trial approach—measuring performance in terms of body weight increase and, when necessary, by carcass analysis. For practical reasons it is also necessary to formulate rations in terms of their percentage content of any given nutrient—amino acid, vitamin or mineral—or in terms of the actual minimum amount needed in each pound of feed.

The Energy Requirement for Growth.—Quantitatively, energy is by far the most important among the several nutrients needed for growth, and for this reason it usually determines the requirement for total feed. The chicken, like other animals, tends to eat whatever amount of feed is necessary to satisfy its energy needs. This does not mean however that it will always eat the right amount of feed to promote maximum growth or maximum feed conversion. If other required nutrients are not present in the right proportions, the amount of growth promoted by voluntary feed consumption will be less than maximum and may be very unsatisfactory.

The exact amount of gross energy in a particular ingredient or ration can be determined by complete combustion of a sample in a bomb calorimeter. The result is expressed as Calories per pound or per kilogram. The gross energy of the feed, minus the fecal and urinary energy in the droppings, represents metabolizable energy. (In the case of ruminants it is necessary to deduct also the energy of combustible gases which result from fermentation, chiefly in the paunch.)

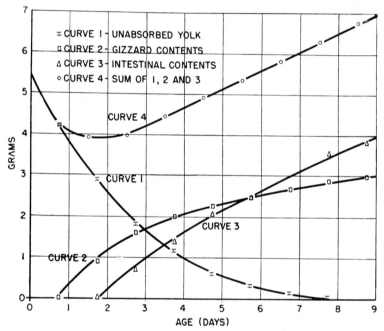

FIG. 120.—Showing how unabsorbed yolk affects chick weight during the first few days after hatching. (*After Barott and Pringle.*)

Not all of the metabolizable energy can be used by the animal because some will be lost in the form of heat. After this cost of utilization is deducted, the remainder is net energy, or the energy which is actually useful to the chicken for maintenance, including muscular activity, and for the production of fat, muscle tissue, and eggs. Productive energy, by definition, is the amount of energy stored in the form of fat or protein in the growing or fattening animal. Productive energy values of feed ingredients will always be less than metabolizable energy values, usually by 30 per cent or more.

The exact energy requirement of growing chickens cannot be stated without qualification. The most efficient ration in terms of energy utilization may not be the most economical when measured by the feed cost for each pound of weight increase, either because of cost per pound of the ingredients used or because of differences in the percentage of carcass fat produced or desired. Furthermore, there must be maintained a reasonable balance among the several feed nutrients. Excess energy will be of little value unless adequate amounts of protein, vitamins and minerals are also present. Some consideration of the interrelationships between protein and energy and of their effects on total feed intake will be helpful to an understanding of the whole problem.

The feed intake of growing chickens will, in general, increase as the energy content of the ration is decreased. This can be shown by adding to a good ration increasing amounts of oat hulls, which contain very little useful energy, with or without an adjustment in the protein content of the ration. As shown in Table 29, with each 10 per cent increase in oat hulls growing chickens responded by eating more feed. So long as the protein level was maintained at 20 per cent, as in Lots 1 to 5, there was no significant effect on growth. But when the original ration was diluted by successive additions of oat hulls (Lots 8 to 12) with consequent reduction in the protein level, a point was soon reached at which the bulkiness of the ration prevented the chickens from eating enough feed to meet their protein needs, and the rate of growth was reduced.

With a constant protein level and a decreasing energy level in the ration (Lots 1 to 5) the total protein intake per chick increased as the energy level was decreased. But when both feed protein and feed energy were decreased, as in Lots 8 to 12, the total protein consumed per chick decreased with each change in energy level.

One other point presented in Table 29 calls for special comment. The chickens in Lots 1 to 5 made essentially equal growth in spite of substantial differences in total energy consumption. The extra energy consumed by Lots 1, 2, 3 and 4 must have been dissipated as heat or stored in the form of fat. Carcass analyses provided the answer. The fat content of the chickens in the five lots at the end of the experiment, when they were eleven weeks old, was 27, 23, 21, 18 and 16 per cent, respectively. Of some interest, too, is the fact that the average gizzard weight of the chickens in Lots 5, 11 and 12, consuming rations containing 40 or 50 per cent of oat hulls, was 38 grams in contrast to 25 grams for the average gizzard weight of Lots, 1, 6 and 7 fed rations without hulls.

Carcass analyses were not reported for Lots 8 to 12, but data from other experiments have shown that the per cent of fat in the carcass will always increase with increased energy intake, provided the protein level of the ration is held constant—either high or low—but that it will decrease with increasing protein level of the ration when the intake of feed energy is held constant—either high or low. On the other hand, with rations adjusted, and with feed intake controlled, so as to give the same energy and nitrogen intake to all lots of chicks, varying the level of corn oil from 0.5 per cent to 30.7 per cent of the ration had no effect on the per cent of carcass fat at either a 15 per cent or a 30 per cent level of protein in the ration. (See Table 32.)

TABLE 29.—EFFECT OF PRODUCTIVE ENERGY LEVEL ON GROWTH, FEED CONSUMPTION AND FEED EFFICIENCY. (10 MALE AND 10 FEMALE CROSSBRED CHICKS PER LOT.) DATA OF HILL AND DANSKY, 1954: POULTRY SCIENCE 33: 112–119, WITH CALCULATIONS TO SHOW PROTEIN INTAKE AND FEED EFFICIENCY.

Lot Ration fed*	Protein level Per cent	Av. weight @11 weeks Grams	Consumption/chick			Feed per gram of gain Grams
			Total feed Grams	Energy Calories	Protein Grams	
1 E-1	20	1491	4364	9374	874	3.01
2 E-1 + 10% hulls	20	1481	4397	8310	880	3.05
3 E-1 + 20% hulls	20	1522	4911	7971	983	3.31
4 E-1 + 30% hulls	20	1461	5099	6996	1020	3.59
5 E-1 + 40% hulls	20	1456	5448	6064	1090	3.85
6 18% protein	18	1448	4304	9424	775	3.06
7 16% protein	16	1440	4450	9883	712	3.18
8 90% E-1 + 10% hulls	18	1510	4963	9593	894	3.37
9 80% E-1 + 20% hulls	16	1464	5007	8602	801	3.52
10 70% E-1 + 30% hulls	14	1394	5048	7592	707	3.73
11 60% E-1 + 40% hulls	12	1371	5329	6869	640	4.00
12 50% E-1 + 50% hulls	10	1207	5678	6098	568	4.86

*See Table 30

TABLE 30.—COMPOSITION OF DIET E–1 AS FED TO LOTS 1 TO 7 INDICATED IN TABLE 29. DATA OF HILL AND DANSKY.

Ingredients	Lot Nos.						
	1	2	3	4	5	6	7
Yellow corn meal	38.4	29.2	19.9	10.7	1.4	42.0	45.6
Crushed wheat	10	7.5	5	2.5	0	10	10
Soybean oil meal	12	13	14.1	15.1	16.2	10.8	8.6
Crude casein	8	8.7	9.4	10.1	10.8	6.6	5.2
Pulverized oat hulls	0	10	20	30	40	0	0
Constant ingredients	31.6	31.6	31.6	31.6	31.6	31.6	31.6
Per cent protein	20.1	20.1	20.1	20.1	20.1	18.1	16.1
Productive energy, Cals./lb.	975	858	741	623	505	994	1008

The Protein Requirement for Growth—The protein requirement could be assessed by amino acid analysis of rapidly growing chicks at, say, weekly intervals, determining by difference the composition of the new tissue added during growth. But amino acids have other functions, so that as much as 50 per cent of the dietary intake of some of them may be catabolized in four- to six-week-old chicks.

Smaller amounts, ranging up to 6 or 7 per cent, will be excreted. For these reasons the practical approach to the determination of specific requirements has been through the use of carefully controlled feeding trials.

TABLE 31.—PERCENTAGE OF CARCASS FAT IN 28-DAY-OLD CHICKS AS INFLUENCED BY THE LEVEL OF DIETARY FAT AND DIETARY PROTEIN UNDER CONDITIONS OF *ad libitum* FEEDING. DATA OF N. T. RAND, PH.D. THESIS, UNIVERSITY OF ILLINOIS, 1957.

Dietary fat Per cent	Dietary protein				
	15%	*20%*	*25%*	*35%*	*45%*
0.2	13.1	10.4	8.6	6.5	4.6
10	13.7	11.4	9.7	7.5	6.0
20	15.9	13.2	11.1	8.6	6.7
25	15.7	13.5	11.6	8.9	6.9

TABLE 32.—PERCENTAGE OF CARCASS FAT IN 28-DAY-OLD CHICKS AS INFLUENCED BY THE LEVEL OF FAT AND PROTEIN IN THE RATION UNDER CONDITIONS OF EQUALIZED NUTRIENT INTAKE. DATA OF N. T. RAND.

Corn oil in the ration Per cent	Energy in the ration Cals./gram	Percentage of carcass fat	
		15% protein series	*30% protein series*
0.5	3.4	9.97	5.44
8.3	3.8	9.50	4.89
18.1	4.3	8.95	4.90
30.7	4.9	9.78	5.54
	Average	9.55	5.19

As individual crystalline amino acids became available, several workers undertook to determine the minimum level that would promote maximum growth when added to a ration so formulated as to be deficient in the amino acid under study but nutritionally adequate in all other respects. This was slow, expensive and often frustrating work. Rarely did the growth obtained equal what could be obtained with practical rations using intact proteins. Furthermore, improvements in practical rations from time to time as a result of newer knowledge of vitamin or mineral requirements meant that the amino acid experiments had to be repeated and new values obtained.

Eventually the cost of crystalline amino acids became low enough to permit some preliminary attempts to grow chicks on diets made up entirely of chemically pure ingredients. But this work was still very costly and often the chicks refused to eat the synthetic mixtures. Little by little the problems were solved and as the cost of crystalline amino acids came down, more and more tests could be run. In time it became possible to formulate mixtures which chickens would eat readily and which would promote sufficiently rapid growth to provide specific answers to the question of exact amino acid requirements.

It still is not possible to obtain on purified diets consistently good growth that will always be equal to that which can be obtained using practical-type rations. Furthermore, the prospect of developing stocks of poultry which are genetically capable of still faster growth than is now considered acceptable, probably means that much more work must yet be done in attempting to define the specific requirements of the rapidly growing chicken for each of the amino acids.

It has already become clear that a stated minimum requirement for a given amino acid has real meaning only under specified conditions—one of the most important being that all other nutrients, including the remaining amino acids, vitamins, minerals and energy, must be present in sufficient quantities so that no one of them will be a limiting factor.

With the demonstration that the efficiency of energy utilization is increased when a substantial part of the energy in a ration for growing chicks comes from fat, it is entirely possible that protein and amino acid requirements in the future may be stated in direct relation to the calorie level which is to be used.

There are a few principles which have been well established and which will continue to apply. If, for example, any one of the dietary essential amino acids (those which the chicken cannot synthesize) is entirely omitted from the ration, there can be no formation of any new protein tissue. A partial deficiency will limit the amount of such new protein which can be formed, and no surplus of any other amino acids will enable the chicken to grow except at a slow rate.

In much the same way, the requirement for the amino acids which are difficult or impossible for the chicken to synthesize varies with the level of protein fed, as well as with the energy content of the ration. The requirement, when expressed as a percentage of the total ration, will increase with an increase in the protein level, but at a decreasing rate.

It has become customary to standardize the protein level in starting rations for chicks at about 20 per cent, but it is well known that the level can be lowered as chickens increase in weight and that 15 per cent, or even less, is satisfactory for adult fowls. What has not been so commonly understood and appreciated is that for maximum early growth, that is, during the first week or so after hatching, the protein level should be raised to perhaps 30 or 35 per cent. This view is supported by the fact that the observed *percentage* rate of growth is highest right after hatching and decreases steadily with increasing body weight. Furthermore, the protein content of the unabsorbed egg yolk, which furnishes the chick with food immediately after hatching, is over 40 per cent on a dry basis. The fat content is over 60 per cent.

TABLE 33.—APPROXIMATE ENERGY VALUES OF SOME COMMON POULTRY FEED INGREDIENTS. (ALL FIGURES FOR CALORIES ARE ROUNDED.)

Ingredient	Fiber %	Productive energy (Calories) per pound	per quart	Metabolizable energy (Calories) per pound
Alfalfa meal, 20%	20.0	380	230	620
Alfalfa meal, 17%	25.0	220	140	350
Barley	6.0	800	890	1130
Blood meal	1.5	1000	1800	1280
Bone meal, steamed	2.5	300	600	450
Buttermilk, dried	0.4	780	950	1240
Casein	0.2	1000	1200	2000
Corn, yellow	2.5	1100	1600	1500
Corn distillers' solubles	4.0	1000	1300	1350
Corn gluten meal	4.0	840	1400	1400
Corn oil	0	—	—	4000
Cottonseed meal, 43%	12.0	800	1200	1100
Fish meal, menhaden	1.0	900	1200	1200
Hominy feed	5.0	800	1000	1400
Linseed meal, o.p.	9.0	550	600	700
Liver and glandular meal	2.0	1000	1650	1400
Meat and bone scrap, 50%	2.5	800	1200	1200
Milo	2.5	1100	1800	1500
Molasses, blackstrap	0	700	2100	900
Oats	12.0	800	700	1200
Oat groats	3.0	1150	2000	1600
Peanut meal, o.p.	11.5	800	1200	1130
Rice bran	12.0	700	560	1000
Skim milk, dried	0.2	760	900	1200
Soybean oil meal, 44%	6.5	760	1080	1020
Tallow	0	—	—	3200
Tankage, 60%	2.1	800	1300	1200
Wheat, hard	3.0	1020	1700	1500
Wheat bran	10.0	500	250	540
Wheat middlings	7.5	700	600	840
Whey, dried	0.2	780	1200	850

Laboratory trials have shown that chicks fed to 28 days of age on rations containing as high as 40 per cent of protein will outgrow others fed lower levels of protein, and exceed them in efficiency of total feed conversion, provided a substantial part of the energy of the ration comes from fat. High fat levels improve protein retention, apparently by reducing the amount of protein converted to heat during metabolism. This is another way of saying that a well balanced ration, with no great excess of any required nutrient, is as important for maximum growth as for promoting any other function.

16

Effect of Feed Intake on Growth.—It is well known that the amount of feed consumed is an important factor in determining how well chickens will grow, but the exact relationship between growth and feed intake is not so generally understood.

In a preceding section dealing with the energy requirement for maintenance, it was shown that there is an increasing demand for energy with increasing size of the animal, and we have seen that the energy requirement is closely related to the total feed intake. The combined effect of this relationship, and of the decreasing rate of

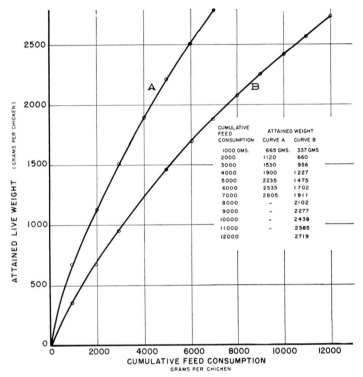

CUMULATIVE FEED CONSUMPTION	ATTAINED WEIGHT CURVE A	ATTAINED WEIGHT CURVE B
1000 GMS.	665 GMS.	337 GMS
2000	1120	660
3000	1530	956
4000	1900	1227
5000	2235	1475
6000	2535	1702
7000	2805	1911
8000	-	2102
9000	-	2277
10000	-	2438
11000	-	2585
12000		2719

FIG. 121.—Growth of chickens in relation to feed consumption. Both curves are for crossbred male chickens. Curve B in 1925; Curve A showing the more rapid and efficient growth possible on the better rations now available.

growth after about the first eight weeks, results in a gradually increasing fraction of the feed supply being used for maintenance and, consequently, a decreasing fraction being used for growth, as the chicken matures. This is merely another way of saying that the law of diminishing increment applies to the utilization of feed for liveweight increase.

With chickens hatched in 1925, Jull and Titus were able to show that for each successive 1000 grams of feed consumed there was a proportionately smaller increase in live weight. The data for one lot of Rhode Island Red × Barred Plymouth Rock crossbred males in their experiment are shown graphically in Figure 121, along with comparable data for the New Hampshire × Barred Plymouth Rock crossbred males referred to earlier in Figure 119 and Table 28.

Curve B of Figure 121 represents what was considered very good growth in 1925. Curve A shows the excellent growth obtained on the more efficient rations available thirty years later. In both cases, however, the value of each 1000 grams of feed, in terms of weight

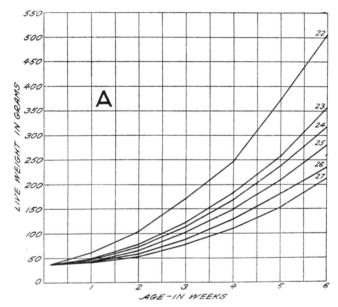

Fig. 122.—Live weight of chicks plotted against age. Compare with Figure 123
(*After Titus and Hendricks.*)

gains was only about 90 per cent of the preceding 1000 grams. It is highly significant that 7000 grams of the better ration produced as much weight in 16 weeks as 12,000 grams of the 1925 ration did in 22 weeks.

Further evidence that growth is a function of feed intake was presented by Titus and Hendricks. The data from one of their experiments are shown graphically in Figures 122 and 123. Six pens of 40 Rhode Island Red chicks were fed the same diet for six weeks but in different amounts. The chicks in one pen were allowed free access to feed at all times. Those in the other five pens were given daily 67, 60, 52, 45 and 37 per cent, respectively, of the amount eaten by the control pen. In Figure 122 the successive weekly average live weights are plotted against age, and the differences in rate of growth are clearly apparent. In Figure 123 the same weekly average live weights are plotted against the total cumulative feed intake, and it will be seen that the data for each of the six lots fall along the same straight line. The authors point out that there is no significance to the fact that the line is straight rather than curved, for in another experiment the corresponding data all fell along a curved line. The point of importance is that the rate of growth was a function of the total (cumulative) feed intake rather than of time. Stated in a practical way, it means that in the case of several lots of chicks fed the same ration, or in all

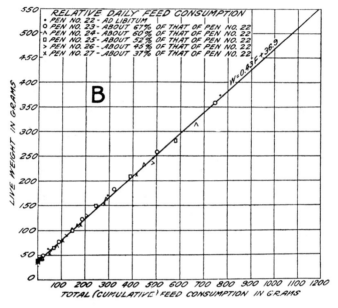

Fig. 123.—Live weight of the same groups of chicks shown in Figure 122, but plotted against the total cumulative feed intake. (*After Titus and Hendricks.*)

probability if fed equally good rations of different makeup, one could more accurately predict or estimate the average live weight at any time during the first six weeks from a knowledge of the total feed consumption than from a knowledge of the age of the chicks. As the chicks grew older, and the maintenance requirement became an increasingly important matter, the relationship failed to hold.

The Mineral Requirements.—Certain mineral elements must be added to rations for young chicks if normal growth is to be obtained. Several others, known to be needed in small amounts, are normally present in the common feed ingredients in sufficient amounts to take care of the requirements for growth.

The recommended allowance of calcium is 1.0 per cent of the total ration. Phosphorus should be supplied at the rate of 0.6 per cent of the feed, and not less than three-fourths of this amount should be in the form of inorganic phosphorus. Much of the phosphorus in feeds of plant origin in phytin phosphorus which must be supplemented by additional phosphorus from such sources as steamed bone meal.

Sodium chloride, or common salt, should be added to the extent of 0.5 per cent of the total ration. It may be iodized salt in order to supply the iodine requirements, and it may also be manganized so as to furnish the needed manganese. Manganese is needed at the rate of about 25 milligrams per pound of total feed, because only about 5 per cent of the manganese eaten is absorbed from the digestive tract.

The Vitamin Requirements.—Most of the vitamin requirements of growing chicks have now been worked out so that they can be stated in exact terms. The requirements for individual vitamins are given in Table 36.

THE REQUIREMENTS FOR EGG PRODUCTION

Since the rate of egg production varies greatly in different individuals and at different seasons of the year, the only way of stating the nutrient requirements specifically is in terms of the nutrients contained in a unit of the product, that is, in an egg of specified weight. From such a statement of the requirements it is then possible to make any necessary allowances for variation in rate of egg laying. An egg weighing 2 ounces will contain about 7.5 grams of crude protein (N $\times$ 6.25), about 2 grams of calcium and about 95 Calories of gross energy. If a hen is laying every day, and if her eggs average 2 ounces in weight, it is obvious that these amounts of nutrients must be added to her maintenance and activity requirements. If she is laying on alternate days, one-half of these amounts of nutrients must be provided daily.

As an example of the method by which the foregoing information may be used in calculating the feed requirements under specified conditions, we shall use a flock of 400 hens, weighing 5 pounds (2268 grams) each, and laying at the rate of 300 eggs a day. We shall assume that the environmental temperature is such that food energy will not need to be used for the express purpose of maintaining body temperature. Calculations will also be made to show to what extent the requirements may be furnished by a good grade of corn.

The Energy Requirements.—The total energy requirement of these hens will consist of their basal heat production, their activity requirements and the energy stored in eggs, assuming that they are neither gaining nor losing weight. The basal energy requirement is found by estimating the basal heat production of the entire flock. The basal heat production of adult hens is about 2.75 Calories per kilogram of live weight per hour. For 400 hens weighing 2268 grams each this would amount to 59,875 Calories every 24 hours.

It has been shown that the net energy value of corn for chickens is 2.8 Calories per gram of corn. By the use of this factor it is seen that (59,875/2.8 =) 21,384 grams, or 47.1 pounds of corn will be required daily to furnish the energy for basal heat production.

Since the energy requirement for normal activity is about one-half of the basal energy requirement, (47.1/2 =) 23.5 pounds of corn will be needed to furnish the energy for normal activity. The "gross" maintenance requirement may then be said to be (47.1 + 23.5 =) 70.6 pounds of corn.

The energy stored in 300 eggs amounts to (300 × 95 =) 28,500 Calories, and to supply this there will be needed (28,500/2.8 =) 10,179 grams, or 22.4 pounds, of corn. Hence, by simple addition, the total energy requirement of this flock of hens under the conditions specified would be met by (47.1 + 23.5 + 22.4 =) 93.0 pounds of corn.

The Protein Requirements.—The protein needed for the various physiological functions of these hens may be calculated in a similar manner. It has been shown that the nitrogen requirement for maintenance, for several species of animals, is 0.002 gram per Calorie of basal heat production. Assuming that the same figure is correct for the fowl, calculation shows that 59,875 × 0.002, or 120 grams of nitrogen will be needed for maintenance. Converted into conventional protein, by multiplying by 6.25, this is 750 grams of protein. Assuming a biological value of 50 per cent for the protein of corn, this would mean a minimum of 1500 grams of digested and absorbed protein. Then, on the assumption that the protein of corn is 75 per cent digestible by the fowl, it would take 2000 grams of dietary corn protein to meet the requirements. Since corn contains only about 9 per cent of protein, it would be necessary to feed (2000/.09 =) 22,222 grams, or 49 pounds, of corn daily to supply the amount of protein required by these 400 hens for maintenance.

In 300 eggs there would be (300 × 7.5 =) 2250 grams of protein. Using the same factors (50 per cent biological value, 75 per cent digestibility and 9 per cent of protein in corn), the quantity of corn needed to supply the protein in 300 eggs is found to be 147 pounds. Hence 49 + 147 = 196, the number of pounds of corn required to make possible the formation of the protein in 300 eggs, as well as to provide the protein used in maintenance. Since muscular activity does not require the expenditure of protein, no calculation in respect to that factor is necessary.

It should be understood that this 196 pounds of corn is not in addition to the 93 pounds required for energy. The quantity that must be fed is determined by whichever of the calculated results is the larger. In this case the feeding of 196 pounds of corn would be required to furnish the minimum amount of protein needed. It would furnish more than the necessary amount of energy. This is one reason why corn alone is neither a suitable nor an economical ration for laying hens.

The protein required in this example could be supplied by 40 pounds of soybean oil meal. Since the 93 pounds of corn calculated to supply the needed energy would also furnish 8 pounds of dietary protein the remaining amount could be supplied by 21 pounds of soybean oil meal. And a mixture of 93 pounds of corn and 21 pounds of 44 per cent soybean oil meal would contain 15.3 per cent of protein, just about what laying hens need.

Following the successful development of crystalline amino acid diets for chicks, the same techniques have been used with laying hens. Minimal requirement levels have been determined for eleven essential amino acids. In the course of the experimental studies, if any one of the amino acids was omitted from the diet, feed intake was immediately reduced so that egg production promptly ceased. Furthermore, if hens were force fed the deficient diets for five days and then returned to a practical ration, egg production was resumed after a total interval of ten days.

The Calcium Requirements.—Calcium is of considerable importance in the ration of laying hens because of the quantities needed in egg shell formation, but not even the maintenance requirement for calcium can be furnished by corn alone. Using the factor mentioned previously, 4 grams of dietary calcium per 100 grams of net protein used for maintenance, calculation shows that $(7.5 \times 4 =)$ 30 grams of calcium will be needed daily for maintenance. Corn contains only 0.02 per cent of calcium. Hence $30 \div 0.0002 =$ 150,000 grams, or 331 pounds, of corn that would be needed to supply the calcium requirements for maintenance. This is about three times as much as the flock would eat if given free access to corn under favorable conditions.

In 300 eggs there would be about 600 grams of calcium. Assuming, as before, that calcium is only about 50 per cent retained by the body, the dietary amount required becomes 1200 grams daily for the conditions specified. In attempting to furnish this from corn alone, calculation shows that it would be necessary to feed $(1200 \div 0.0002 =)$ 6,000,000 grams, or $6\frac{1}{2}$ tons of corn daily to a flock of 400 hens in order to provide the calcium needed in the formation of 300 eggs each day. This, of course, reduces the matter to an absurdity. Even granting that on a restricted calcium intake there might be a great increase in the percentage retained, and assuming for the moment that all of the calcium in corn might be utilized, it is still apparent that it is physically impossible to supply the calcium requirement from corn alone. In actual practice the need for calcium is usually met by feeding crushed oyster shell or ground limestone *ad libitum*. Seven pounds of oyster shell would furnish the daily calcium requirement of this flock.

An adequate supply of calcium in the ration is unfortunately no guarantee against the production of eggs with rough or thin shells. Furthermore, the mere feeding of extra calcium will not overcome the well-known decrease in shell quality which is characteristic of many high-producing hens and flocks during the latter part of the laying year, and may even make matters worse. Added manganese has been shown to help in some instances, but there are other unknown factors involved.

The feeding of extra calcium, up to 3.5 or 4.0 per cent of the total ration, may be justified in hot weather but it is unfortunately no guarantee against the production of some eggs with rough or thin shells. A decrease in shell quality during the latter part of the laying year is characteristic of many high-producing hens and flocks. Its prevention is one of the unsolved problems confronting both commercial poultrymen and research workers.

There is a marked increase in calcium deposition in the bones of pullets just before they begin to lay, and it is therefore important to provide oyster shell free choice for about a month before egg laying is expected to begin.

Other mineral requirements of hens are summarized in Table 36.

The Vitamin Requirements.—Some of the vitamin requirements of laying and breeding hens are more intense than the corresponding requirements for growing chicks, and it is often said that the most critical test of a poultry ration is to find out whether it will enable a flock of breeding hens kept indoors to produce eggs of high hatchability.

The requirements of breeding hens for vitamin A are nearly twice those of young chicks, and for vitamin D two and one-half times.

Riboflavin is an exception to the general rule in that the requirements of breeding hens are slightly less, and those of laying hens producing market eggs are distinctly less than those of young growing chicks.

The actual recommended amounts are indicated in Table 36.

The Total Feed Requirement.—The foregoing calculations have all been based upon a specific weight of hen and a specific rate of egg production. In actual practice, it is necessary to allow for variation in average weight, and for variation in rate of lay. Total feed intake will also be influenced by the size of eggs laid, as well as by the environmental temperature and the amount of voluntary activity.

In terms of annual egg production it is reasonable to assume that small eggs will be offset by large eggs, and that the effect of low temperatures will be offset by periods of high temperature. The effect of activity can also be considered in terms of average conditions. This leaves body weight and rate of lay as the two variables which are of most importance.

Assuming that the ration is reasonably well balanced for egg production, the total amount required by a hen in one year can be calculated very closely from the formula $F = 25 + 8W + E/7$, in which F is the number of pounds of feed required, W is the average weight of the hen in pounds, and E is the number of eggs laid during the year.

Thus, for a hen weighing 5 pounds and laying 210 eggs, the total feed required would be 25 plus 8 × 5 plus 210/7, or 25 plus 40 plus 30, a total of 95 pounds.

TABLE 34.—POUNDS OF FEED REQUIRED BY HENS OF DIFFERENT WEIGHTS IF THEY LAY THE INDICATED NUMBERS OF EGGS IN ONE YEAR

Average weight, pounds	Number of eggs per year					
	0	70	140	210	280	350
3.5	53	63	73	83	93	103
4.0	57	67	77	87	97	107
4.5	61	71	81	91	101	111
5.0	65	75	85	95	105	115
5.5	69	79	89	99	109	119
6.0	73	83	93	103	113	123
6.5	77	87	97	107	117	127
7.0	81	91	101	111	121	131

TABLE 35.—AVERAGE AMOUNTS OF FEED REQUIRED PER DAY AND PER DOZEN EGGS BY 100 HENS OF DIFFERENT WEIGHTS AND EGG PRODUCTION (TWO-OUNCE EGGS ARE ASSUMED.)

Feed consumed by:

Eggs per 100 hens per day	4-pound hens		5-pound hens		6-pound hens	
	Per day	Per dozen eggs	Per day	Per dozen eggs	Per day	Per dozen eggs
0	15.6	—	17.8	—	20.0	—
10	17.0	20.5	19.2	23.2	21.4	25.7
20	18.5	11.1	20.7	12.4	22.9	13.7
30	19.9	8.0	22.1	8.8	24.3	9.7
40	21.3	6.4	23.5	7.1	25.7	7.7
50	22.8	5.5	25.0	6.0	27.1	6.5
60	24.2	4.8	26.4	5.3	28.6	5.7
70	25.6	4.4	27.8	4.8	30.0	5.1
80	27.0	4.1	29.2	4.4	31.4	4.7
90	28.5	3.8	30.7	4.1	32.9	4.4
100	29.9	3.6	32.1	3.9	34.3	4.1

Each added pound of live weight adds 8 pounds to the yearly feed requirement, and each 7 eggs laid adds one pound. It takes as much feed to maintain an extra pound of live weight of hen as it does to produce an extra 56 eggs of average weight.

According to the formula (see also Table 34), a 4-pound hen laying 210 eggs would require 87 pounds of total feed in one year, while a 6½-pound hen would require 107 pounds of feed to do the same job. Or to put it in another way, the 107 pounds of feed consumed by a 6½-pound hen laying 210 eggs would be sufficient for a 4-pound hen laying 350 eggs.

The same relationship can of course be applied to the daily feed intake of a flock, with average live weight and rate of lay as the other variables. In this case the formula becomes $F = 6.85 + 2.2W + E/7$, in which F is the daily feed intake of 100 hens of "W" pounds average weight when laying at the rate of "E" eggs per 100 hens per day. Daily feed requirements for 100 hens weighing 4, 5 and 6 pounds each, and laying at different rates, are shown in Table 35. Since the formula is derived from figures for annual feed consumption it will underestimate the requirement in cold weather and overestimate it in hot weather. A correction will also be needed when applying either formula to rations which are very high or very low in energy content.

OTHER SPECIAL REQUIREMENTS

Maintenance, growth and egg production are the important considerations in the feeding of most poultry flocks, but there are certain other processes that at times become quite important.

The Requirements of Molting Hens.—By the chemical analysis of a large number of chickens at different weights, it has been shown that in White Leghorns ranging from 1 to 5 pounds in weight the feathers contain from 20 to 25 per cent of the protein in the entire bird, and that except in the case of nearly mature pullets, in which body fat becomes of great significance, the feathers also contain from 12 to 21 per cent of the gross energy. This at once suggests that the requirements for feather growth are no small item in the metabolism of the molting hen.

The gross weight of feathers on a 4-pound pullet will be about 100 grams, and of this amount 12 grams will be nitrogen. This is equivalent to the nitrogen in 10 eggs, but it undoubtedly represents a much greater requirement for dietary protein than does the production of 10 eggs. This is because of the relatively high sulphur content of feathers, which presupposes a rather intense requirement for dietary sulphur that is available only in the amino acids cystine and methionine.

It is sometimes considered that because egg production ceases during the molt, the feed supply may be reduced. As a matter of fact, this is usually not advisable. If molting hens are in good flesh their feed requirements are probably somewhat less than when they are laying. If they are in poor physical condition, as often happens, they should be well fed so that they will gain in weight.

The Requirements for Fattening.—It is ordinarily assumed that there is very little wastage of energy in the metabolism of fat deposition. In the mature animal that is being fattened the energy requirement appears to be about 7 Calories per gram of weight increase during a fattening period, and the protein requirement about 0.2 gram of net protein per gram of gain. Presumably these values would apply, at least approximately, in the case of fattening poultry. The feed energy would have to be higher than the stated amount by the quantity necessary to allow for losses in digestion, and the feed protein would have to be sufficient to allow for losses in both digestion and metabolism.

The Water Requirements.—The uses of water in the body of the fowl, especially as they relate to digestion, metabolism and the regulation of body temperature, have been discussed in a previous chapter. Some facts concerning water requirements will be presented here.

The entire physiological mechanism in the fowl is admirably adapted to the conservation of water. Water used in digestion is used again in other ways. Even the rather large amount of water used in carrying away the waste products from the kidneys is largely reabsorbed from the cloaca and used again in various body processes.

The water balance in the fowl may be indicated by saying that the water consumed is equal to the sum of (1) the water stored in the tissues; (2) the water used in egg formation; (3) the water vaporized; and (4) the water excreted in urine and feces; minus (5) the amount of metabolic water formed in the oxidation of food materials. The amount of water required would have to include that used in digestion but, since it may be used also for any of the other four purposes, it does not become an additive fraction of water consumed.

The average water intake of laying hens is about 35 to 40 pounds per 100 hens per day. Large hens laying at a high rate in hot weather may require 50 to 60 pounds. This is equivalent to about 9 pounds of water for each dozen eggs produced. When there is no egg protion, water intake is closely related to the consumption of dry matter. High-protein rations, and those high in salt or in any diuretic, increase the normal needs for water.

FORMULATING RATIONS

Important as is the conception of minimum nutrient requirements in setting up feeding standards, any careful student of the subject will soon come to the conclusion that it is possible to determine the specific requirements for any purpose far more accurately than they can be supplied in practice. Furthermore, the practical application of feeding standards, after they have been set up in detail, is likely to be found chiefly in evaluating certain feeding practices, rather than in any revolution in the methods of formulating rations. To be useful to the practical feeder, the results of such scientific material as has been discussed in the early part of this chapter must be translated into terms that can be applied easily and quickly.

The data in Tables 36, 37 and 38 furnish the basis for such application when used in conjunction with the usual tables of feed composition. They have been taken from publications of the National Research Council prepared by its sub-committee on poultry nutrition.

It must be emphasized that the requirements listed in these tables are for rations containing 20 and 15 per cent of protein, respectively,

TABLE 36.—NUTRIENT REQUIREMENTS OF CHICKENS (IN PERCENTAGE OR AMOUNT PER POUND OF FEED)[1] AS RECOMMENDED BY THE NATIONAL RESEARCH COUNCIL.

	Starting chickens 0–8 weeks	Growing chickens 8–18 weeks	Laying hens	Breeding hens
Total protein, per cent	*20*	*16*	*15*	*15*
Vitamins:				
Vitamin A activity (U.S.P. Units)[2]	1200	1200	2000	2000
Vitamin D (Int. Chick Units)	90	90	225	225
Thiamine, mg.	0.8	?	?	?
Riboflavin, mg.	1.3	0.8	1.0	1.7
Pantothenic acid, mg.	4.2	4.2	2.1	4.2
Niacin, mg.	12	*5.0*	?	?
Pyridoxine, mg.	1.3	?	1.3	1.3
Biotin, mg.	0.04	?	?	?
Choline, mg.	600	?	?	?
Folacin, mg.	0.25	?	0.11	0.16
Minerals:				
Calcium, per cent	1.0	1.0	2.25[3]	2.25[3]
Phosphorus, per cent[4]	0.6	0.6	0.6	0.6
Sodium, per cent[5]	0.15	0.15	0.15	0.15
Potassium, per cent	0.2	0.16	?	?
Manganese, mg.	25	?	?	15
Iodine, mg.	0.5	0.2	0.2	0.5
Magnesium, mg.	220	?	?	?
Iron, mg.	*9.0*	?	?	?
Copper, mg.	*0.9*	?	?	?
Zinc, mg.	20	?	?	?

[1]The figures are estimates of requirements and include no margin of safety. Figures shown in italics are still tentative.
[2]May be vitamin A or pro-vitamin A
[3]This amount of calcium need not be incorporated in the mixed feed. Calcium supplements fed free choice are considered as part of the ration.
[4]At least 0.45 per cent of the total feed of starting chickens should be inorganic phosphorus. About 30 per cent of the phosphorus of plant products is non-phytin phosphorus and may be considered as part of the inorganic phosphorus required. The requirement for older chickens is not so well defined.
[5]The indicated amount is equivalent to 0.37 per cent of sodium chloride.

for starting chicks and laying hens, on the assumption that these levels of protein will meet the requirements for growth and egg production. Since a ration containing 20 per cent of protein is not adequate for maximum rates of growth, especially when these rates of growth are supported by rations high in energy, it is frequently necessary to revise the requirements upward under both laboratory and field conditions. When the energy content of a ration is substantially increased in order to promote maximum growth, the levels of all other nutrients must be increased also in order to insure an

TABLE 37.—ESSENTIAL AMINO ACID REQUIREMENTS FOR CHICKS AND LAYING HENS AS RECOMMENDED BY THE NATIONAL RESEARCH COUNCIL.

Amino Acid	Starting Chicks (Per cent of ration)	Laying Hens (Per cent of ration)
Arginine	1.2	?
Lysine	1.0	0.5
Histidine	0.3	?
Methionine	0.8	0.53
or		
Methionine	0.45	0.28
and Cystine[1]	0.35	0.25
Tryptophan	0.2	0.15
Glycine[2]	1.0	?
Phenylalanine	1.4	?
or		
Phenylalanine	0.7	?
and Tyrosine[3]	0.7	?
Isoleucine	0.6	0.5
Leucine	1.4	1.2
Threonine	0.6	0.4
Valine	0.8	?
The above are for protein levels of	20 per cent	15 per cent

[1]Cystine will replace methionine for chicks as long as the ration contains not less than 0.45 per cent of methionine.
[2]The chick can synthesize glycine, but the synthesis does not proceed at a rate sufficient for maximum growth.
[3]Tyrosine will replace phenylalanine for chicks as long as the ration contains not less than 0.7 per cent phenylalanine.

adequate intake of these other nutrients on the lower level of total feed consumption which is the usual response to high energy rations. Thus 25 per cent of protein may be needed for maximum rates of growth on certain high-energy rations, and levels as high as 30 or 35 per cent may give the maximum rate of feed conversion.

An illustration of the principle involved is given in Tables 39 and 40. Two lots of male chicks, each lot containing three replicates of ten chicks, were fed a highly purified diet on an *ad libitum* basis. Previous tests had shown that a minimum of 30 per cent of protein was necessary in this particular diet in order to obtain maximum growth. The diet fed to Lot A consisted of 49 parts of a protein-vitamin-mineral premix, 34 parts of glucose and 7 parts of corn oil. This mixture provided 33.4 per cent of protein and 3.82 Calories of metabolizable energy per gram. The diet for Lot B consisted of 49 parts of the premix and 21 parts of corn oil—all of the glucose being replaced by corn oil. It provided 42.3 per cent of protein and 4.91 Calories of metabolizable energy per gram.

TABLE 38.—AMINO ACID COMPOSITION OF INGREDIENTS COMMONLY USED IN POULTRY RATIONS. (ALL FIGURES ARE PERCENTAGES.)

	Crude protein	Arginine	Lysine	Methio- nine	Cystine	Trypto- phan
Alfalfa meal	20	1.0	1.0	0.36	0.38	0.35
Barley	12	0.5	0.3	0.13	0.20	0.13
Barley	9	0.4	0.2	0.10	0.15	0.10
Blood meal	84	3.0	7.2	1.00	1.50	1.18
Buttermilk, dry	32	1.0	2.2	0.67	?	0.41
Corn	9	0.4	0.2	0.21	0.15	0.07
Corn gluten meal	42	1.3	0.7	0.97	0.68	0.33
Cottonseed meal	43	3.5	1.6	0.71	0.97	0.46
Distillers solubles, dry	26	0.8	0.8	0.41	0.26	0.12
Fishmeal	70	5.0	6.4	2.20	1.18	0.98
Fishmeal	65	4.6	5.9	2.00	1.10	0.91
Fishmeal	60	4.0	5.4	1.80	1.00	0.84
Fish solubles, condensed	35	1.5	1.7	0.60	0.21	0.12
Linseed meal	35	2.7	1.1	0.84	0.66	0.56
Liver meal	56	2.9	3.4	0.84	0.78	0.70
Meat scrap	55	3.9	3.4	1.10	0.77	0.44
Meat scrap	50	3.0	2.7	0.70	0.60	0.35
Meat scrap	45	2.7	2.2	0.50	0.45	0.27
Milo	11	0.4	0.3	0.16	0.20	0.09
Oats	12	0.7	0.4	0.23	0.19	0.14
Oats	9	0.5	0.3	0.17	0.14	0.10
Peanut meal	44	4.4	1.3	0.49	0.70	0.44
Peas, dry	24	1.7	1.4	0.19	0.34	0.19
Rice, rough	8	0.6	0.2	0.11	0.10	0.10
Rye	12	0.5	0.4	0.16	?	0.16
Sesame meal	45	4.0	1.3	1.44	0.59	0.54
Skim milk, dry	35	1.1	2.5	0.81	0.42	0.45
Soybean meal	45	2.8	2.7	0.62	0.66	0.53
Sunflowerseed meal	45	3.7	1.9	1.53	0.72	0.59
Wheat	13	0.5	0.3	0.21	0.24	0.14
Wheat	10	0.4	0.3	0.16	0.19	0.11
Wheat bran	15	0.9	0.5	0.17	0.19	0.21
Wheat middlings	16	0.9	0.4	0.14	0.19	0.14
Whey, dry	12	0.4	1.0	0.32	0.41	0.18
Yeast, dry	45	2.0	3.1	0.84	0.54	0.55

At the end of 28 days the chicks in Lot A had consumed 545 grams of feed and weighed 439 grams each. Those in Lot B had consumed only 439 grams but weighed 438 grams each. The relative feed conversion rates were 1.52 and 1.22 grams of feed per gram of gain, respectively.

TABLE 39.—SHOWING THE EFFECT OF SUBSTITUTING FAT FOR CARBOHYDRATE IN A HIGH-PROTEIN PURIFIED DIET FOR YOUNG CHICKS.

	Lot A	Lot B
The ration:		
Protein-vitamin-mineral premix	49 parts	49 parts
Glucose	34	—
Corn oil	7	21
Total	90 parts	70 parts
Protein, by analysis, per cent	33.4	42.3
Metabolizable energy, Calories/gram	3.82	4.91
Total protein in 90 grams of Ration A	30.0 grams	—
Total protein in 70 grams of Ration B	—	29.6 grams
Metabolizable energy in 90 grams	343.8 Cals.	—
Metabolizable energy in 70 grams	—	343.7
Results:		
Average weight after 28 days, grams	439	438
Total feed consumed per chick, grams	545	439
Feed per gram of gain, grams	1.52	1.22
Total protein eaten per chick, grams	182	186
Protein per gram of gain, grams	0.51	0.52

TABLE 40.—AMINO ACID INTAKE OF CHICKS ON RATIONS SHOWN IN TABLE 39.

	Lot A		Lot B	
	Actual (grams)	*Per cent of ration*	*Actual (grams)*	*Per cent of ration*
Essential amino acids:				
Arginine	15.1	2.8	15.4	3.5
Histidine	4.7	0.9	4.8	1.1
Isoleucine	11.8	2.2	12.1	2.8
Leucine	13.6	2.5	13.9	3.2
Lysine	12.4	2.3	12.6	2.9
Methionine	3.2	0.6	3.3	0.8
Phenylalanine	9.1	1.7	9.3	2.1
Threonine	7.1	1.3	7.3	1.7
Tryptophan	1.8	0.3	1.9	0.4
Valine	10.0	1.8	10.2	2.3
Total	88.8	16.4	90.8	20.8
Non-essential amino acids:				
Alanine	6.6	1.2	6.7	1.5
Aspartic acid	11.3	2.1	11.5	2.6
Cystine	1.1	0.2	1.1	0.3
Glutamic acid	35.5	6.5	36.3	8.3
Glycine	8.0	1.5	8.2	1.9
Proline	4.6	0.8	4.7	1.1
Serine	12.6	2.3	12.8	2.9
Tyrosine	6.2	1.1	6.3	1.4
Total	85.9	15.7	87.6	20.0
All amino acids	174.7	32.1	178.4	40.8

Table 40 shows the individual amino acid intake per chick, calculated from the known amino acid composition of the protein used and the total protein intake. Also shown is the percentage that each amino acid provided relative to the total ration. The difference between the two lots in total intake of protein and of individual amino acids was insignificant, but the *percentage* of protein consumed by Lot B was substantially higher than for Lot A. The same relative difference existed for each individual amino acid as well as for each vitamin and each mineral. Note that it is the absolute intake of each nutrient that is important, not the percentage. In fact, percentages can be very misleading unless other pertinent conditions are specified.

Changing the caloric density of the ration from 3.82 Calories per gram (Lot A) to 4.91 Calories per gram (Lot B) induced a voluntary decrease in total feed consumption for the four-week period of 19.4 per cent. But since the level of amino acids, vitamins and minerals was increased by 21 per cent (42.3 compared with 33.4) there was no loss in attained weight. Furthermore, because of the increased concentration of energy in the ration of Lot B, actual feed conversion was improved substantially. This results from the fact that as fat is substituted for carbohydrate, a higher percentage of the available energy is useful to the chick, and less is lost in the form of heat.

As a broad principle, any condition which results in a substantially lowered feed intake for more than a day or two, will make it necessary to increase the concentration of all nutrients in the diet if maximum growth or egg production is to continue. The feed intake of laying hens will be reduced by high environmental temperatures, but if the concentration of protein and other essential nutrients is raised enough to compensate for the lower rate of consumption, egg production will usually continue at a very satisfactory rate. Total feed consumption seems to be closely related to the need for energy, and this must always be kept in mind both in the formulation of rations and in practical poultry feeding.

EVALUATING A RATION

In order to determine the value of a ration for a particular purpose, it is necessary to consider not only its content of specified nutrients, but also its acceptability to the chicken, its physiological effects on the fowls to be fed, its possible effect on the product (meat or eggs), and its cost.

Acceptability.—Both chicks and hens often show distinct preferences for certain feed ingredients or mixtures, and they do not take readily to new feeds. It may be as difficult to get adult fowls to eat yellow corn if they have been fed exclusively on wheat and oats, as to get another flock to change from corn to wheat. Some hens will carefully pick out corn from a mixture of several grains while others will just as carefully select wheat.

Attractiveness, as influenced by sparkle and by color, is of some importance. Grits which shine and sparkle are usually chosen in preference to those which are dull. Green is a favorite color, as determined by attractiveness of feed or water. Water which has been colored green is usually taken in preference to other colors or to clear water. Green marbles are often used by turkey growers to attract young poults to their feed. Other colors are much less effective.

Feed consumption is also affected by the physical condition of the feed. Very fine mixtures are not so readily eaten as are feeds which are more coarsely ground. Similarly, feeds which become very sticky when moistened are not relished, as a rule. And it is obvious that size of ingredients is of some importance, depending on whether one is mixing a ration for baby chicks or for laying hens.

Unless care is taken in formulation, the fiber content of a starting ration may easily be so high as to prevent chicks from eating as much as they would voluntarily consume, thereby reducing both weight gains and the efficiency of feed conversion.

Physiological Effect.—It is necessary to consider the physiological effect of a feed or ration as well as the various nutrients which it contains. Linseed meal, for example, though high in protein, cannot be used to advantage in poultry rations except in small quantities, unless it is given special treatment. At levels above 3 per cent it is very laxative and reduces both the rate and efficiency of gain. The unfavorable effects of rye have been mentioned previously.

Many other ingredients affect the character of the droppings, and this becomes important in the feeding of baby chicks. Rations containing soybean meal as the only protein supplement have been observed to cause more "pasting up" in chicks than rations supplemented with fish meal or milk products. Dehulled solvent-process meal causes less trouble, suggesting that some constituent of the beans is responsible for the sticky condition of the droppings. In some trials, antibiotics have apparently eliminated the problem. The pasting can also be avoided by feeding 25 to 50 per cent cracked grain during the first few days after hatching. Presumably the pasting is merely one symptom of a digestive disturbance which is caused by some constituent of soybean meal. The young chick is particularly susceptible to this trouble, while older ones are less easily affected. Further research is needed to determine exactly what is involved.

Some feeds enhance, while others partially inhibit the deposition of yellow pigment in the shanks of growing chickens.

Milk has a definite diuretic effect, as does common salt if it is fed at levels much above 1 per cent.

Certain weed seeds are very unpalatable to poultry, and others are definitely toxic. Corn cockle is an example.

17

Effect on Product.—Though the composition of the feed usually has little effect on the composition of eggs, certain feeds do have an undesirable effect on the flavor of the eggs and on the flesh of fowls.

Green feed and yellow corn help to give the rich golden yellow color in the yolk which is greatly desired in some markets, while discriminated against in others. Tests at the Georgia Station showed that the feeding of 0.5 gram of dried ripe Pimiento pepper per hen per day imparted a desirable color to the yolks of eggs, and that the color or yolk could be deepened to a dark reddish-brown by feeding as much as 5 grams daily. Chicks hatched from the pimiento-colored eggs had more pigment in their shanks than did control chicks after both lots had received the same ration for a period of six weeks.

The effect of cottonseed meal on yolk color has been discussed in connection with the use of that product as a protein supplement. Another related plant, the common cheeseweed, *Malva parviflora*, also has an undesirable effect on eggs. Experiments conducted at the California Station have shown that if this weed is eaten in appreciable quantities by laying hens, the whites of their eggs will develop a pinkish color after being placed in cold storage.

Tests conducted at the National Poultry Institute, Newport, England, showed that greenish yolks were produced by hens fed the seed pods of the common weed, Shepherd's purse (*Capsella bursa-pastoris*). Seed pods of another weed, pennycress (*Thlaspi arvense*), are also suspected of causing a similar discoloration.

Acorns, if germinated, were responsible for greenish-brown yolks, probably because of their content of gallic acid. Green, immature acorns caused no trouble, even when fed at the rate of 2 ounces per hen per day.

Cost.—A very important factor in any ration is its cost. The best ration, all things considered, is the one which gives the greatest economic returns. This does not mean either the greatest production or the cheapest ration. The greatest production might be obtained only from a ration that cost more than the product was worth, and the cheapest ration might result in such limited production that it would be as unprofitable as the most expensive ration. To find the most profitable mean between these two unprofitable extremes is the nice problem which confronts every practical feeder.

PLATE III

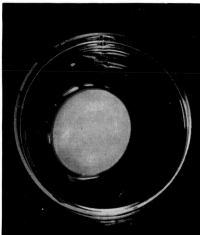

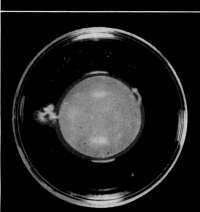

**Yolk Color Is Directly
Influenced by Feed**

———

Extremely Pale Yolk

Produced by hens fed a mixture
of—

Oats	50%
Bran	50%

Occasional table scraps
No green forage

———

Medium-Colored Yolk

Produced by hens fed a ration
of—

Yellow corn	50%
Wheat	25%
Oats	25%

No green forage

———

Deep Orange Yolk

Produced by hens fed a mixture
of—

Corn	52%
Wheat	24%
Oats	14%
Dried milk and soy bean meal	10%

Green grass pasture

———

These three examples of the influence of feed on yolk color were observed in three flocks near Urbana, Illinois. The spots appearing on the yolks are merely light reflections.

*Courtesy of the Illinois
Agricultural Experiment Station.*

Chapter 11

Controlling Diseases and Parasites

Losses from disease and from parasites can be very serious, and it is important for the poultryman to be familiar with the most effective means of prevention and control in order to keep such losses at a minimum. Constant vigilance is the price of success in this phase of poultry management.

Various estimates place the monetary loss to the poultry industry at more than $300,000,000 a year. Not all of this loss can be prevented, but ways of reducing it are certainly worthy of special study. Of much more direct concern to the individual flock owner are such losses as 30 or 40 per cent of a flock of young chicks from bronchitis or pullorum disease, or more than a month's egg production following an outbreak of Newcastle disease.

THE NATURE OF DISEASE

The disease problem may be looked upon as a constant struggle between the host and the invading organisms. The flock owner sits as a sort of referee whose interests and sympathies are entirely with the host but who is too often helpless to do much more than watch a losing battle, while all of his profit and some of his capital are hauled away to an incinerator or disposal pit.

If the poultryman is to avoid this unhappy circumstance, he must become, in effect, a health officer for his flock. He must plan and carry out a program of flock management which will turn the tide of battle always, or nearly always, in favor of the host. There are three distinct approaches to such a program. The first is to adopt strict sanitary and quarantine procedures which will keep host and disease organisms apart. For example, it is obvious that if chickens can be kept continuously under conditions such that the cholera organism can never gain entrance, they will not be exposed to or suffer from fowl cholera. Chickens can be kept indoors, in buildings screened against flies and other insects, so that they will probably never become infested with tapeworms. Complete protection against all diseases and parasites is very difficult, if not impossible, to carry out on a commercial scale, but many practices can be adopted that will aid materially in the control of these troubles.

The second general method is to weaken the attacking agent so that it is unable successfully to invade the host and establish itself. This is usually accomplished by placing various sorts of barriers in the way, or by destroying large numbers of the invaders through the use of strong disinfectants. Specific examples are the use of drugs to reduce coccidial infections, the spraying of poultry houses with malathion emulsion to control lice and mites, and the maintenance of high humidity in separate hatchers together with formaldehyde fumigation to eliminate the spread of pullorum organisms from infected to healthy chicks.

The third method of approach is to strengthen the position of the host so that it is better able to withstand the constant onslaught of invading organisms of various kinds. This objective may be partially accomplished through natural means, such as breeding for increased resistance to specific diseases, improved nutrition which helps to insure the physical well-being of the fowls, and provision for clean and comfortable surroundings. It may also take the form of purely artificial protection, such as vaccination against fowl pox or laryngotracheitis.

In actual practice, all three methods of disease control are used, as well as occasional treatment for specific maladies. As a general rule, medicinal treatment is ineffective, and dependence must be placed on other methods in attempting to reduce or prevent mortality. The poultryman needs information of three sorts in solving this problem:

1. How to avoid disease outbreaks by proper methods of management,
2. How to recognize disease outbreaks when they do occur, and
3. Procedures to follow in obtaining a correct diagnosis and specific directions for control.

Each of these will be discussed briefly in the following pages.

DISEASE PREVENTION

Maintenance of flock health is one of the prerequisites to profitable poultry and egg production, and this implies a need for some knowledge of the more important disease-inducing agents, the methods by which they are spread from flock to flock, and the weak points at which they may be most easily controlled or eliminated. Most of the economically important diseases of poultry are infectious and contagious. They are readily transmitted from one individual to another, though sometimes by widely varying means.

The Causes of Disease.—Many diseases are caused by bacteria. Common examples are tuberculosis, fowl cholera, pullorum disease, coryza. Most of them, fortunately, are not transmissible to other farm animals or to man. Effective methods of control include the elimination of carrier fowls, and the adoption of quarantine and sanitation procedures which will help to prevent infection.

Certain important diseases are caused by ultra-microscopic agents called viruses. Some of these are extremely virulent, and the diseases which they cause can be very costly to flock owners. Fowl pox, laryngotracheitis, and the avian leukosis complex are examples. Effective vaccines have been developed for the first two, and constitute a means of providing adequate protection for individuals and flocks.

Two of the most destructive diseases of poultry, coccidiosis and blackhead, are caused by microscopic animal organisms known as protozoa. Chickens develop a certain degree of immunity to coccidiosis following a mild infection. This fact is made the basis of control in thousands of flocks of broilers which are deliberately exposed to coccidiosis, while the infection is kept within bounds by feeding a coccidiostatic drug.

Fowls are also susceptible to a few mycoses or fungous diseases. These are of much less frequent occurrence than the types of disease already mentioned, but they can cause serious losses on occasion. The two examples most often encountered are aspergillosis and thrush.

Finally, there are numerous parasitic infestations to which fowls are peculiarly subject. These include internal parasites such as the large intestinal roundworm, the cecal worm, and various tapeworms; and external parasites such as body lice, sticktight fleas, roost mites, and the northern fowl mite.

So-called nutritional diseases result chiefly from deficiencies of certain vitamins and minerals. These have been discussed in Chapter 8.

The Spread of Disease.—Poultry diseases are spread in many different ways, and the common means by which each particular disease is disseminated must be known before one can proceed intelligently to break the cycle of infection and prevent further losses. In controlling ordinary colds, for example, it is much more important to keep the pullets entirely away from the older hens, *i. e.*, housed separately, than to go to extreme lengths in providing clean quarters. Hens which have recovered may act as carriers and are a constant source of infection for other susceptible individuals.

Similarly, hens which have survived an outbreak of pullorum disease as chicks may become carriers. The danger of spreading the infection to other adults may be rather slight, but such hens if retained in the flock, are the direct means of infecting the next generation of chicks. Many eggs laid by these carrier hens will be infected with the pullorum organism and, in consequence, chicks from such eggs already have the disease when they are hatched.

Certain infections are apparently air borne. Others are readily transmitted by means of contaminated soil or water. Still others are spread by contact. Some may be disseminated by vectors, i. e., flies, mosquitoes, ticks, and the like, which without becoming infected themselves never-the-less transmit infectious material from one fowl to another. Finally, there is always danger of disease dissemination by purely mechanical means—on the shoes and outer clothing of persons who may pass from one flock to another, on feed bags which are re-used without sterilization, in crates which are used to transport fowls, or on the feet of wild birds which fly from farm to farm.

Specific methods of transmission can be guarded against when they are known to be important in connection with a particular disease, but because of the many other possible means of spreading disease, and because the primary method of dissemination is not always known, it is necessary also to make use of those general sanitary and quarantine measures which are effective for almost any type of infection.

Methods of Sanitation and Quarantine.—The practice of sanitation is not always simple, and it is not easy. If carelessly or only partially followed it is of very little value, but if rigidly carried out it can be highly effective. An excellent example of what a careful sanitation and quarantine program can accomplish is furnished by the experience of the Regional Poultry Research Laboratory at East Lansing, Michigan. Through a period of 11 years after the laboratory was established, the stock was kept free from all diseases other than the one with which they were working, namely, the avian leukosis complex. The only exception was the infrequent occurrence of coccidiosis, and this disease was kept under control. During the eleven years they had no pullorum disease, no bronchitis, no colds or coryza, no cholera, no typhoid, no laryngotracheitis, no Newcastle, no fowl pox, no lice, no mites, no roundworms, no tapeworms. In other words, the sanitation procedures actually worked. Not until the spring of 1950 did any contagious virus disease, other than lymphomatosis, occur. In May of that year there was an outbreak of infectious bronchitis. The source of the infection was not positively determined, but circumstantial evidence pointed strongly to an unfortunate break in the sanitation procedures.

The essential points in the sanitation and quarantine plan in effect at the laboratory are:

1. A "closed" breeding flock is maintained. Hatching eggs were purchased at the beginning, and no stock has been added since. This is highly important.
2. Quarantine measures are rigidly carried out, as indicated in some detail in the following statements.
3. No chickens from outside sources are accepted for diagnosis.
4. No one can go on the plant without passing through a locker room in which shoes and outer clothing are changed.

Lunch buckets, watches, pocket knives and other personal items are passed through an ultra-violet sterilizing cabinet before being taken into the plant. Working clothes are furnished by the laboratory as a protection to the experiments being conducted.

5. The plant is divided as between isolation breeding flocks and those used for transmission experiments. Individual caretakers work exclusively on one side or the other. Furthermore, a change of shoes is made on leaving or entering each house.

6. No visitors are allowed on the plant at any time.

7. Employees are prohibited from keeping chickens at home, simply as an added safeguard against introducing infection.

8. All chicks are started in batteries and transferred to brooder house pens with wire panel floors.

9. All buildings are screened against wild birds, flies and mosquitoes. Insects have been controlled also by the use of DDT, Lindane, and pyrethrins in oil-base sprays.

10. All feed is delivered in bulk, and elevated to bins in the feed house, so that neither truck nor driver is ever on the plant. Furthermore, the truck is washed before leaving the mill, and the driver makes no intermediate deliveries before reaching the laboratory. A similar type of small bulk delivery is used on the plant itself.

11. The plant has its own water supply from a deep well and an enclosed water tower.

12. All chickens are raised and maintained in complete confinement within screened buildings.

13. The pens and equipment are cleaned regularly and thoroughly, and steam sterilized after each cleaning.

14. The litter used in the laying and brooding pens was chosen because it is subjected to high temperatures during the manufacturing process.

15. A vigorous campaign is maintained to keep out rats, mice, and other wild rodents.

16. All refuse, litter, feces, etc., go to a compost pile in a remote corner of the plant. The composted material is removed by way of a back entrance about once in two years. Carcasses and offal are buried in a trench with quicklime. Those involved in autopsy are incinerated.

Such a complete program would of course be difficult to carry out on a commercial basis, and it probably has no place in the management of farm flocks. But the principles on which it is based are sound, and many of them can be applied much more widely than at present, with distinctly profitable results. Simpler programs have repeatedly been shown to be practical and reasonably effective.

What, then, are the steps in a practical sanitation and quarantine plan which can be carried out in connection with the management of both farm and commercial flocks? Most authorities and experienced operators would agree on the following procedures, with certain variations and additions under special conditions.

1. Avoid the introduction of partly grown or adult stock. Breeders should maintain closed flocks. Others should make necessary introductions by means of eggs or chicks from best known sources.

2. Isolate and rear chicks away from adult stock. Grow chicks indoors, or provide enough land so that range-grown chicks do not occupy a given area more often than once every three years. If chicks from two or more sources are to be grown at the same time, isolate them from each other during the first two months.

3. Avoid traveling directly from the adult flocks to the chick range, if at all possible. If the business is large enough to make it practical, have separate caretakers for chicks and hens.

4. Keep visitors out of the houses and yards, especially those whose business takes them from farm to farm.

5. Maintain clean, sanitary quarters. Have a clean water supply. Use feeders which reduce waste to a minimum, and prevent contamination of feed by the chickens. Avoid spillage of feed where it will attract wild birds and rodents.

6. House pullets and hens separately. This is not only good management, but it protects the pullet flock from infections which may be spread by "carrier" hens.

7. If such diseases as fowl pox and laryngotracheitis are a problem on the farm or in the community, vaccinate all fowls on the premises, and continue to vaccinate each new crop of chickens year after year. (See also discussion under Newcastle disease and bronchitis.)

8. Follow procedures which will keep the fly nuisance at a minimum. In certain areas it may be equally important to control mosquitoes and other biting insects.

9. Keep the poultry areas sufficiently well fenced to prevent the escape of chickens to neighboring farms, and to prevent chickens from other flocks from gaining access to the premises.

10. If a breeding program is being conducted on the farm, practice rigid selection in order to make use of high-viability families, year after year.

HOW TO RECOGNIZE DISEASE

Since complete protection through sanitation and quarantine is rarely possible under farm or ranch conditions, it is important to be able to recognize disease and parasitic infestations in their early stages. Most poultrymen have to acquire this ability through costly experience, because no amount of written information can take the place of knowledge gained by daily contact with a poultry flock and close observation of conditions as they change and develop from season to season.

The experienced poultryman is constantly on the alert for signs of unthriftiness. He quickly identifies hens which are inactive, or those which stand in a corner with their feathers all ruffled up instead of competing with their pen-mates at the feed hopper. Such conditions may be only temporary, or they may be signs of more serious trouble, and the responsibility of deciding which they are rests squarely on the flock owner in most instances.

Since many death losses, especially in fowls of laying age, are of a non-specific type, not known to be related to disease organisms, and therefore not capable of spreading to other fowls in the flock, the poultryman must learn to distinguish between various sorts of morbidity before he can hope to apply control measures effectively. This calls for experience, and can be only partially learned from books.

Pathologists at the California Station, in autopsying about 7000 chickens of laying age, more than two-thirds of which came from commercial flocks, found that more than half of the deaths resulted from pathological conditions quite unrelated to infection, parasitism, or other specific disease manifestations. This non-specific mortality is a serious poultry problem to which there is as yet no completely satisfactory answer. Selection of breeding stock on the basis of family survival offers a most encouraging prospect for successful control.

WHAT TO DO WHEN DISEASE OUTBREAKS OCCUR

A sick or dead bird should be considered as a warning, depending somewhat on conditions, and not merely as something to be disposed of promptly. An attempt should be made to determine the cause of death in order that one may decide what steps need to be taken to prevent further loss. Prompt and accurate diagnosis is absolutely essential to any intelligent plan of disease eradication and control. Many local veterinarians have received special training in the diagnosis and control of poultry diseases, and are in a position to give expert assistance. If such a man is located in the community, by all means make use of his services. If no competent help is available, specimens may be sent to a state laboratory for diagnosis. Obviously, not every chicken that dies should be sent to the laboratory for examination, but any indication of more than a normal loss should be the occasion for getting diagnostic help as soon as possible.

It is, of course, important to remember that mere post-mortem examination is not always sufficient for making a diagnosis. Special tests, bacteriological cultures, or animal inoculations may be necessary. These take time. But effective control measures depend, first of all, on an accurate diagnosis. If specimens have decomposed before arrival at the laboratory it is usually quite impossible to

Fig. 124.—A poultry farm incinerator which is fired by LP gas. Such equipment is essential on many large commercial farms. (*Courtesy of Pacific Poultryman.*)

determine the exact cause of death. The following suggestions on how to select and ship specimens for diagnosis were prepared by the Department of Veterinary Medicine at the Oregon Agricultural Experiment Station, and should be equally applicable elsewhere.

1. Select birds showing symptoms typical of the disease in the flock. Do not choose a bird because it "acts differently."
2. Select 2 or 3 mature birds or 5 to 7 brooder chicks for examination. Autopsy of a single bird may be misleading.
3. Live specimens are the most satisfactory for examination.
4. If dead birds are sent in, they should be strongly wrapped to prevent seepage from the carcass. In warm weather they should be packed in ice.
5. Diseased organs or tissues may be packed solidly in powdered borax, in a can with a tight-fitting lid.
6. Specimens should be sent prepaid by express, parcel-post, or truck. Avoid such unnecessary delays as may be caused by holidays and week-ends.

It is also important to send along a description of the flock giving the total number and age of birds in the flock, the number affected, how long the disease has existed, what the death loss has been, what the specific symptoms are, together with a brief description of the housing, feeding, and management methods in use. All of this can be helpful in arriving at a correct diagnosis.

COMMON DISEASES OF YOUNG CHICKENS

Poultry diseases may properly be classified and discussed on the basis of cause, *e. g.*, bacterial, virus, protozoan, and the like, but the poultryman is usually confronted with the disease first and the cause later—after a diagnosis has been made. For convenience, they will be discussed here as diseases of young chickens and diseases of hens, with parasites as a third classification.

Pullorum Disease.—Probably more has been written about this disease than about any other infection in poultry and no doubt more flock owners are familiar with it than with any other ailment, with the possible exception of colds. Under the provisions of the National Poultry Improvement Plan, millions of hens are tested every year for the purpose of detecting reactors which are the means of transmitting the disease to a new generation of chicks.

The cause of the disease is the microörganism *Salmonella pullorum*. In baby chicks, the disease takes the form of an acute, highly fatal septicemia, and most of the deaths occur during the first two weeks after hatching. In female chicks which survive, the organism frequently becomes localized in the ovary so that eggs laid by such individuals are very likely to be infected. After three weeks in an incubator, under conditions which are almost ideal for bacterial growth, the chicks which hatch from infected eggs are literally teeming with the organism, and early death is almost a certainty. Because of this peculiar method of transmission from generation to generation, elimination of the carrier hens is an important step in controlling the disease. The agglutination test, applied by mixing antigen with a drop of blood under field conditions, or with a small amount of blood serum in the laboratory, is the accepted means of identifying reactors. It is important to use an antigen which will show a reaction with the known variant strains, as well as with the standard strain of *S. pullorum*.

Because the disease is so readily spread from chick to chick at hatching time, it has become common practice to fumigate incubators as a precautionary measure. Either the potassium permanganate or the cheesecloth method may be used. The following practical recommendations are taken from Bulletin 416 of the Kentucky Station entitled "Effect of Formaldehyde Fumigation on Mortality of Chick Embryos."

1. The incubator and eggs should be clean and should otherwise conform to the best practices in sanitation.

2. Fumigation at high concentrations should not be made during the first three days of incubation because the embryos are then most susceptible to formaldehyde.

3. Eggs in the separate hatching compartments of an incubator should be fumigated on the eighteenth to twentieth days of incubation.

4. Eggs may be fumigated at time of hatching, but in no case should fumigation be delayed until the chicks have dried.

5. The formalin should be standard 40-per cent, commercial grade. It should be stored in a well-stoppered bottle.

   WARNING: Do not permit formalin to come in direct contact with the hands, for it may cause serious skin trouble. Wear rubber gloves when handling it.

6. Potassium permanganate should be kept in a colored bottle or moisture-proof container.

7. Just before fumigation the humidity in the incubator should be raised to 92° to 94° F. wet-bulb reading. The fumigation should be performed at normal operating temperature.

8. Fumigation by the permanganate method requires the following items:

   (a) Measuring graduate or bottle for the formalin.

   (b) Small balances or standardized measure for the permanganate.

   (c) Large earthenware or enameled dish for combining formalin and permanganate. A large enameled wash basin or cooking utensil may be used.

9. Effective germicidal fumigation for pullorum organisms by the permanganate method requires about 35 cc. of 40-per

cent formalin and 17.5 grams of potassium permanganate per 100 cubic feet. Converted to the standard usually employed by hatcherymen, this proportion is equivalent to 1.2 fluid ounces of formalin and 0.6 ounce permanganate per 100 cubic feet.

10. The dish should be placed on the floor of the incubator (or in the intake air channel), the permanganate placed in the dish, and the formalin poured over the permanganate.

11. Ammonium hydroxide may be used after fumigation to shorten the period in which the disagreeable odor of formaldehyde is present. Some reduction in embryo mortality may occur with its use.

12. Control of mushy-chick disease requires two to three times stronger fumigation than the control of pullorum. Seventy to 100 cc. formalin and 35 to 50 grams permanganate per 100 cubic feet is the concentration recommended for effective control of mushy-chick disease.

    Mortality with three times normal fumigation is not serious, and if necessary the treatment could be increased still more, provided the fumigating is done after the fourth day of incubation.

13. Fumigation by the cheesecloth method requires the following items:
    (a) Measuring graduate or bottle for the formalin.
    (b) Cheesecloth of appropriate size.
    (c) Small hooks, tacks, or rods, for holding cloth in place.
    (d) Bucket or basin in which to immerse cheesecloth in the formalin.
    (e) Rubber gloves to be worn while handling the cheesecloth saturated with formalin. *Warning! Serious skin trouble may occur if formalin comes in direct contact with the hands.*

14. When the cheesecloth method is used, pieces of cheesecloth about 1 yard square should be immersed in a sufficient quantity of formalin to supply 20 cc. formalin per 100 cubic feet in incubator space. The cloth should then be hung over rods near the fan and allowed to remain for 3 hours. (This method requires approximately two-thirds the quantity of formalin needed in the permanganate method.)

15. Treatment by either method should last not less than 1 hour nor more than 3 hours.

16. If suitable measuring and weighing facilities are not available the operator should consult his local pharmacist or photographer about the weighing or measuring of the needed materials.

17. The recommendations of the incubator manufacturer should be considered in fumigating with formaldehyde.

Infectious Bronchitis.—This is popularly known as chick bronchitis or as "gasping disease." The cause is a filterable virus. The disease occurs most frequently in chicks from 3 or 4 days to 3 or 4 weeks of age, and spreads so rapidly that nearly every chick in the flock may be affected by the time the trouble is recognized. Mortality may run to 80 or 90 per cent of the affected chicks, though in some instances nearly all recover.

Adult stock is also susceptible. Mortality among hens is low, but egg production usually drops to zero and may not return to normal for a month or longer.

The disease is easily transmitted from infected to susceptible chickens by contact, and carrier birds may be a source of infection for several weeks under field conditions.

No effective treatment has yet been found, but recovered birds are usually immune and control can therefore be accomplished through the use of modified live-virus vaccines. The vaccine may be applied intranasally to individual birds, but the more common procedure is to vaccinate flocks on a mass basis by using a spray or dust, or by adding the vaccine to drinking water in appropriate amounts.

Since mortality among baby chicks is nearly always high, hatcherymen should brood surplus chicks in quarters which are completely separated from the areas in which incubators and hatching equipment are located.

Coccidiosis.—This is one of the most widespread and destructive diseases of chickens. It is caused by various protozoan parasites belonging to the genus *Eimeria*. One species, *Eimeria tenella*, characteristically invades the lining of the ceca, producing the cecal type of the disease, while others are found in the lining of the small intestine where they cause the intestinal type. The cecal type is usually the more acute, and is often designated by poultrymen as "bloody diarrhea." Most outbreaks occur in chickens ranging from 4 to 12 weeks of age, but older chickens may become infected. A certain degree of resistance is established by mild exposure, but resistance to one species does not protect against infection with any of the other species. Furthermore, the recovered resistant individuals may act as carriers and be a source of infection for other susceptible birds with which they come in contact for some time after their recovery.

The life cycle of the parasite is such that freshly discharged oöcysts, which pass out with the droppings, are not infective if eaten by other chickens. Within a few days, however, under suitable conditions of moisture and temperature, these oöcysts go through a process known as sporulation, after which they are highly infective. Whether eaten soon after sporulation or not for as long as several months, they become activated in the intestinal tract of the chicken and produce the characteristic infection of the cecal or intestinal lining.

Sporulated oöcysts are quite resistant, and ordinary disinfectant solutions have little effect on them. Extreme dryness is destructive to them, and so is excessive heat. It is therefore desirable to maintain dry litter in brooder houses as an aid in both prevention and

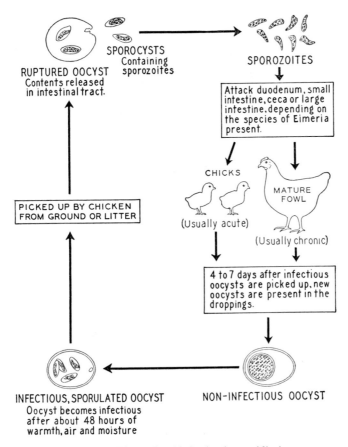

SPOROCYSTS
Containing sporozoites

SPOROZOITES

RUPTURED OOCYST
Contents released in intestinal tract.

Attack duodenum, small intestine, ceca or large intestine, depending on the species of Eimeria present.

CHICKS

MATURE FOWL

PICKED UP BY CHICKEN FROM GROUND OR LITTER

(Usually acute)

(Usually chronic)

4 to 7 days after infectious oocysts are picked up, new oocysts are present in the droppings.

INFECTIOUS, SPORULATED OOCYST
Oocyst becomes infectious after about 48 hours of warmth, air and moisture

NON-INFECTIOUS OOCYST

FIG. 125.—The cycle of infection in coccidiosis.

control. Outbreaks are particularly common following spells of warm, wet weather which provide ideal conditions for the coccidia to develop.

The fact that some time is required after oöcysts are passed out in the droppings before they can become infective for new hosts, affords an opportunity for breaking the life cycle. If affected chickens are confined indoors, if the house is kept warm and dry, and if the litter and droppings are removed daily, so that reinfection is prevented, the disease will quickly run its course. Wire-mesh platforms to support the water and feed containers, and wire-screened roosting sections which prevent the chickens from coming in contact with the droppings are also very helpful in combating this disease. Wire panel floors may be used for the entire brooder house.

Following a mild infection, chickens normally develop a considerable degree of resistance to coccidiosis. With the introduction of practical coccidiostatic drugs, especially the newer sulfonamides, it became possible to make use of controlled infection in the widespread reduction of losses from this disease. It is most easily accomplished by brooding chicks on old litter, in which some coccidia are almost certain to be present, while at the same time using a coccidiostatic drug in the feed or in the drinking water. The whole idea is to prevent a "runaway" infection while the chicks are developing sufficient resistance to protect themselves. Both the time and the level of feeding of the drug vary with conditions existing at the time of use.

COMMON DISEASES OF HENS

The most important diseases of hens, in terms of economic loss to the industry, are those belonging to the group caused by filterable viruses. These include Newcastle disease, fowl pox, laryngotracheitis, and the avian leukosis complex as major offenders.

The Avian Leukosis Complex.—This disease, known commonly as fowl paralysis, has become widespread, and has caused enormous losses to the industry. Recognition of these losses, and of the need for much more exact information concerning the disease led directly to the establishment of the U. S. Regional Poultry Research Laboratory at East Lansing, Michigan.

The avian leukosis complex takes many different forms, and this has added to the difficulties of investigators who have worked diligently to determine both cause and methods of prevention. There are six recognized types of the disease. Visceral lymphomatosis is at present the most common, and accounts for 70 to 85 per cent of all cases. In second place, accounting for 10 to 25 per cent of the cases, is neural lymphomatosis. The remaining 5 per cent of the cases are distributed among ocular lymphomatosis, osteopetrosis, leukemia or the blood form of the disease, and myelocytomatosis.

Visceral Lymphomatosis.—As the name suggests, this is a type of the disease in which the internal organs are affected. No one of the visceral organs is exempt from attack, and it often happens that several different organs are affected in the same fowl. The liver, spleen, heart, ovary, kidneys, and intestines are most frequently involved. The liver, in particular, is often greatly enlarged, and the name "big-liver disease" has often been applied to this type of lymphomatosis.

The involvement may be generalized through one or more entire organs, or restricted to local tumor areas. As in other forms of the disease, the tumors are formed by infiltration of malignant cells of the lymphocytic series into the various organs.

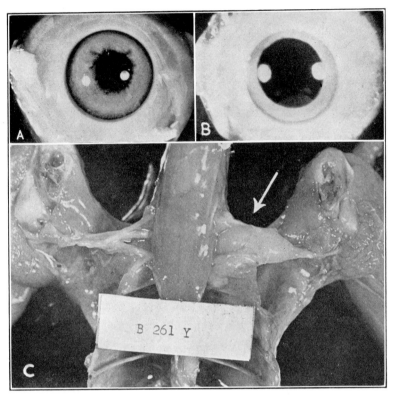

Fig. 126.—Common symptoms of the avian leukosis complex. *A*, Distorted pupil characteristic of the ocular type of the disease; *B*, a normal eye; *C*, enlarged nerve trunk characteristic of the neural form of the disease. (*Courtesy of U. S. Department of Agriculture.*)

Neural Lymphomatosis.—This is the nerve type most familiar to poultrymen, and commonly called fowl paralysis or range paralysis. One or both legs or wings may be affected to the extent of partial or complete paralysis. The large nerves leading to the affected parts are infiltrated with tumor cells which impair their function and lead to eventual paralysis. At the Regional Poultry Research Laboratory symptoms of respiratory distress, as shown by gasping, have frequently been observed in young chickens shown to

18

be affected with the disease. This is related to involvement of the vagus nerve. The abnormal condition often may readily be seen at post-mortem examination as enlarged, grayish watery nerves. At other times it is necessary to make use of the microscope to determine the abnormal condition.

Ocular Lymphomatosis.—This is the eye type of the disease, sometimes referred to as "gray eye" or "white eye." It is also known as iritis. The gray discoloration of the iris is often accompanied by a distortion of the pupil of the eye. In severe cases the fowl becomes blind. The change is brought about by infiltration of tumor cells. It is primarily a disease of young adults—those five to ten months of age. It is less common now than a few years ago because it is easily recognized and poultrymen have made conscious selection against it.

Osteopetrosis.—This term means hardening of the bone, and is therefore used to designate the bone type of the avian leukosis complex. The long bones of the wings and legs are the ones affected, and they become greatly enlarged, with very thick, hard walls. The flat bones of the body become rarified, pitted and more fragile, through the loss of calcium salts, perhaps by transfer to the enlarged long bones.

Leukemia.—The fifth type of the disease is leukemia, or the blood form, and this can be of two different sorts, depending on the type of blood cell affected. If the red cells are involved, it is known as erythroblastosis. If the white cells are affected, it is granuloblastosis. An individual fowl may have either or both. The red cell type commonly appears first. If the white cell type follows, it may eventually predominate in the fowl so affected. The internal organs reflect by their color the abnormal character of the blood circulating through them. The liver and spleen are usually cherry red in color, brighter than normal.

Myelocytomatosis.—This form of the disease is mainly of academic interest up to the present time. It is characterized by small chalky white tumors which occur principally in the liver, in some other internal organs, and on the internal surface of the breast muscles along the sternum and ribs.

Transmission.—The visceral form of the disease is transmitted both by simple contact and through the hatching egg. The virus is shed in the feces and saliva of infected chicks. At the Regional Poultry Research Laboratory it was shown that visceral tumors were readily induced by inoculating chicks through the eye, mouth, nasal passages, trachea or cloaca, as well as by spraying the virus into the air breathed by baby chicks. Neural lymphomatosis is transmitted chiefly by contact. Since young chickens are more susceptible than older stock, the incidence of this form of the disease can be greatly reduced by rearing chicks in complete isolation from infected stock or premises. Little is known about transmission of the ocular type of the disease.

Prevention and Control.—No method of treatment is known for any of the forms of lymphomatosis, and all attempts to control the disease by vaccination have been unsuccessful. The most effective means of prevention and control at present are:

1. Strict sanitation to prevent contamination of feed, water, litter, and the poultry premises by infective fecal material.
2. Rearing young chicks under strict isolation from older fowls. Such isolation is particularly important during the first two weeks of life. Persons who care for the chicks should have no contact with older fowls.
3. Selection of breeding stock on the basis of hereditary natural resistance to the avian leukosis complex.

Fowl Pox.—This highly infectious disease, caused by a filterable virus, is also known as chicken pox, avian diphtheria, and sore-head. It shows up in two different forms, commonly designated as the skin or comb form, and the diphtheritic or throat form. Both types may occur in the same individual. In the skin type there are numerous small, raised, blister-like spots on the

FIG. 127.—Appearance of fowl pox lesions on the comb and wattles about ten days after natural infection.

comb, wattles or face. These soon dry up and form brownish scabs. They may be scattered, and few in number, or they may cover almost the entire surface of the comb, face, and wattles. Light infection may cause little inconvenience to the fowls, but more often it is severe enough to cause loss of appetite, followed by loss in weight and a marked reduction in egg production.

In the diphtheritic form of the disease there are yellowish, raised, necrotic patches in the mouth and throat. They are firmly adherent to the mucous membrane, and may become so extensive as to interfere with eating and with breathing. The eyes are often involved, showing a watery discharge and, later a yellowish pus-like accumulation. The death rate is likely to be greater than with the skin type of the disease.

FIG. 128.—Laryngotracheitis. Characteristic position during inspiration. (*Courtesy of California Agricultural Experiment Station.*)

Treatment is of little value, but vaccination with egg-propagated live virus or with the older type of virus recovered from scabs grown on artificially infected fowls, furnishes almost complete protection against infection. Vaccination actually gives the chicken a mild infection which is sufficient to develop a high degree of immunity. The vaccine is most easily administered by the "stick" method while the chickens are 6 to 16 weeks of age. Vaccination should be a routine annual procedure on farms where the disease has appeared. Pigeon pox vaccine is recommended in the case of fresh outbreaks in laying flocks.

Laryngotracheitis.—This disease, known also as chicken "flu," is a highly contagious respiratory infection which often causes high mortality. It is a comparatively new disease in the United States but it has been reported from coast to coast. The cause is a filterable virus to which chickens are extremely susceptible.

The outstanding and most characteristic symptom is gasping. When inhaling, the fowl extends its head and neck upward with the mouth wide open. When exhaling, the head is drawn back and lowered, with the mouth closed. Coughing, rattling, wheezing, and occasional loud cries are frequently heard, as the fowls attempt to dislodge the accumulations of mucus in the air passages.

A vaccine prepared from the membranes of artificially infected embryos or from the tracheal exudate of infected fowls, and applied to the mucous membrane of the cloaca, gives protection against later infection. Since the live virus must be used for vaccination purposes, and since it is capable of causing the disease to break out in virulent form, great care must be taken to see that it is properly used. For this reason, vaccination is ordinarily not recommended unless the disease is prevalent in the community, or occurs regularly on the farm from year to year because of the presence of recovered carriers. If several flocks are housed on a single farm and the disease occurs in one of them, the others may be protected by prompt vaccination. When annual vaccination is practised, the usual procedure is to apply it when the new crop of chickens is 16 weeks old or older.

Chronic Respiratory Disease.—This disease, often abbreviated to CRD, is widespread and is probably the most serious respiratory infection in poultry today. It affects both young and adult stock and is characterized by nasal discharge, a foamy condition of the eyes, respiratory rales, slow rate of spread, and great persistency of symptoms.

The principal cause is an organism (or perhaps more than one) belonging to the pleuropneumonia-like group (PPLO). Severe field cases are often the result of secondary infections by intestinal organisms. The disease is spread by contact and may also be transmitted through the egg.

There is some evidence to indicate that spread of the disease can be reduced by dipping suspected eggs in antibiotic solutions. Absorption of the solution through the shell may be sufficient to prevent growth and development of the PPLO organisms.

No effective method of treating infected fowls has yet been found.

Fowl Plague.—The filterable virus which causes fowl plague, or fowl pest, is highly infectious, even in minute amounts. The disease is characterized by an extremely rapid course and high mortality. It is reported to be rather prevalent in Europe, but only two serious outbreaks have occurred in this country, one in 1925 and one in 1929. In both instances the disease was eradicated by prompt action of sanitary officials.

Since the virus is contained in the blood, intimately associated with the red blood cells, there is usually a generalized hemorrhagic condition evident at autopsy. This, together with the rapid onset of the disease and the high death rate, ranging from 50 to 100 per cent, will usually be sufficient for diagnosis. Medicinal treatment is of no benefit whatever. Prompt and complete eradication of affected flocks is essential for the protection of the entire industry. If this disease is suspected, Federal and State officials should be notified immediately.

Newcastle Disease (Avian Pneumoencephalitis).—This virus disease has been known for many years in various parts of the world, but not until the middle forties did it become of major importance in the United States. It is a highly infectious respiratory disease. In young chickens there are varying degrees of muscular incoordination, including many peculiar motions such as walking backward or in circles. In older flocks egg production commonly drops to zero within three to five days after an outbreak. When egg laying is resumed after 4 to 6 weeks, many of the eggs are abnormal in shape with rough and thin shells. Interior quality is also adversely affected. Death losses are usually low among fowls of laying age, but may range up to 25 per cent or more in chicks.

Control is possible through vaccination, but authorities differ in their recommendations as between live and killed virus, and whether the wing-web or intranasal method should be used. In areas where the disease is not too common, killed virus vaccine has been very helpful. In areas where the disease is quite general, and flocks of commercial size are close together, the tendency is to use intranasal or eye-instilled vaccination with live virus on day-old chicks, or the wing-web method with live virus at 3 to 4 weeks of age, followed in either case by a second vaccination at 4 to 6 months using the wing-web or stick method.

Recovered females confer a certain degree of parental immunity on their chicks, and this lasts for one to four weeks after hatching. It tends to interfere with the efficacy of wing-web vaccination if done prior to three weeks of age. Apparently there is less interference when the intranasal or intraocular method is used. Intranasal vaccination does not confer the same degree of parental immunity as does the stick method, nor the single stick method as much as vaccination at both three weeks and 4 to 6 months.

Poultrymen are still learning to live with this disease, and continued research will no doubt make the problem easier than it is at present.

Tuberculosis.—Fowl tuberculosis is of common occurrence, especially in the West North Central States. Tests have shown from 10 to 15 per cent of fowls in farm flocks in certain sections to be infected with this disease, but there has been considerable improvement in this respect in recent years.

The cause of the disease is the bacterial organism known as *Mycobacterium avium*, and the symptoms are similar to those of tuberculosis in other animals. Tuberculosis is characteristically slow to develop and chronic in form. Fowls over 18 months of age are much more likely to show infection than are younger members of a flock.

Since the causative organism may remain in the soil of poultry yards for many months, and perhaps years, and since comparatively few cases are found in young fowls, control and eventual eradication can be obtained by the simple procedure of disposing of all fowls as they reach the end of their first laying season, at about 18 months of age, and by keeping all laying flocks confined indoors so that they do not come in contact with contaminated soil. Of course it is likewise essential to raise the young stock on clean ground, away from any lots over which chickens have ranged. This recommendation should not be taken to mean that all poultrymen everywhere should dispose of all laying stock at 18 months of age. There may be economic reasons for doing so, but as far as tuberculosis is concerned, it is recommended only when the disease has become established in a community, or when one has reason to believe that it is present on a particular farm.

The tuberculin test, simply and quickly made by means of a wattle injection, will identify infected fowls. This is an easy method of determining whether or not the disease is present in a flock, and is a means of saving valuable breeding birds from slaughter when the disease is known to be present and old hens are to be disposed of. The possibility of tuberculosis infection is an excellent reason for keeping pullets and older hens in separate houses. No medicinal treatment is of any value.

Since the disease is readily spread by contact with infected carcasses, and since avian tuberculosis is transmissible to swine, diseased carcasses should never be thrown out where other fowls or hogs may have access to them. This is particularly important in those sections of the country where fowl tuberculosis is common and where large numbers of hogs are raised for market. For the same reason, the poultry flock and the swine enterprise should be entirely separated. Many farmers who perhaps are not greatly concerned over a few losses among the chickens, will take an entirely different view of the matter when they realize that allowing the chickens and the pigs to mingle freely may be a cause for retentions or rejections of hog carcasses at the terminal markets.

Coryza or Colds.—Perhaps the most common ailment of fowls is the common cold, or infectious coryza. The primary cause is a microörganism called *Hemophilus gallinarum*, but certain other organisms may be associated with it under conditions which increase the severity of the disease. The infection may be of a very mild type, with a slight nasal discharge persisting over several weeks or months, with few other symptoms, or it may be severe and be accompanied by swelling of the face below and behind the eye, or by inflammation and partial occlusion of the respiratory passages. Unfortunately, there is always the danger that the mild type of the disease may change to the severe type at any time.

Fig. 129.—Eggs laid for some time after an outbreak of Newcastle disease may have soft or thin shells. Affected chickens commonly assume peculiar positions such as those shown here. (*Courtesy of Illinois Agricultural Experiment Station.*)

Fowls which recover may continue to be carriers for months, and are a constant source of danger to all healthy individuals with which they come in contact. For this reason it is highly important to house pullets on a given farm entirely away from the older hens. Other sanitary or control procedures are of very little value unless this is done.

Fowl Cholera.—A positive diagnosis of fowl cholera can be made only by a bacteriological examination, because neither symptoms nor lesions are sufficiently characteristic. If the disease is suspected, specimens should be submitted to a diagnostic laboratory at once.

The disease has long been known and is wide spread, but by comparison with others which have been described it is of much less economic importance. This may explain why no satisfactory method of treatment or prevention has ever been developed.

Poultrymen are likely to become familiar with it only in the case of an acute outbreak which may occur without warning. Several fowls may be found dead under the roosts some morning when all were apparently healthy the day before. The disease often strikes on farms where excellent management and feeding methods are used, and when flocks are laying at a high rate. The sick birds should be killed and burned along with those dead from the disease. The healthy fowls may be removed to clean and disinfected quarters if any are available. Since recovered fowls may become carriers of the infection, it is usually considered better to dispose of all fowls in the house where the outbreak occurred and, after thorough cleaning and disinfection, to leave the house empty for several weeks or months before restocking it.

Other Diseases of Hens.—There are several other infectious diseases of fowls which occur from time to time. They are always serious to the flock-owner affected, but in the aggregate they are of less consequence than the ones which have been described. Among them are fowl typhoid, paratyphoid infections, erysipelas, and so-called blue comb or pullet disease.

Poisons.—Fowls frequently have access to poisonous substances and, under certain circumstances they are subject to acute or chronic poisoning. Actually, however, cases of poisoning are not common when considered in relation to the many other ailments of poultry.

Drugs and Chemicals.—Chickens are able to tolerate considerable quantities of arsenic over extended periods, so that there is little danger to them from eating poisoned grasshoppers, or from such drip as may normally occur following the use of arsenical sprays on fruit trees.

Cyanides are extremely toxic for fowls of all ages. In fact, calcium cyanide in both dust and flake forms has been used for the destruction of large numbers of fowls during control work in outbreaks of such diseases as European fowl pest.

Kamala, often recommended as a tapeworm remedy, is a gastrointestinal irritant, and has a strong purgative action. A decline in egg production and a decrease in egg weight are to be expected following its use.

Metallic lead consumed in the form of lead shot is poisonous for water fowl and presumably also for chickens. Metallic mercury is also toxic to fowls. If mercurial ointment is used as a treatment for lice, it is important that no excess be left on the feathers where the fowls can pick it off. Mercurial ointment should never be used on setting hens because the small amount of mercury absorbed by the skin is sufficient to prevent normal hatching of the eggs.

Nicotine sulphate is a violent poison, and extreme care should be exercised in connection with its use.

Certain organic sulphur compounds used for the chemical treatment of seed grains in the routine control of plant diseases may become a potential hazard for poultry. Arasan is an example. If treated seed grain is fed without previous washing to remove the chemical there is danger of retarded growth in chicks, reduced egg production, or of soft-shelled and misshapen eggs not unlike those produced by flocks infected with Newcastle disease or infectious bronchitis.

Common salt is poisonous to fowls if fed in a large enough amount, especially when the fowls do not have free access to water. The minimum lethal dose is about 4 grams per kilogram of live weight. As much as 8 per cent salt in the feed can be tolerated over considerable periods of time.

Plants and Seeds.—Certain plants and seeds to which fowls sometimes have access, or which may inadvertently be included in mixed rations, are poisonous. Corn cockle seed is an example. It is highly unpalatable to fowls and the danger from poisoning is therefore slight unless the seed is present in the mash mixture in fairly large amounts.

The seed of *Crotalaria* and of *Daubentonia*, both of which are grown rather extensively in the southern states, are poisonous to fowls. They should be so handled that chickens do not have access to the seed. Certain other seeds are known to be poisonous, but they normally are not consumed voluntarily by fowls and hence are not of great importance.

Insects.—The rose chafer is definitely poisonous to young chickens, and chickens will feed upon these insects ravenously if given the opportunity. Loss from this cause can easily be prevented under most conditions by so managing the flocks of growing chickens that they do not have access to fields or gardens where rose chafers are numerous during May and early June.

Commercial Feeds.—Poultry workers are confronted every year with numerous cases in which some proprietary feed mixture is suspected of having caused the death of chicks or older fowls. Very rarely are such feeds actually poisonous, as when they have been loaded in cars or trucks which previously were used for some poisonous substance without proper cleaning before re-use. Hundreds of suspected feed samples have been tested by feeding to young chickens and nearly all of them have proved to be harmless. Corn, barley, and wheat grown in certain limited areas in central South Dakota contain sufficient selenium to cause poisoning. Selenium from this source, fed at the rate of 15 parts per million of the total ration, caused hens to lose weight and reduced the hatchability of their eggs to zero.

Cannibalism.—Although not properly considered as a disease, this vice may develop at any time. It occurs as toe-picking in baby chicks or as feather pulling, vent picking, or tail picking in adult flocks. The causes are chiefly environmental, and control is therefor a matter of management.

Certain nutritional deficiencies may cause irritability which leads to outbreaks of cannibalism. Rations high in corn, and therefore low in niacin unless properly supplemented, cause chickens to become nervous and irritable. Attempts to cause experimental outbreaks of cannibalism by various means have more often failed than succeeded. Hereditary differences in temperament may be involved but they have not been demonstrated experimentally.

The Maryland Station recommends a scatter or "shotgun" program for controlling outbreaks, on the theory that different methods work at different times and under different conditions. Some of the procedures suggested are:

1. Give the flock more room, or reduce the size of the flock by culling.

2. Use an anti-pick salve on at least 25 per cent of the flock—both picked and unpicked birds.

3. Sprinkle fine salt, free of lumps, generously over the mash for three to five days.

4. Feed whole, heavy oats either free-choice in hoppers or by hand to the extent of 5 or 6 pounds daily to 100 hens.

5. Keep the chickens busy by hanging a pulled cabbage or other attractive material in such a position that the chickens have to jump up slightly to peck at it.

6. Make use of commercial appliances such as shields over the vent, or guards on the beak or in front of the eyes.

7. Debeak the offenders by cutting the upper mandible back to the quick, or by using a commercial electric debeaking outfit.

Since vent picking often starts while hens are at the feed hoppers, it is good practice to place the hoppers at floor level, just high enough to clear the litter, or high enough so that a hen eating from the hopper cannot be picked by another standing on the floor.

Salt in the drinking water is often effective. It should be used for a half-day at a time on two or three successive days. A heaping tablespoonful to each gallon of water is about right.

POULTRY PARASITES

Chickens are subject to infestation by a large number of internal and external parasites but, fortunately, only a few of them are of sufficient importance to need special consideration. Certain ones are more important in one section of the country than in another, and some show a seasonal variation in frequency of occurrence. Some are easily kept under control by ordinary good sanitation practices, whereas others require special methods for their elimination.

Internal Parasites.—Most important among the internal parasites are the large roundworm of the small intestine, the cecal worm, the gapeworm, and the several varieties of tapeworms.

The Large Roundworm.—This is the common intestinal worm, known to most poultrymen, and usually found in the small intestine. It ranges in length from $1\frac{1}{2}$ to 4 inches, and in numbers from two or three specimens in a single fowl to so many that the bowel is completely filled for a distance of several inches. Prevention is best accomplished by general sanitation, including rotation of lots and ranges, and elimination of low wet areas, or damp spots around the watering devices. Such practices reduce the opportunity which chickens may have for picking up worm eggs. There is no known spray or disinfectant which is effective in killing roundworm eggs.

Tests at the Georgia station, involving 24 lots of broilers over a two-year period, showed that normal sanitary management procedures without the use of any anthelmintics were sufficient to prevent any serious infestation with roundworms. These broilers were grown in pens known to have been contaminated, half on dirt floors and half on concrete.

There may be times when treatment of affected fowls is warranted, and carbon tetrachloride has long been the drug recommended for removing large roundworms. The dosage rate is 4 cc. per kilogram of body weight, given individually. A drop in egg production following its use must be expected. Various piperazine compounds, such as piperazine citrate, have recently been found to be highly effective, either in individual doses of 300 to 500 milligrams per kilogram of body weight or when added to the drinking water at the rate of 2 to 4 grams per gallon.

The Cecal Worm.—The cecal worm of chickens is very small, not over $\frac{1}{2}$ inch in length, and grayish-white in color. It is frequently found in great numbers in the ceca, where it produces severe inflammation. The life cycle of this parasite is practically identical with that of the large roundworm, and therefore the same methods of prevention and control are effective, namely, general sanitation, rotation of lots and ranges, and strict separation of young and old stock.

Treatment should not be necessary in well-managed flocks, but the drug phenothiazine has been found to be effective in killing and expelling the worms. The dosage is $\frac{1}{2}$ gram per chicken, and flock treatment has been reported to be as effective as individual treatment.

Tapeworms.—These parasites are flat, segmented, ribbon-like worms, which vary in size, depending on the species, from those so small as to be barely visible, to types which are as much as 10 inches long. So far as is known, all tapeworms require an intermediate host for the completion of their life cycle, and this is the key to their prevention and control. If chickens can be so managed that they have no opportunity to eat any of these intermediate hosts, which consist of various beetles, flies, and slugs, there is no possibility of their becoming infested with tapeworms. Prevention is therefore the logical method of control.

Frequent removal of poultry manure to prevent it becoming a breeding place for flies is important. If roosting racks are used, the manure beneath them should be treated regularly to keep down the fly nuisance. Slugs may be eliminated, or their numbers greatly reduced by the use of certain poison baits when necessary.

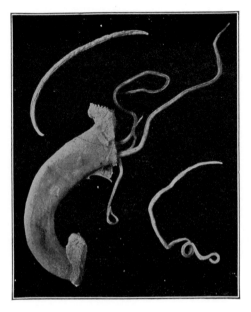

FIG. 130.—Section of intestine showing roundworms protruding from a cut end. (*Courtesy of California Agricultural Experiment Station.*)

Earthworms, which may serve as mechanical carriers of the eggs of various parasites, can be kept under control by eliminating wet areas, and seeing that the ranges are well drained throughout.

More than 200 different substances have been tested by many different workers in attempting to find a medicinal agent which would be effective for the removal of tapeworms from chickens. Several different drugs will cause quantities of segments to be detached and removed, but if the heads of the tapeworms remain attached to the wall of the intestine they promptly regenerate so that the infestation is soon as bad as before the treatment was given. Recently, however, a tin compound—di-n-butyl tin dilaurate, sometimes referred to as butynorate—has been shown to be an effective and safe material for the removal of certain species of tapeworms from chickens. The compound was used at the rate of 500 mg. per kilogram of feed (0.05 per cent) or as a single 125-mg. dose by capsule. Removal of the entire tapeworm of several species was accomplished.

External Parasites.—The control of external parasites is an important practical problem wherever fowls are kept. In most instances control measures are comparatively simple and effective, but if they are omitted the loss caused by the parasites may be very serious.

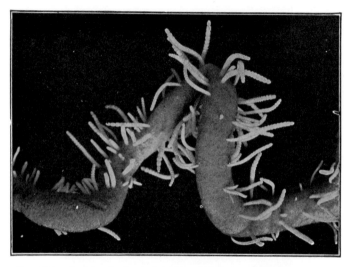

Fig. 131.—Inside of a hen's intestine showing attached tapeworms. (*Courtesy of California Agricultural Experiment Station.*)

Lice.—Several different kinds of biting and chewing lice infest chickens. They are permanent parasites in the sense that they live and reproduce on the body of their host. Furthermore, there is a tendency for each species of lice to prefer a certain location on the body of the fowl. Among their special characteristics are flattened bodies, legs which are peculiarly well fitted for clinging to skin and feathers, and a remarkable ability to move about so as to remain out of sight among the feathers.

The three common species of chicken lice are the head louse, the body louse, and the shaft louse. Others are seen occasionally, but cause much less damage. Since one method of treatment may be used for all, the exact species present is of little consequence to the flock owner.

The older methods of treatment—dusting, dipping and greasing —involved handling of each individual fowl. They are still effective, but they have been replaced by the much simpler and faster method of using a malathion spray in the poultry house. Malathion is effective as a one per cent liquid water spray (1 pint of 57 per cent malathion emulsion in 8 gallons of water) applied to the roosting areas to the point of run-off. It has the further advantage that it will control the red mite or roost mite at the same time with a single spray application.

Fig. 132.—Eggs (nits) of the common large louse, attached to the shafts of body feathers.

Roost Mites.—The common roost mite is a familiar pest in all parts of the country. The habits of this parasite are quite different from those of lice. The mites spend most of their time in cracks and crevices about the house, especially the roosts and roost supports, going on the fowls mostly at night. Since they are blood-sucking parasites, they are especially destructive. Malathion spray, as recommended for lice, is a simple and effective method of control.

Scaly-leg Mites.—These mites are so named because they are responsible for the condition known as scaly leg in fowls. Scaly leg is rarely seen on well-managed poultry plants but it may become serious when fowls are kept for long periods under insanitary conditions. Control is most effectively accomplished by disposing of all mature fowls, giving the house and adjacent yard a thorough cleaning, and then restocking with young pullets. If treatment is to be practiced, it is necessary to find some material which will penetrate beneath the scales of the shanks in order to reach the minute parasites. It must be strong enough to kill the mites without being too irritating to the fowls. Soaking the shanks three times at intervals of 2 to 4 weeks in a 0.5 per cent solution of sodium fluoride is said to be effective, as is also dipping in a mixture of 1 part kerosense and 2 parts raw linseed oil. Since the mites spread readily from fowl to fowl, treatment of the roosts as for the roost mite is also important.

Northern Fowl Mites.—The northern fowl mite, also sometimes called the feather mite, is a serious pest. Since they may reproduce either on the fowls or in the nests, single treatments are not always sufficient for complete eradication. They are most commonly found around the base of the tail and around the vent, and frequently they prefer male hosts. Their feeding habits are such as to cause the formation of large scabs which spoil the appearance of dressed carcasses. Outbreaks occur sporadically, and often are rather severe before they are discovered. They are sometimes found by reason of the dirty appearance which they give to the plumage of white fowls.

Several methods of control are effective. One of the best, especially in cold weather, is to dust each fowl thoroughly with finely divided orchard spray sulphur. The nests should also be liberally dusted. Since English sparrows harbor this parasite, nests near the poultry house should be destroyed and burned.

Nicotine sulphate applied to the skin, one drop below the vent, one on the back of the neck, and one under each wing, has been found highly effective in controlling these mites.

Heavy infestations have also been controlled by individual treatment with 4 per cent malathion dust.

Fowl Ticks.—The fowl tick is common in the southern part of the country and is a serious pest. It is a powerful blood sucker, and its habits are similar to those of the roost mite. The same general methods of control are recommended, but they must be more rigorously applied. Control is difficult not only because the ticks crawl into any deep cracks which are available, but because the seed ticks can live for five or six months, and the nymphal stages for eight to fifteen months without any food. It is necessary to do a very thorough job of cleaning, burning all litter and trash, and even treating nearby trees as well as other outbuildings to which the chickens have access, in order to accomplish complete control. Treatment consists of applying 1 per cent malathion spray under high pressure to the inside and outside structural portions of infested houses.

Sticktight Fleas.—These parasites are common throughout the southern states, from Florida to California. They attack dogs, cats, and rats, but find chickens an ideal host. They attach themselves to the comb, face, wattles and earlobes in large numbers, and since they are voracious feeders they cause serious injury. Eggs laid by the adult females fall to the floor or ground, and the remainder of the life cycle, through larval and pupal stages to adult is passed there. Control measures must include treatment of the floor of the poultry house and nearby infested soil, as well as the affected fowls.

According to reports from the California Station, sprinkling the yards two or three times weekly for a short period will greatly reduce the breeding of these pests, since they cannot thrive in damp surroundings. The effectiveness of the treatment is increased by scattering salt freely about the yards before wetting the soil.

The Florida Station has reported that complete control was secured by a combination of feeding 5 per cent of commercial sulphur flour in the mash for a period of three weeks and dusting sulphur on the surface soil and in the poultry house at the rate of 2 pounds for each 100 square feet. Neither feeding nor dusting alone was effective.

Affected fowls may be treated by the application of 2 per cent carbolic ointment, or tincture of iodine. Great care must be taken not to get either of these materials into the fowls' eyes.

All litter, manure, and other refuse from the house should be burned or spread on distant fields where it can be promptly plowed under. Otherwise the flea larvæ will continue to develop and will soon be ready to attack any dogs, cats, or humans in the neighborhood.

Rat control is especially important in preventing flea infestations in the poultry flocks.

Other External Parasites.—Various other parasites occasionally become a nuisance to poultry flocks, and special control methods are sometimes necessary. Chiggers or "red bugs," common bed bugs, Mexican chicken bugs, black flies, and depluming mites may cause trouble at times, but they are usually not a problem on well-managed farms and ranches where sound sanitation practices are continuously followed.

DISINFECTANTS AND THEIR USE

Disinfectants are substances which have the power to kill microorganisms. They are very valuable materials to use under certain conditions, but in good poultry management they are always secondary to scrupulous cleanliness. Not only is cleanliness more important as a means of preventing losses from disease, but it is an essential preliminary to effective disinfection. The action of most disinfectants is greatly retarded in the presence of accumulated organic matter of any kind. Furthermore, the use of copious amounts of water will both wash away infective organisms and dilute them to the point that they are much less dangerous.

Direct sunshine is an effective germicide, and it can often be used to advantage for equipment which is portable and so constructed that it can be fully exposed to the sun's rays.

When disinfection is necessary it is important (1) to do a thorough job of cleaning first, (2) to apply the disinfectant while it is warm or hot if possible, (3) to use it liberally and to apply it thoroughly, and (4) to allow plenty of time for the disinfectant to act.

19

Steam applied under pressure is probably the most effective of all disinfectants, but it is not available under average farm conditions. Boiling water is also effective, and frequently can be used on the farm.

Chlorine is a good cheap disinfectant that may be used freely. The addition of a wetting agent or detergent when using chlorine solutions will increase their effectiveness.

Quaternary ammonium compounds are very effective against bacteria, but not so satisfactory for viruses. Time is the important factor in cleaning up after a virus infection. Material contaminated with a virus may become safe in as short a time as three weeks after thorough cleaning if moisture and temperature conditions have varied during that period.

Formaldehyde gas is effective in spaces which can be tightly closed, especially if the air is warm and moist. Directions for the use of this material for incubator fumigation have been given in connection with the discussion of pullorum disease.

Common lye (sodium hydroxide) is a powerful disinfectant, especially if applied in a solution of hot water. A 2 per cent solution is made by adding 1 pound of lye to 6 gallons of hot water. Lye must be kept in tightly closed containers because it very soon becomes inactive on exposure to the air.

Saponified cresol solutions are prepared by several different manufacturers and are usually available through local drug and supply houses. The commonly recommended dilution is 4 ounces to a gallon of water. Soft water should be used if available, because the cresol solutions do not mix so readily with hard water.

Since most disinfectants are very irritating, it is important to protect the eyes, face, and hands from contact with the solution being used. If cresol solutions are used in small brooder houses or other confined space, ample time should be allowed for drying before chicks are introduced.

Chapter 12

Marketing Eggs

THE marketing of eggs involves buying and selling, and the physical movement and distribution of eggs between the point of production and the point of consumption. To be effective, marketing must be concerned with those phases of production which influence egg quality, as well as with the preferences of consumers for certain characteristics of the retail product and for the type of package in which it is offered for sale. Between these two extremes come the many details of assembling, grading, standardization, processing, transportation, storage, financing and merchandising. Obviously, the system of purchase, distribution and sale is extensive and complicated, and the costs involved are considerable.

The Marketing Problem.—The ultimate objective of the market ing process is to put eggs in the hands of consumers with their original quality unimpaired. In practice this is seldom accomplished in a full and complete sense except where direct marketing from producer to consumer is involved. It will be the purpose of this chapter, however, to emphasize that objective and to point out the ways in which it may most nearly be attained.

The seasonal nature of egg production, though still presenting something of a marketing problem, is not nearly so important as it was twenty or more years ago. In April, 1929, for example, receipts of shell eggs at New York City were nearly four times the receipts in November of that year, and 29 per cent of the year's receipts arrived in the two months of April and May. But in 1959 the difference between April and November receipts was only 5 per cent.

The Geographical Nature of Egg Production.—The distribution of poultry flocks does not coincide with the geographical distribution of population, though there has been a growing tendency for market eggs to be produced close to the large centers of population. New York State, with about 10 per cent of the population, produced less than three per cent of the Nation's eggs in 1959, while California, with about 9 per cent of the population, produced over eight per cent of the eggs. Excess production over local consumption needs occurs chiefly in the West North Central States. Iowa, with less than two per cent of the population, produced eight per cent of the 1959 egg crop.

(291)

Eggs or poultry from a single state or area may be widely distributed over the country, but the bulk of shipments often go to a single terminal market. In 1959 Maryland shipped 60 million pounds of processed poultry to the eight principal markets, but 50 million pounds of that total went to New York City. Of Ohio's shipments of over a million cases of eggs in 1959, 57 per cent went to Detroit and 39 per cent went to Pittsburgh.

Fig. 133.—A view of Chicago's South Water Market. (*Courtesy of U. S. Egg and Poultry Magazine.*)

A single terminal market, such as New York City, may receive eggs from as many as thirty different states in a single year, but most of its receipts come from five states. For the eight principal markets combined, 94 per cent of the receipts of shell eggs in 1959 came from the states listed in Table 42, and 67 per cent came from the five states of California, Iowa, Minnesota, New Jersey and Pennsylvania.

The Maintenance of Quality.—Because of the seasonal nature of poultry and egg production, and because of the differences in geographical distribution of poultry and human population, the matter of maintaining the quality of poultry products during the time that elapses between their production and their delivery to the final consumer is of great importance. Its successful accomplishment requires that every individual who has anything to do with the marketing of eggs or poultry shall be "quality conscious," and interested in reducing the loss of original quality to a minimum.

The advantage gained from strict attention to production factors that affect quality may be quickly lost if the products are not properly handled after they leave the farm.

The demand for high-quality eggs is growing, and is likely to continue to grow for a long time. If producers are to receive the full benefit from this growing demand they must know what constitutes high quality in eggs, how such eggs can be produced, and how they should be marketed.

TABLE 41.—EGG PRODUCTION PER CAPITA AND AVERAGE FARM PRICE OF EGGS BY REGIONS, EXPRESSED AS PERCENTAGES OF U. S. CONSUMPTION PER CAPITA, AND AVERAGE U. S. FARM PRICE, RESPECTIVELY, 1953–1955. AS REPORTED BY THE U. S. DEPT. OF AGRICULTURE.

Region	Per capita production as a percentage of U. S. per capita consumption	Farm price of eggs as a percentage of the U. S. average farm price
New England	83	130
Middle Atlantic	74	121
East North Central	103	92
West North Central	327	80
South Atlantic	71	117
East South Central	86	99
West South Central	78	96
Mountain	80	102
Pacific	100	110
United States	107*	100

*Production exceeds consumption, as reported, because quantities of eggs are exported, used for hatching and other non-food purposes, and purchased by the Armed Forces for use outside the United States.

Eggs are among the most delicate and perishable food products, are subject to rapid deterioration, and are easily affected by unfavorable surroundings. In food value, flavor and general attractiveness, they are better when first laid than at any later time. Because consumers are quick to discriminate against poor eggs, it is important not only that the right kind of eggs be produced, but that they be so handled as to reach the consumer with the least possible loss of their original quality.

Consumer Preferences.—The consumer is the final judge of what constitutes quality in eggs and her measures or preferences do not always coincide with the measures used by the egg trade. Some consumers, for example, actually prefer eggs with medium or thin white over those with firm thick white. In general, consumers are not so much concerned with minor details representing egg quality as they are with size of the eggs and assurance of freshness.

With graded eggs available through retail outlets all over the country, most consumers obtain their needs from supermarkets or neighborhood grocery stores, although many patronize roadside

TABLE 42.—STATES SHIPPING AS MANY AS 100,000 CASES OF SHELL EGGS TO ANY ONE OF THE INDICATED CITIES IN 1959. AS REPORTED BY THE U.S. DEPARTMENT OF AGRICULTURE.

	Baltimore	Boston	Chicago	Detroit (1000 Cases)	Los Angeles	New York	Philadelphia	San Francisco
California	—	—	—	—	3,349	—	—	1,670
Illinois	—	—	640	148	—	99	—	—
Indiana	223	113	174	215	—	—	—	—
Iowa	—	685	1,043	—	—	1,537	160	—
Maine	—	—	—	—	—	—	—	—
Maryland	125	—	—	—	—	—	—	—
Massachusetts	—	385	—	—	—	—	—	—
Michigan	—	—	—	561	—	922	—	—
Minnesota	328	—	817	215	—	—	—	—
New Hampshire	—	323	—	—	—	—	—	—
New Jersey	—	—	—	—	—	999	256	—
New York	—	—	—	—	—	422	—	—
North Carolina	128	—	—	—	—	—	—	—
Ohio	—	—	—	574	—	—	—	—
Pennsylvania	360	—	—	—	—	481	882	—
Wisconsin	—	—	1,169	—	—	—	—	—
All other	107	161	131	103	41	526	190	12
Total	1,269	1,667	3,974	1,816	3,390	4,887	1,458	1,682

stands and some buy eggs delivered by producers. A 1957 study in Rochester, New York, showed that 9 per cent of the 1029 families interviewed bought eggs at a farm, and 23 per cent had eggs delivered by a farmer, while 56 per cent bought from a supermarket or neighborhood grocery. The remaining 12 per cent obtained their eggs in other ways. Among these same families 44 per cent preferred eggs of AA quality, 21 per cent preferred A quality, while 15 and 20 per cent preferred B and C quality, respectively.

FIG. 134.—A convenient egg washer and sanitizer for farm use.
(*J. C. Allen and Son Photo.*)

About 40 per cent of these families preferred white eggs and 13 per cent preferred brown eggs, while 50 per cent had no preference as to shade of yolk color.

Tests of transparent plastic cartons have shown that consumers definitely prefer this type of package because they can see what they are getting. They also find the transparent cartons attractive and many feel that these cartons provide better protection for the

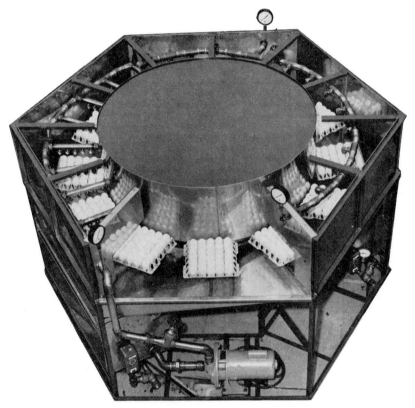

Fig. 135.—A mechanical rotary egg washer for one-man operation. It will handle 25 cases per hour. (*Courtesy of Kuhl Poultry Equipment Company.*)

eggs than is given by the regular carton. An opinion survey in six Maine cities showed that 70 per cent of consumers preferred the plastic carton. In actual test sales, about half of the customers chose the plastic carton, even though the price of eggs so packed was marked at 3 and 5 cents a dozen above eggs in regular cartons.

Measures of Egg Quality.—Quality in eggs, with reference to food value or market desirability, is measured: (1) by external appearance; (2) by candling; and (3) by odor, flavor and physical character of the opened egg. For the most part, these measures give only a gross picture that is sufficient for trade purposes. Exact measures of quality, in the scientific sense, have been almost totally lacking, though considerable progress in that direction has recently been made.

Fig. 136.—A conveyor egg washer which spray washes and dries the eggs. Note the hand-operated vacuum lift. (*Courtesy of Kuhl Poultry Equipment Company.*)

External Appearance.—Under this heading may be mentioned size, shape, shell color and texture, cleanliness and uniformity of eggs within a given sample or lot. While small eggs of high interior quality may be worth more than large eggs of low quality, it is none the less true that size is a most important factor in determining the price received for eggs in any market. The standard size is 2 ounces each, or 24 ounces to the dozen, and it has become customary to refer to 22, 23, 24 or 26-ounce eggs when what is meant is the weight of a dozen. Eggs weighing up to 26 ounces to the dozen may sell at a premium over 24-ounce eggs, but extremely large eggs (30 ounces or more to the dozen) are not in great demand because of the greater danger of breakage when handled in ordinary containers, and the extra expense involved in handling them in special packages. These objections do not, of course, apply to a strictly local market where extra size many occasionally be made the basis of extra premiums. Eggs weighing less than 24 ounces to the dozen will have to be sold at a discount in most, if not all markets, during a large part of the year.

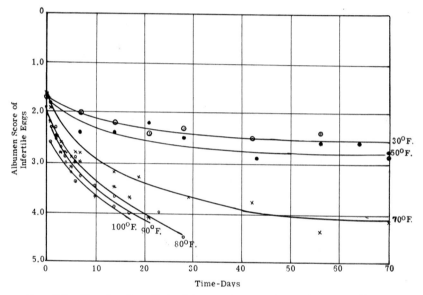

Fig. 137.—Showing the effect of temperature on change in egg quality as measured by the albumen score. (*Courtesy of Missouri Agricultural Experiment Station.*)

Workers at the Massachusetts Station studied the relation between egg quality and price in retail stores in Springfield, Worcester and Boston. The most definite and significant relationship found was that prices were directly related to weight under all conditions. Weight was most important, both relatively and actually, in August, each additional ounce per dozen causing an increase of 4.5 cents a dozen in price. The corresponding figures for April and November were 2.4 cents and 3.2 cents, respectively.

Shape is not often of great importance, and in any event it is easily controlled by selection. It should be remembered, however, that short, round eggs do not make the best appearance in an ordinary case or carton, and that long eggs are much more likely to be broken during shipment than are eggs of normal shape.

Shell color is, in the main, a breed characteristic, though there is often wide variation among individual hens in a particular flock when all are of the same breed and variety. If white eggs are to sell at a good price in a competitive market, they must be chalk white. A few tinted or creamy eggs in a case of white ones will cause buyers to turn to other shipments that are more nearly uniform. With brown eggs there is more tolerance because of the natural variation in brown shell color, but it is nevertheless true that of two cases that are equal in other respects, the one that is most nearly uniform in shade of brown color will be likely to sell first. All of this simply means that uniformity of shell color gives the seller a price advantage. While there is no relation between shell color and interior quality, there is enough color preference in certain markets to warrant consideration by shippers. Thus New York City has long been known as a white-egg market. In the course of a year it receives many more brown eggs than white eggs, but there is a special demand for large white eggs of strictly top quality and this has meant worth-while premiums to many producers. Boston, on the other hand, has long been regarded as a brown-egg market.

Eggs with rough, thin, or uneven shells are always discriminated against, and should not be shipped to central markets. They should either be used at home or disposed of locally to customers who will appreciate the opportunity to get eggs of high interior quality at less than the regular market price. If the quantity of such eggs warrants, they may be broken out and sold as liquid eggs.

Stained or dirty eggs are unattractive in appearance and must always be sold at a discount. Furthermore, dirty eggs will spoil more quickly than clean eggs, and careless washing makes matters worse because it increases the chance of spoilage. For these reasons it becomes important to do everything possible to prevent the production of dirty eggs.

Studies at the Missouri Station have shown that the percentage of dirty eggs can be very materially reduced by following suitable management practices. When eggs were gathered only once daily, 31 per cent were either dirty or slightly dirty, but when gathered four times daily the percentage dropped to 15. During a six-months period 12.5 per cent of eggs laid in trapnests were soiled, while 29.4 per cent of those laid in open nests were dirty. In the Missouri tests White Leghorns gave more than twice as many dirty eggs on a percentage basis, as did all other breeds combined. Many more dirty eggs were found among those laid before nine o'clock than among those laid later in the day. Perhaps the most significant finding in these tests was that more than 99 per cent of all eggs were clean at the moment of laying and before they came in contact with the nest.

Uniformity helps to sell any product, and eggs are no exception to the rule. A case of eggs weighing 23 ounces to the dozen, if all eggs in it are alike, will be much easier to sell than a heavier case in which there is wide variation in size, shape and color. It nearly always pays to sort eggs before sale or shipment in order to secure reasonable uniformity within each package.

Candling Quality.—External appearance is not an accurate indication of what is to be found inside the shell, and it is therefore customary to make use of the practice known as candling in order to measure interior quality. Accurate candling can best be done in a darkened room with some arrangement for passing the light from a lamp or an electric light bulb through the eggs to the observer.

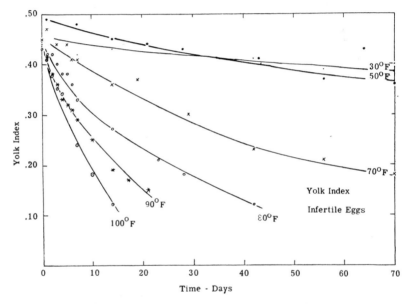

Fig. 138.—Showing the effect of temperature on change in egg quality as measured by the yolk index. (*Courtesy of Missouri Agricultural Experiment Station.*)

Many of the important differences in interior quality can then be plainly seen. Candling equipment may range from a simple home-made affair costing but a few cents, to an elaborate mechanical device, with which is combined an automatic grader (according to egg weight), costing several hundred dollars. Regardless of the type of equipment, each egg must be individually examined.

The characters used in measuring quality on the basis of candling appearance are shell, air cell, yolk, white and germ. Eggs that have thin, porous or cracked shells are easily detected. None but sound shells should be passed when candling eggs for shipment.

The air space or air cell is usually at the large end of the egg.

and can be plainly seen when the egg is candled. It develops between the two membranes that line the shell, and increases in size according to the amount of moisture evaporated from the egg. It should be fixed in position with no tendency to bubble or move about. A bubbly air cell is an indication of staleness and a weak shell membrane, or of rough handling, while an air cell that moves freely to any part of the egg is the result of a broken inner membrane.

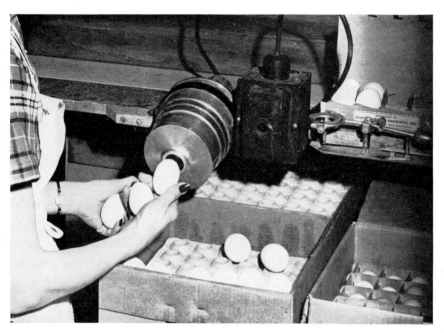

Fig. 139.—The so-called "black-lamp" candler does an excellent job of detecting certain low-quality eggs. (*Courtesy of Poultry Processing and Marketing.*)

When a strictly fresh egg is candled, the yolk cannot be seen except as a faint shadow. It should remain close to the center of the egg. In an egg of lower quality the yolk moves more freely and casts a darker shadow because it floats nearer to the shell. Much of this difference in appearance is really due to changes in the white, or albumen, rather than to changes in the yolk. In an egg of top quality the white is firm and clear, and so thick or viscous that the yolk does not move freely in it. Under usual holding conditions the egg-white gradually becomes thin, weak and watery in appearance so that the yolk is permitted to move about as the egg is turned. As a result of this condition, the yolk floats close to the shell where it casts a dark shadow and is therefore more plainly seen in candling.

High-grade eggs must not show any visible germ development. The greater the germ development the lower the quality. When it has reached the stage at which blood begins to show, the egg is considered unfit for food. This stage will be reached within forty-eight hours when fertile eggs are held at temperatures of 100° to 103° F. The best method of avoiding loss from this cause is to produce no fertile eggs except during the hatching season.

Although most eggs are of excellent interior quality when first laid, there are some faults that occasionally appear in eggs from flocks that are receiving the best of care in every way. Blood clots, bloody eggs, meat spots and body checks may be mentioned as examples. A blood clot is due to the rupture of a small blood-

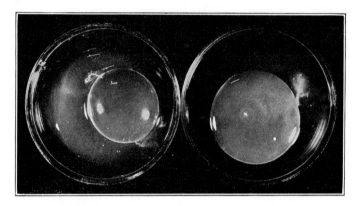

Fig. 140.—Heat is the principal cause of loss in egg quality. A firm yolk and a dense white (left) are quickly changed by heat. The egg shown at the right had been incubated for three days.

vessel while the yolk is being formed. The result is that a small clot of blood is enclosed within the egg, usually on the surface of the yolk. Less frequently the clot may be so large as to color most of the white and give it a pink appearance before the candle. It is then referred to as a bloody egg and is unfit for food. Small blood clots can easily be removed after the egg is opened, so that the egg may be used, but such eggs should not be marketed.

Blood and meat spots present a serious problem for the industry, as shown by examination of samples from twenty different flocks in seven midwestern states made by the Illinois Station in May, 1944. Of 3600 eggs from ten Leghorn flocks, 12.5 per cent contained blood spots and 12.8 contained meat spots. Among 3600 eggs from ten commercial flocks of Plymouth Rocks, New Hampshires, and Rhode Island Reds, 36.7 per cent contained blood spots, and an additional 6.1 per cent contained meat spots.

More recently, workers at the Minnesota Station made a detailed examination of nearly 3000 eggs laid by 36 crossbred hens (Table 44). They found, as had other workers, that most of the meat spots from white eggs were white or very light in color, whereas 70 per cent of those from brown eggs were intermediate or dark brown in color. They also observed that meat spots from brown eggs would fluoresce under near ultra-violet light in a manner

FIG. 141.—A walk-in cooler for holding eggs. (*Courtesy of Poultry Tribune.*)

similar to the shell of such eggs. Blood spots and degenerated blood do not possess this quality. Spots similar to meat spots in eggs were found in the oviducts of autopsied hens, chiefly in the uterus, but their exact origin has not been determined.

A "body check" is an egg in which the shell appears to have been cracked while in the uterus or shell gland, presumably before all of the shell material was formed. The break is then sealed by the deposition of additional shell material, so that after being laid it appears normal when given but casual inspection. The weak shell is easily detected by candling. Such eggs should not be shipped because of the greater likelihood of breakage.

TABLE 43.—SUMMARY OF UNITED STATES STANDARDS FOR QUALITY OF INDIVIDUAL SHELL EGGS*

Quality factor	U.S. AA quality	U.S. A quality	U.S. B quality	U.S. C quality
Shell	Clean, unbroken, practically normal	Clean, unbroken, practically normal	Clean to very slightly stained, unbroken, may be slightly abnormal	Clean to moderately stained, unbroken, may be abnormal
Air cell	$\frac{1}{8}$ inch or less in depth, practically regular	$\frac{3}{16}$ inch or less in depth, practically regular	$\frac{3}{8}$ inch or less in depth, may be free but not bubbly	May be over $\frac{3}{8}$ inch in depth, may be free or bubbly
White	Clear, firm	Clear, may be reasonably firm	Clear, may be slightly weak	Clear may be weak and watery; small blood clots or spots may be present*
Yolk	Well centered, outline slightly defined, free from defects	May be fairly well centered, outline may be fairly well defined, practically free from defects	May be off center, outline may be well defined, may be slightly enlarged and flattened, may show definite but not serious defects	May be off center, outline may be plainly visible, may be enlarged and flattened, may show clearly visible germ development but no blood, may show other serious defects

For eggs with dirty or broken shells, the standards of quality provide three additional qualities:

Dirty	Check	Leaker
Unbroken, may be dirty	Checked or cracked but not leaking	Broken so contents are leaking

*Effective December 1, 1946, Amended July 1, 1960

*If they are small (aggregating not more than $\frac{1}{8}$ inch in diameter)

	Meat Spots Per cent	Blood Spots Per cent	Clear Eggs Per cent
Incidence . .	38.1	9.3	52.6
Size of spots:			
Pinpoint . .	13.9	33.9	
Up to ⅛ inch .	76.9	45.2	
⅛ to ⅜ inch .	8.9	12.8	
Over ⅜ inch .	0.3	8.1	
Location of spots:			
Albumen . .	58.6		
Chalazæ . .	29.1	Nearly 100% on yolk	
Yolk . . .	12.3		
Color of spots:			
Dark . . .	17.7		
Intermediate .	26.8	All red	
Light . . .	55.5		

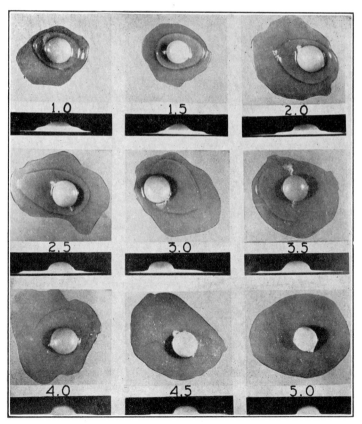

FIG. 142.—Successive stages in the "broken out" appearance of eggs. No. 1 is approximately equivalent to U. S. AA quality, No. 2 to U. S. A quality, No. 3 to U. S. B quality, and No. 4 to U. S. C quality. (*Courtesy of Institute of American Poultry Industries.*)

20

The official United States standards for quality of individual eggs with clean unbroken shells are summarized in Table 43. These have been in effect since December 1, 1946.

TABLE 45.—SUMMARY OF U.S. CONSUMER GRADES FOR SHELL EGGS.

U. S. consumer grade	At least 80 per cent must be:	Tolerance permitted	
		Per cent	Quality
Grade AA or Fresh Fancy Quality	AA Quality	15 to 20 Not over 5	A B, C or Check
Grade A	A Quality or better	15 to 20 Not over 5	B C or Check
Grade B	B Quality or better	10 to 20 Not over 10	C Dirty or Check
Grade C	C Quality or better	Not over 20	Dirty or Check

TABLE 46.—U.S. WEIGHT CLASSES FOR CONSUMER GRADES FOR SHELL EGGS.

Size or weight class	Minimum net weight per dozen	Minimum net weight per 30 dozen	Minimum weight for individual eggs at rate per dozen
	Ounces	Pounds	Ounces
Jumbo	30	56	29
Extra Large	27	$50\frac{1}{2}$	26
Large	24	45	23
Medium	21	$39\frac{1}{2}$	20
Small	18	34	17
Peewee	15	28	—

Detailed definitions of terms used in describing eggs which conform to the various standards and grades have been reprinted from the Federal Register, and may be obtained from the U. S. Department of Agriculture, Washington 25, D. C.

Quality of Opened Eggs.—There are some characteristics of eggs that cannot be observed until the eggs are opened. These include odor, flavor and color of yolk. Since eggs will very quickly absorb odors of various sorts, it is important that they be handled at all times in such a way as to prevent contact with any materials that might cause an undesirable odor or flavor. If eggs are laid in nests which have been recently treated with creosote, they may be tainted in flavor. Fumigation of fowls or poultry houses with such substances as nitrobenzene may also result in the production of strong-

TABLE 47.—GRADE WORKOUT OF EGGS BOUGHT DIRECTLY FROM FARMERS BY THREE ILLINOIS FIRMS COMPARED WITH THE GRADE WORKOUT OF EGGS FROM THE CHICAGO TERMINAL MARKET, 1947 AND 1948. ILLINOIS AG. EXP. STATION BULLETIN 619.

	A Large	A Medium	A Small	Total Grade A	B Large	Checks and Under-grades	B Medium	Loss	Total Under-grade
				(Per cent)					
Grading stations									
1947	66.5	15.4	2.9	84.8	8.6	6.1	—	.5	6.6
1948	62.0	15.9	2.9	80.8	12.9	5.7	—	.6	6.3
Chicago wholesale									
1947	38.2	7.4	.8	46.4	33.0	14.4	4.9	1.3	20.6
1948	38.5	6.8	.6	45.9	34.5	18.4	—	1.2	19.6

flavored eggs. Hens on range have been known to eat large numbers of army worms and, in consequence, lay eggs which are decidedly off in color and flavor. Undesirable flavors and odors are supposed to result from the feeding of such materials as onions, rape and garlic, and it has also been suggested that the feeding of grain which has recently been treated with formalin will likewise cause an undesirable odor in the eggs laid.

TABLE 48.—KINDS OF EGGS BOUGHT BY TYPICAL EGG-GRADING STATIONS IN ILLINOIS, OHIO AND UTAH, 1954. ILLINOIS AGR. EXP. STATION BULLETIN 619.

	Total Large	A Large	Medium and Small	Undergrades
			(Per cent)	
Annual:				
Illinois	64	51	28	8
Ohio	57	42	36	7
Utah	62	57	32	6
February:				
Illinois	76	63	17	7
Ohio	78	55	16	6
Utah	77	73	17	6
October:				
Illinois	39	30	53	8
Ohio	30	19	63	7
Utah	36	35	59	5

The color of yolk is almost entirely a matter of feeding, though it appears to be influenced somewhat by the rate of laying of an individual hen. The liberal use of xanthophyll-bearing feeds, such as fresh or dried green roughage and yellow corn, will result in the production of deep yellow yolks, whereas the feeding of rations in which these materials are restricted will cause the production of pale yolks. This has already been discussed in some detail in connection with feeding. Except as certain feeds supply both vitamin A and yellow pigment, and hence affect the product in both particulars, there is probably no correlation between yolk color and the nutritive value of eggs.

The differences, seen in candling, between an egg with a firm white and a well-centered, dimly-visible yolk, and an egg with a watery white and prominent yolk, are even more pronounced when the eggs are opened. The yolk of the first egg will appear well rounded, while that of the second will be flattened and spread out. The white of the first egg will stand up well, suggesting the original shape of the unopened egg, while that of the second will be watery in appearance and quite without shape. Attempts to influence this condition by feeding have, as a rule, been unsuccessful. Although it has been shown that holding conditions affect the rate of change in viscosity of the white, it appears that the individual hen is a more important factor. The most promising means of bringing about improvement in this respect are selection and breeding, using hens that possess the desired characteristics, and sons of such hens.

TABLE 49.—COSTS AND MARGINS FOR GRADED EGGS SOLD IN FOUR MAJOR MIDWESTERN CITIES, 1952–1954. ILLINOIS AGR. EXP. STA. BULLETIN 619.

	City A	City B	City C	City D
		(Cents per Dozen)		
1952				
Uncandled cost	42.8	41.4	46.2	40.9
Store cost	52.5	50.2	51.8	47.7
Average retail price	57.0	53.9	56.0	51.8
Retail margin	4.5	3.7	4.2	4.1
Processing cost	9.7	8.8	5.6	6.8
Retail margin (per cent of average retail price)	7.9	6.9	7.5	7.9
Processing cost (per cent of average retail price)	17.0	16.3	10.0	13.1
1953				
Uncandled cost	49.0	47.7	50.7	45.8
Store cost	57.1	56.0	57.4	55.4
Average retail price	61.2	59.4	61.3	58.8
Retail margin	4.1	3.4	3.9	3.4
Processing cost	8.1	8.3	6.7	9.6
Retail margin (per cent of average retail price)	6.7	5.7	6.4	5.8
Processing cost (per cent of average retail price)	13.2	14.0	10.9	16.3
1954				
Uncandled cost	35.3	34.5	37.2	36.3
Store cost	42.9	42.2	43.6	43.4
Average retail price	46.0	45.5	46.3	46.7
Retail margin	3.1	3.3	2.7	3.3
Processing cost	7.6	7.7	6.4	7.1
Retail margin (per cent of average retail price)	6.7	7.3	5.8	7.1
Processing cost (per cent of average retail price)	16.5	16.9	13.8	15.2

Other Measures of Quality.—Various attempts have been made to devise more exact measures of egg quality in order that careful scientific studies can be undertaken of the factors that influence quality. The yolk index is a measure of the standing-up quality of the yolk. It is obtained by dividing the height of the yolk by its average diameter. The measurements are made after the egg is broken out into a small plate. Average values for fresh eggs usually fall between 0.42 and 0.40. As the yolk becomes flattened the yolk index is lowered. When the value of the index is 0.25 or lower, the yolk is so weak that it is extremely difficult to handle it for measurement without breaking.

Deterioration in the eggs of individual hens has been measured by recording the percentage of thick and thin egg-white. As the yolk increased in weight due to absorption of water from the white, the percentage of thick white decreased. The rate of change in percentage of thick white, under uniform holding conditions, was a characteristic of individual hens, and there was considerable variation among hens in this respect. The concentration of water in thick white remained exactly equal to that in the associated thin white, regardless of losses to the yolk and to the atmosphere.

Albumen score has been used by workers at the Cornell Station, and is in many respects the simplest of all measures to apply. The scale of scores is illustrated in Figure 142.

Workers at the California Station have described a method for the study of egg-shell porosity, and have suggested a set of standards of comparison to be used with the method. The standards are shown in Figure 143. These workers found that the initial porosity in fresh eggs was normally low, that it was rather uniformly distributed over the egg surface, and that it increased with holding time, more rapidly at higher temperatures. In eggs held for twenty-five days at room temperature the porosity increased from about Score 4 or 5 to Score 8 or 9.

Producer Control of Egg Quality.—It has already been stated that eggs are highly perishable. A fact of equal significance is that no process has yet been found for improving an egg of poor quality. It is rather obvious, then, that in any successful marketing plan emphasis must be placed on those practices that will insure the production of high-quality eggs, and on handling methods that will preserve their original quality as long as possible. The importance of selection and breeding for desired egg characteristics, and of feeding and management looking toward high-quality eggs, have been discussed in previous chapters. Care and handling of eggs before they leave the farm is also important.

Care and Handling of Eggs on the Farm.—Except for those quality factors that are definitely controlled by inheritance and by feeding, the production of high-quality eggs is a matter of careful attention to a few details that do not require any elaborate buildings or equipment.

The first rule to remember is that fertile eggs should not be produced except for hatching purposes. As mentioned in connection with incubation, when a fertile egg is held at a temperature above 80° F., the germ begins to develop. In the early stages the development is referred to by market men as a "hatch spot," but in a very short time blood appears and thereafter the egg must be classed as inedible. A lower temperature at this stage will kill the tiny embryo and then decomposition will begin.

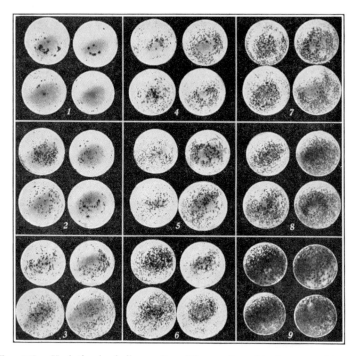

FIG. 143.—Variation in shell porosity. The numbers *1* to *9* represent increasing shell porosity as shown by the increasing number of small spots on the interior of the shells. Both halves of each shell are shown, with air-space ends to the left. (*Courtesy of California Agricultural Experiment Station.*)

Since dirty eggs must always be sold at a discount in a competitive market, more and more producers are routinely washing eggs before they leave the farm. Several types of mechanical egg washers are available. The smaller ones depend on swirling wash water containing a detergent-sanitizer and maintained at a temperature which is warmer than the eggs by as much as 30° or 35° F. Larger installations use a spray method of washing and then convey the eggs automatically to a drying unit from which they pass on to the candler and grader. Prompt drying after washing is important.

There are also available abrasive mechanical cleaners which do a very satisfactory job on white eggs. They may remove some of the color from brown eggs.

Even the best of eggs will reach the market in poor condition unless they are properly handled between the time they are laid and the time they leave the farm. A few simple practices, if rigidly carried out, will reduce this loss to a minimum. Eggs should be gathered from the nests at least twice a day at all seasons of the year, and in very hot weather they should be collected three or more times every day. This practice helps to prevent damage from heat and cold, reduces the proportion of cracked and broken eggs, and results in fewer dirty eggs. The marketing of high-quality eggs simply cannot be accomplished unless frequent gathering is made a part of the plan.

As soon as the eggs are gathered they should be taken to a cool place and kept there until sold. Warm eggs should be left in an open tray or basket until they have cooled. In this way they will lose heat much more quickly than if they are packed in egg cases as soon as gathered. Prompt cooling is an important step in preserving quality.

The final step that can be taken by the producer in the interest of quality eggs is frequent marketing. Although it will be subject to variation in individual cases because of the holding place available, the trouble and expense of delivery, and the demands of a particular market, a good rule is to market eggs twice a week. If no additional expense is involved, the more often eggs are delivered the better.

Workers at the California Station made a field survey to determine actual deterioration in quality of commercially produced eggs, and to measure the relative influence of various factors on this deterioration. They found that during the first week after laying, actual interior egg quality—as measured by albumen score, *i. e.*, height of the thick white—deteriorated more than did the estimate obtained by candling.

They further found that the greatest loss in quality of the white occurred during the first 24 hours after laying, and that as much as 73 per cent of the variance observed was accounted for by factors operating before the eggs left the ranch where they were produced. During summer, influences operating after the first 24 hours, but before the eggs left the ranch, were important. These changes could be largely controlled by proper cooling and frequent marketing.

Pullets consistently produced better eggs than did hens, as measured by albumen score. No effect of rations or of feeding practices could be found. The loss in height of thick white was about 1.5 mm. during the first 24 hours, and an additional 1 mm. during the remainder of the time on the ranch, regardless of season. Additional loss between ranch and market, including an overnight truck trip of 75 to 100 miles, averaged less than 0.5 mm.

These results serve to emphasize the extreme importance of farm and ranch practices in controlling egg quality.

PLATE IV

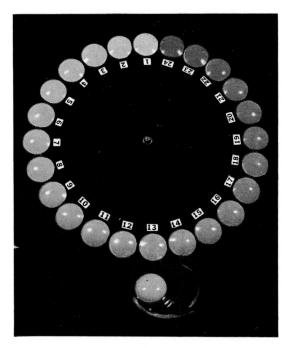

A

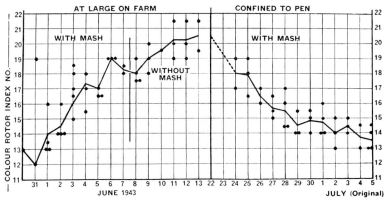

B

A, Heiman-Carver Yolk Color Rotor, a device for measuring yolk color by direct comparison.

B, Effect of feed on yolk color. Pullets which had been laying eggs with pale yolks (Rotor Nos. 12 to 14) when confined indoors, quickly produced darker yolks (Rotor Nos. 19 to 22) when turned out on range, especially when deprived of mash. When the pullets were returned to the original quarters and method of feeding, yolk color quickly became pale, as before. (*Courtesy of Ontario Department of Agriculture.*)

Dealer Control of Egg Quality.—In the usual marketing process the eggs from an individual farm lose their identity when sold to the first buyer, and are sold by him along with the product of many other farms. The second buyer, in turn, receives eggs from a number of buyers of the first type, so that the eggs of commerce are often far different in average quality from the eggs of a particular farm. This naturally complicates the problem of controlling quality. In the important commercial egg-farming sections this condition is largely avoided by direct shipment to jobbers, or by sale through coöperative organizations.

The Importance of Proper Equipment.—One of the major reasons for the poor quality of many of the eggs reaching the central markets has been the lack of proper facilities for handling eggs on the part of hucksters, local egg buyers and country storekeepers. Too many persons fail to realize that eggs are a perishable commodity. The obvious fact that each egg is enclosed within a shell is apparently taken to mean that any sort of handling methods will suffice. It never occurs to many people that eggs deteriorate rapidly in quality when held under ordinary room conditions. But this state of affairs is being changed both through education and through voluntary and compulsory installation of suitable equipment on the part of nearly all handlers of eggs from assembly points to retail stores.

How Deterioration Occurs.—Deterioration of eggs comes about in several ways, some of which have been mentioned briefly in connection with measures of egg quality. It will be profitable to inquire more fully into the specific processes by which deterioration is brought about.

Shrinkage.—Shrinkage is caused by the evaporation of moisture from within the egg. The amount of shrinkage is usually measured by the size of the air cell as seen in candling. The rapidity with which it progresses depends upon the temperature at which the egg is kept, the humidity of the surrounding air, the rate of ventilation and the porosity of the shell. In actual practice, temperature is the most important controlling factor. The vapor tension of water is about one-fifth as much at 30° F. as at 80° F., so that the lower the temperature of storage, at least down to near the freezing-point of eggs, the better will be the quality of the eggs at the end of the storage period. The favorable effect of low temperature is, of course, not due entirely to the reduced evaporation, but the fact remains that low temperatures constitute the most important practical means of controlling egg quality during the marketing process.

The increase in porosity of the shell which occurs in held eggs, a change that is more rapid at high than at low temperatures, is also an important factor in shrinkage. Since the increasing porosity leads to an increasing rate of evaporation, it is evident that eggs should be placed under conditions of low temperature at the earliest possible moment after being laid.

The overall importance of low temperatures in maintaining egg quality is readily shown by the fact that infertile eggs of AA quality will drop to C quality by the end of 3 days if held at 99° F. If held at 75° they drop to C quality in about 9 days, at 60° in about 25 days, and at 45° in 65 days. But if held at 37° they can be kept for 100 days before dropping to C quality.

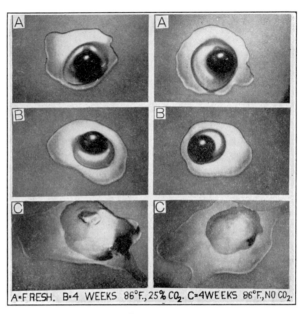

A=FRESH. B=4 WEEKS 86°F., 25% CO_2. C=4WEEKS 86°F, NO CO_2.

Fig. 144.—Showing the effect of carbon dioxide in preserving interior egg quality, *A*, the broken out appearance of fresh eggs; *B*, eggs held four weeks at 86° F., in an atmosphere of 25 per cent CO_2; *C*, eggs held four weeks at 86° F., but without added CO_2. (*Courtesy of P. F. Sharp.*)

Liquefaction.—Reference has been made to the increased visibility of yolk which results from a lowered viscosity of the white, permitting the yolk to float nearer to the shell and thus cast a darker shadow before the candle. The reasons for this liquefaction of the white, as it occurs under different sorts of conditions, are not yet fully explained, but some of the related facts are being brought to light. It has been shown, for example, that under the influence of osmotic pressure there is an actual passage of water from the white into the yolk. This may amount to as much as 2 grams per egg within a ten-day period with eggs held at 86° F. The vitelline membrane is compelled to stretch in order to make room for this incoming water, and is thereby weakened; and the contents of the yolk is made more fluid in character. These facts, together with the loss of mechanical support as a result of the disappearance of the thick white, explain the flattening of the yolk when such an egg is opened.

Shrinkage and liquefaction can be made to occur independently by imposing the right experimental conditions. If eggs are held in a desiccator over calcium chloride in an atmosphere maintained at 5 per cent carbon dioxide, water will be removed from the eggs at a rapid rate by the calcium chloride. But if eggs are stored in a desiccator over a 5 per cent solution of sodium hydroxide, a high humidity is maintained while carbon dioxide is rapidly removed from the air and, consequently, from the eggs. After twenty-six days all eggs subjected to the first treatment had air spaces from $\frac{1}{4}$ to $\frac{1}{2}$ inch in depth, showing extensive shrinkage, yet the interior quality as shown by white viscosity was excellent. Thick white made up 52 per cent of the total white. In the second lot there was very little shrinkage, but the eggs were badly liquefied, only 30 per cent of the white being thick white. In this case the watery eggs actually contained more water than did the eggs with viscous whites. In practice, on the other hand, it is usually true that the eggs with "watery" whites are those that have undergone considerable shrinkage, *i. e.*, an egg becomes more "watery" as it loses water by evaporation. The explanation is found in the fact that there is no necessary relation between these two processes. They simply happen to occur together. The loss of water which is so evident when a shrunken egg is candled is, after all, a relatively minor type of deterioration.

Gaseous Exchange.—Loss of carbon dioxide is not only something that can be made to occur under experimental conditions, but a process which occurs normally under usual holding conditions. Carbon dioxide is liberated from an infertile egg at a rate which decreases from the time the egg is laid, at first rapidly, and then more and more slowly over a period of at least one hundred days. Even after one hundred days at 10° C. (50° F.) there is still an appreciable output amounting to 0.1 to 0.2 mg. of carbon dioxide per egg per day.

Hydrogen-ion Concentration.—The hydrogen-ion concentration of fresh egg white, expressed as pH, has been variously reported as from 7.6 to 8.2, whereas that of eggs held for some time may be low enough to give a pH value of 9.5, especially if they have been held in a well-ventilated room at a fairly high temperature. This results directly from the loss of carbon dioxide, and it makes egg white under these conditions one of the most alkaline of natural biological fluids. Such a change means an increase in alkalinity (hydroxyl-ion concentration) of about 80 times. It is significant that this change takes place less rapidly at low temperatures, which is another reason for holding market eggs at low temperatures from the time they are laid until they are ready to be consumed.

If eggs are held at room temperature it takes approximately 10 to 12 per cent of carbon dioxide in the atmosphere to hold the pH of the egg white down to 7.6, while at temperatures near freezing 3 per cent of carbon dioxide will have the same effect. If sufficient carbon dioxide is introduced to hold the pH down to near that of the fresh egg, the thick white becomes turbid, but this turbidity quickly disappears with the escape of carbon dioxide after the eggs are removed from the storage room.

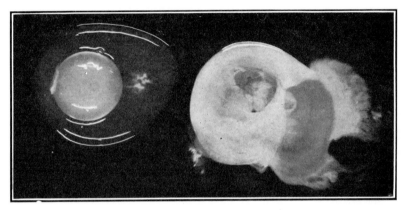

Fig. 145.—These fertile eggs were held four days at 100° F. The egg on the left was thermo-stabilized by dipping in hot water to prevent embryonic development and normal break-down of the thick white. (*Courtesy of Missouri Agricultural Experiment Station.*)

The point of interest seems to be that the carbon dioxide tends to reach an equilibrium between the concentration in the egg white and that in the air in which the eggs are kept. If newly-laid eggs are stored in a confined space, that is, in a room or other container that is full of eggs, and unventilated, the carbon dioxide concentration of the air surrounding them will soon be higher than that of normal outdoor air, and the equilibrium point will be reached at a pH value for the egg white that is intermediate between the 7.6 and 9.5 values previously mentioned. If more carbon dioxide is introduced into the surrounding air, some of it will be taken up by the egg white and the pH will fall. Hence it may be said that the pH of the white of the egg is one of the controllable factors in the storage of eggs. Considerable practical use has already been made of this knowledge through the introduction of carbon dioxide into egg-storage rooms.

Bacterial Decomposition.—That the contents of normal fresh eggs are, as a rule, sterile has been shown by a number of different investigators. As long as the shells of eggs are kept clean and dry there is little danger of bacterial invasion. The soiling of shells, especially with fecal matter, favors the entrance of bacteria, as does the presence of moisture. The increase in shell porosity with age has already been mentioned, and this undoubtedly makes conditions more favorable for bacterial infection. Once bacteria have gained an entrance, increased temperature will hasten decomposition.

Washing dirty eggs always increases the likelihood of bacterial spoilage, and most workers who have studied the problem are firm in their opinion that washing should be done only when eggs are going directly into consumption channels, and not into cold storage. A California study involving about 79,000 eggs furnishes a good illustration. The eggs were oil processed, stored for six months, and then broken for examination.

Unwashed clean eggs stored as controls showed only 0.2 per cent spoilage among 14,000 eggs. Unwashed slightly dirty eggs showed 0.4 per cent spoilage. The average spoilage for all washed eggs was 3.6 per cent. When storage eggs were held for ten days on the floor of the candling room before being broken for examination, washed eggs showed a 10.6 per cent loss, compared with 7.4 per cent for unwashed very dirty eggs, and only 0.6 per cent for unwashed clean eggs. Dry-cleaned eggs in the same test showed a spoilage of 1.0 per cent.

Much of the bacterial spoilage in storage eggs is of the sour egg type caused by *Pseudomonas* organisms. These bacteria not only produce some of the substances which are responsible for the sour odor, but they also produce a pigment which spreads through the white of the egg, and which has a greenish fluorescence when illuminated with ultraviolet light. It has been found by workers at the California station that ultraviolet light of the right wavelength and intensity will penetrate the shell of white eggs and cause those which are infected with *Pseudomonas* to fluoresce with a bright green glow. Commercial candlers using this long wave ultraviolet or "black" light are already available, and are being widely used in the industry.

Studies of the growth of bacteria in egg white have shown that, with the exception of a few organisms, bacteria will grow in white of pH 7.6 or slightly higher, but that egg white of pH 9.5 is germicidal. Since the white may change as much as 1 pH unit in twenty-four hours at room temperature, it is easy to understand why the majority of studies carried out with "reasonably fresh" eggs have shown egg white to have bactericidal properties.

Certain other microörganisms, including molds, are found in eggs at different times, and some of them develop at cold-storage temperatures. It appears probable also that some of these microorganisms may, under certain conditions, be involved in the breaking down or liquefaction of egg white during storage.

Preservation and Cold Storage.—The uneven seasonal production of eggs results in a surplus during the spring months and a scarcity during the fall and winter months. For many years cold storage was about the only means of bringing about a balance between the seasonal changes in production and the much more nearly uniform rate of consumption. Now that seasonal variations in egg production have been greatly reduced by improved breeding and management methods, fewer eggs have to be stored. Total holdings on August 1 are about one-third as great as they were twenty years ago.

Cold Storage.—Because of the seasonal nature of egg production, the normal movement of eggs into storage begins in March, is most active during April and May, and reaches a peak, in terms of total holdings, about August 1. Prior to 1920, storage holdings consisted almost entirely of shell eggs, but the percentage of frozen eggs has been increasing at a rather steady rate. During the ten years from 1941 to 1950, total holdings on August 1 were about evenly divided between shell and frozen eggs, (See Table 50) but the ratio now is about 20:80.

TABLE 50.—COLD STORAGE HOLDINGS OF EGGS ON AUGUST 1, BY 5-YEAR PERIODS, 1916-1960, AND PERCENTAGE OF TOTAL HOLDINGS IN FORM OF FROZEN EGGS.

	Shell eggs, cases*	Frozen eggs		Total, case equivalent*	Per cent frozen
		Pounds*	Case equivalent*		
1916–1920 . . .	6.8	15	0.4	7.2	6
1921–1925 . . .	9.5	34	1.0	10.5	10
1926–1930 . . .	10.3	84	2.3	12.6	18
1931–1935 . . .	8.5	112	3.0	11.5	26
1936–1940 . . .	7.5	143	3.8	11.1	34
1941–1945 . . .	7.8	295	7.9	15.7	50
1946–1950 . . .	4.9	221	5.9	10.8	55
1951–1955 . . .	2.0	176	4.6	6.6	70
1956–1960 . . .	1.1	162	4.2	5.3	80

* Millions

Eggs intended for storage should be carefully candled to remove low-quality eggs, cracked eggs and dirty eggs, and should then be packed in new cases made of odorless white wood, and in new odorless fillers. Eggs that are packed especially for storage purposes are quoted during the storage season as "storage packed" and usually bring slightly higher prices than do those packed according to less rigid specifications. When they are brought out of storage for sale during the fall or winter they are quoted as "refrigerator eggs." The temperature of an egg-storage room should be maintained at from 29° to 30° F., 30° F. being the temperature usually

TABLE 51.—STATES SHIPPING AS MUCH AS 500,000 POUNDS OF FROZEN EGGS TO ANY ONE OF THE INDICATED CITIES IN 1950. AS REPORTED BY THE U.S. DEPARTMENT OF AGRICULTURE.

	Boston	Chicago	Detroit	New York	Philadelphia	Pittsburgh
			(Thousands of Pounds)			
Illinois	1,124	534	3,194	2,344	1,895	783
Indiana	—	470	—	1,054	662	774
Iowa	3,980	5,858	—	3,100	1,264	—
Kansas	—	—	—	518	—	—
Minnesota	770	4,067	—	570	1,870	—
Missouri	1,074	1,533	—	3,013	2,178	1,487
Nebraska	1,348	765	594	3,270	721	—
North Dakota	—	698	—	—	—	—
Ohio	—	—	499	1,784	1,003	—
South Dakota	—	2,741	—	—	1,711	—
Tennessee	—	—	2,160	—	—	—
Wisconsin	—	1,897	—	519	—	—
All other	870	519	1,117	1,456	1,318	1,360
Total	9,166	19,082	7,564	17,628	12,622	4,404

preferred. No other products can be stored in the same rooms with eggs because of the danger of imparting undesirable flavors to the eggs.

Shell Protection.—Various methods of shell treatment designed to preserve interior quality have been tried from time to time. Some of these have been intended only for home use and others have been used commercially. Most "shell-protected" eggs are placed in cold storage if they are to be held for any length of time, the process of shell treatment being used to prevent evaporation rather than as a substitute for cold storage.

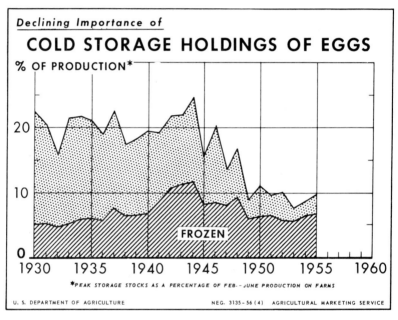

Fig. 146.—Cold storage holdings of eggs have declined in importance since the peak in 1944. (*U.S. Department of Agriculture.*)

Large quantities of eggs have been treated by dipping in lightweight mineral oils which are colorless, odorless, and tasteless. Evaporation is retarded, and much of the original carbon dioxide is retained inside the eggs so treated.

Spray oiling is done in packing plants by automatic machines installed for the purpose. It may easily be done on a small scale by the use of small cans from which the oil spray is released under pressure.

Tests at the Missouri Station have shown that quality can be stabilized effectively by dipping eggs for ten to fifteen minutes in water heated to 130° to 140° F. Eggs treated by this process retained their fresh broken-out appearance, and therefore their commercial grade, much longer than untreated eggs. Embryonic development in fertile eggs was completely arrested.

The only disadvantages found were that the whites from thermostabilized eggs required more time for whipping, and the volume of foam was reduced. The incidence of stuck yolks during storage was increased, especially when lower grade eggs were thermostabilized.

Frozen Eggs.—A method of preservation which has become of considerable importance during the last fifteen or twenty years is that of breaking eggs out of the shell and freezing them. When

Fig. 147.—Spray oiling is an effective means of retarding the loss of quality in shell eggs. (*Courtesy of Poultry Tribune.*)

21

frozen solid they can be held for a long time. The peak in holdings of frozen eggs was reached in August, 1944, when the U. S. Bureau of Agricultural Economics reported a total of 389 million pounds (equivalent to 10.4 million cases) in cold storage. This was more than double the quantity held on the corresponding date five years earlier.

Eggs to be frozen are first carefully candled so that all inedibles can be removed. The dirties, checks, and leakers are usually taken out for separate handling, because of the higher bacterial count of the product made from such eggs.

Fig. 148.—Eggs are individually broken by hand, using special equipment shown here. (*U.S. Department of Agriculture. Photograph by Forsythe.*)

The eggs are broken individually by hand, one or two to a cup, and inspected by sight and smell before being emptied into a clean container. If a spoiled egg is found, the entire equipment which the operator is using is washed and sterilized before further use.

The liquid eggs are mixed thoroughly by churning, after which they may be pumped through filters for removal of bits of shell, and part of the chalazæ and vitelline membranes. The liquid material is then packed in 30-pound tin cans and placed in the freezer at temperatures of 0° to −30° F. Air blast freezers are sometimes used to accomplish the job quickly without expansion of the egg material.

After freezing, the eggs may be held at temperatures of 0° F., or below, for several years without deterioration. They are shipped in frozen condition and are not thawed until they are to be used. Thawing is something of a problem. It is accomplished either by holding the cans in running or circulating cold water for 12 to 18

country merchant. An egg assembler or shipper may have a number of buying stations in his supply area, or he may operate truck routes and pick up eggs at the farm. The common practice today is to buy eggs according to grade so that a producer who consistently has high quality eggs to sell will be rewarded for the extra care which such an operation requires.

Direct Shipment to Dealers in Cities.—Producers who have sufficient volume of eggs to enable them to ship in case lots at reasonably frequent intervals often find this the most satisfactory outlet. Regular shipments of uniformly high quality will enable the flock owner to obtain a premium over the quoted price in a great many instances.

Fig. 150.—Eggs are often sold at retail in heavy paper bags. These are held in a refrigerator until time of sale. (*Courtesy of Pacific Poultryman.*)

FIG. 151.—This refrigerated egg vending machine is in operation 24 hours a day in San Jose, California. (*Courtesy of Poultry Tribune.*)

FIG. 152.—Roadside stands like this one near Champaign, Illinois, attract many customers. (*Courtesy of J. R. Hayes.*)

FIG. 153.—Clinton G. Park delivers eggs from his 7,500-hen flock in Warrensburg to a special outlet in Decatur, Illinois. (*J. C. Allen and Son Photo.*)

FIG. 154.—Insulated trucks help prevent loss of egg quality between farm and grading station. (*Courtesy of U.S. Egg and Poultry Magazine.*)

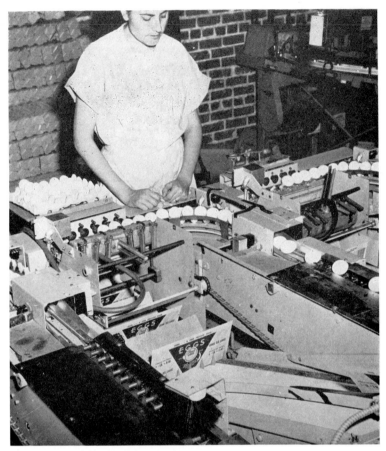

Fig. 155.—This equipment grades and cartons eggs at a rate of 7,200 eggs an hour. (*Courtesy of Poultry Tribune.*)

Fig. 156.—Weighing, shell-protecting and packaging are automatic in this plant at Modesto, California. (*Courtesy of Poultry Processing and Marketing.*)

(328)

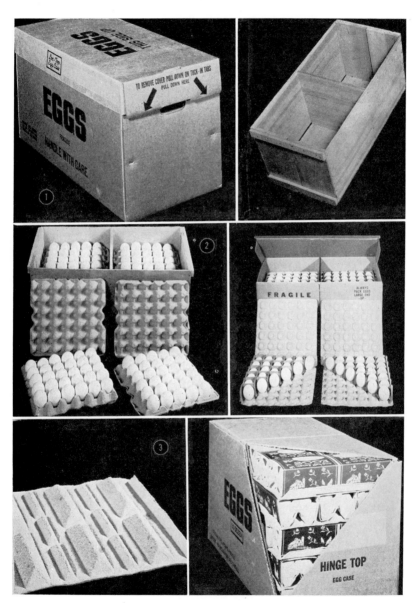

FIG. 157.—Examples of fiber and wood cases and filler flats in common use. Shown at the bottom, left, is a molded pulp flat designed to reduce breakage in cartoned eggs. (*Courtesy of Poultry Processing and Marketing.*)

Sale Through Coöperatives.—Coöperative associations that have been able to succeed have probably accomplished more in the way of real improvement of egg quality than have any other agencies. By establishing standard practices for their members to follow, by paying for all eggs on the basis of grade, and by careful sorting of their eggs so as to be able to sell a uniform product, some of these organizations have been able to develop enviable reputations on the important markets.

Auction Selling.—Another development that has been giving very satisfactory returns to producers is the auction market located close to the producing area. Buyers from the neighboring central markets come to the auction, which is held one or two days a week, and bid for the lots of eggs they want. Selling costs are low, and the keen competition that soon develops from the desire of buyers to obtain the output of certain flocks, results in very favorable prices to the producers of high-quality eggs. Such auctions have been operating successfully in New Jersey, Connecticut, Pennsylvania, Ohio and possibly in other states.

Just what method of marketing will prove to be most important in the future it is impossible to state, but present trends would indicate that it will be some method that will insure to the careful producer of high-quality eggs an adequate return for his efforts, and that will at the same time protect the progressive egg buyer from the practical necessity of paying more for poor eggs than they are worth.

Chapter 13

Marketing Poultry

Most of the poultry marketed in this country formerly came from farm flocks—essentially as a by-product of egg production. With the increase in commercial broiler growing and in turkey production this is no longer true.

Commercial broiler production has developed most extensively in the southern and eastern states, and many millions of pounds of processed broilers are trucked long distances to market. Georgia, Arkansas and Alabama, the three leading states in broiler production in 1959, have only 5 per cent of the population, but produced 36 per cent of the commercial broilers.

Until a few years ago, over 40 per cent of total shipments of dressed poultry to the four principal markets, New York, Chicago, Philadelphia and Boston, were received during the three months of October, November and December. Today, the slaughter of young chickens—about 75 per cent of total poultry slaughter—is fairly well distributed throughout the year, rising to 10 per cent of annual slaughter in July, August, September and October, and falling to about 7 per cent in January, February and March.

Other forms of poultry show a distinctly seasonal marketing pattern. About 75 per cent of all turkeys are slaughtered during the four months of September to December, and 90 per cent of all geese during November and December. The season for duck slaughter is concentrated between May and September, while the bulk of mature poultry from farms is slaughtered from August through December.

Poultry slaughtered under the U. S. Department of Agriculture inspection service in 1959 totaled nearly five billion pounds on a ready-to-cook basis, as follows:

Million Pounds

Young chickens, mostly broilers	3,431
Mature chickens	393
All turkeys	883
Other poultry	44

Market Classes and Grades of Poultry.—The U. S. Department of Agriculture has set up specifications for classes and grades of live poultry, dressed poultry, and ready-to-cook poultry. The following classes of chickens are specified:

Broiler or Fryer. — A broiler or fryer is a young chicken (usually under 16 weeks of age), of either sex, that is tender-meated with soft, pliable, smooth-textured skin and flexible breastbone cartilage.

Roaster. — A roaster is a young chicken (usually under 8 months of age), of either sex, that is tender-meated, with soft, pliable, smooth-textured skin and breastbone cartilage that is somewhat less flexible than that of a broiler or fryer.

TABLE 52.—SUMMARY OF STANDARDS OF QUALITY FOR LIVE POULTRY ON AN
INDIVIDUAL BIRD BASIS

(Minimum Requirements and Maximum Defects Permitted)

Factor	A or No. 1 quality	B or No. 2 quality	C or No. 3 quality
Health and vigor	Alert, bright eyes, healthy, vigorous	Good health and vigor	Lacking in vigor
Feathering	Well covered with feathers showing luster or sheen. Slight scattering of pin feathers.	Fairly well covered with feathers. Moderate number of pin feathers.	Complete lack of plumage feathers on back. Large number of pin feathers.
Conformation: Breast bone	Normal Slight curve, $\frac{1}{8}''$ dent (chickens), $\frac{1}{4}''$ dent (turkeys)	Practically normal Slightly crooked	Abnormal Crooked
Back	Normal (except slight curve)	Moderately crooked	Crooked or hunched back
Legs and Wings	Normal	Slightly misshapen	Misshapen
Fleshing	Well fleshed, moderately broad and long breast	Fairly well fleshed	Poorly developed, narrow breast, thin covering of flesh.
Fat covering	Well covered, some fat under skin over entire carcass. Chicken fryers and turkey fryers and young toms only moderate covering. No excess abdominal fat.	Enough fat on breast and legs to prevent a distinct appearance of flesh thru skin. Hens or fowl may have excessive abdominal fat.	Lacking in fat covering on back and thighs, small amount in feather tracks
Defects: Tears and broken bones	Slight Free	Moderate Free	Serious Free
Bruises, scratches and callouses	Slight skin bruises, scratches and callouses.	Moderate (except only slight flesh bruises)	Unlimited to extent no part unfit for food.
Shanks	Slightly scaly	Moderately scaly	Seriously scaly

Standards effective March 1, 1955

Capon. — A capon is an unsexed male chicken (usually under 10 months of age) that is tender-meated with soft, pliable, smooth-textured skin.

Stag. — A stag is a male chicken (usually under 10 months of age) with coarse skin, somewhat toughened and darkened flesh, and considerable hardening of the breastbone cartilage. Stags show a condition of fleshing and a degree of maturity intermediate between that of a roaster and a cock or old rooster.

Hen or Stewing Chicken or Fowl.—A hen or stewing chicken or fowl is a mature female chicken (usually more than 10 months old) with meat less tender than that of a roaster, and non-flexible breastbone.

Cock or Old Rooster.—A cock or old rooster is a mature male chicken with coarse skin, toughened and darkened meat, and hardened breastbone.

Standards of quality for live poultry on an individual bird basis are summarized in Table 52, and those for individual carcasses of dressed and ready-to-cook chickens in Table 53. Detailed specifications for the various grades are based on these standards of quality, and copies may be obtained from the U. S. Department of Agriculture, Washington 25, D. C.

FIG. 158.—The wax method of plucking gives a clean, smooth appearance to the finished carcass. It is now seldom used except for ducks and geese. (*Courtesy of Institute of American Poultry Industries.*)

Marketing Processed Poultry.—Ready-to-cook poultry is available for purchase in supermarkets throughout the country, but only because there has been developed a highly commercialized operation for killing, dressing, eviscerating, cutting up and packaging chickens and transporting them over long distances. Poultry processing is no longer a farm operation but a highly specialized business. Furthermore, because of the speed and efficiency with which the various operations are carried out, most of this poultry reaches the market fresh chilled. Less than 10 per cent is frozen. Turkeys are still marketed on a highly seasonal basis and about 80 per cent of the crop has to be frozen for future consumption. The corresponding figure for ducks and geese is 40 per cent.

As of January 1, 1958, the number of commercial slaughter plants in the country—meaning those which slaughtered at least 30,000 pounds of poultry a week, live weight basis, was 594. Average

TABLE 53.—SUMMARY OF SPECIFICATIONS FOR STANDARDS OF QUALITY FOR INDIVIDUAL CARCASSES OF DRESSED AND READY-TO-COOK CHICKENS

(Minimum Requirements and Maximum Defects Permitted)

Factor	*A quality*		*B quality*		*C quality*	
Conformation:						
Breastbone	Normal		Practically normal		Abnormal	
	Slight curve, $\frac{1}{8}$″ dent		Dented, curved, slightly crooked		Seriously crooked	⎫
Back	Normal (except slight curve)		Moderately crooked		Seriously crooked	⎬ If fairly well fleshed
Legs and Wings	Normal		Moderately misshapen		Misshapen	⎭
Fleshing:	Well fleshed, moderately long and broad breast		Fairly well fleshed on breast and legs		Poorly fleshed	
Breastbone	Not prominent		Not prominent		May be prominent	
Fat covering	Well covered—some fat under skin over entire carcass		Sufficient fat on breast and legs to prevent a distinct appearance of flesh through skin		Lacking in fat covering over all parts of carcass	
	Broilers or fryers only moderate covering					
Pinfeathers:	Breast and legs	Elsewhere	Breast and legs	Elsewhere		
Dressed						
Pins and hair	Pract. free	Pract. free	Relatively few	Sl. scattering	Numerous	
Ready-to-cook						
Non protruding pins	Pract. free		Few scattered		Scattering	
Protruding pins and hair	Free		Free		Free	

Cuts and Tears:[1]	Free	1½"	No limit
Missing skin[2]	None	3 areas totaling not more than ¾ inch; 1½"; 3" Tail to hip bones width of feather tract	No limit
Disjointed bones	1	2	No limit
Broken bones	None (except one non-protruding wing bone if fryer)	1 Non-protruding	No limit
Missing parts	Wing tips	Wing tips and if ready-to-cook 2nd wing joint and tail	Wing tips and if ready-to-cook wings and tail
Discolorations:[3]			
Flesh bruises	0"	½"	No limit[4]
Skin bruises	½"	½"	No limit[4]
All discolorations	1"	1½"	No limit[4]
Freezer burn	Few small (⅛" diameter) pockmarks	Moderate-dried areas not in excess of ½" in diameter	Numerous pockmarks and large dried areas

The quality designations specified herein are not applicable to birds possessing any of the following conditions: dirty or bloody head or carcass, dirty feet or vent, fan feathers or neck feathers or garter feathers, or feed in the crop.

[1] Total aggregate length of all cuts and tears including incision for removal of the crop or its contents.
[2] Total to be included in total permitted cuts and tears.
[3] Maximum diameter of aggregate areas of all flesh bruises, skin bruises and discolorations.
[4] No limit on size and number of areas of discoloration and flesh bruises if such areas do not render any part of the carcass unfit for food.

Standards effective March 1, 1955

weekly slaughter in these plants was 209,000 pounds. Large plants, slaughtering 300,000 pounds or more a week, made up 21 per cent of the plants and accounted for 51 per cent of the output. Twenty per cent of the large plants were located in the South Atlantic region and they accounted for 45 per cent of all slaughter in large plants.

Since most processed poultry is now Federally inspected under uniform regulations, processors have a better basis for comparing their operations with the average of the industry, and they are alert to all means of keeping quality up so as to avoid condemnations and undergrade poultry. In one recent study of 23,000 random-sampled broilers selected by graders in six different processing plants from over two million birds, defects causing undergrades showed up as:

	Per cent
Procurement bruises	15.0
Breast blisters	6.5
Poor fleshing	5.9
Poor bleeding and discolorations	4.5
Weight	3.7
Bloody wings	3.4

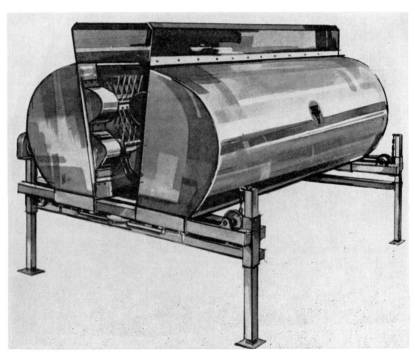

FIG. 159.—An efficient mechanical picking machine which makes use of four interacting picking reels. (*Courtesy of Gordon Johnson Company.*)

TABLE 54.—NUMBER AND DISTRIBUTION OF POULTRY SLAUGHTER PLANTS, AND WEEKLY SLAUGHTER IN 1957, AS REPORTED BY THE U.S. DEPARTMENT OF AGRICULTURE. REFERENCE, AMS-379, APRIL, 1960.

Region	Plants as of Jan. 1, 1958 (Number)				Weekly slaughter, 1957* (1,000 pounds)			
	Small	Medium	Large	Total	Small	Medium	Large	All
New England	8	10	8	26	472	2,099	4,512	7,083
Middle Atlantic	36	18	6	60	1,119	3,491	2,741	7,351
East North Central	43	32	5	80	2,402	5,188	1,963	9,553
West North Central	37	52	15	104	2,171	9,030	6,219	17,420
South Atlantic	22	49	51	122	1,217	10,615	28,993	40,825
East South Central	13	21	18	52	765	4,346	8,720	13,831
West South Central	19	49	10	78	1,024	9,083	4,425	14,532
Western	24	34	14	72	1,249	6,298	6,046	13,593
United States	202	265	127	594	10,419	50,150	63,619	124,188

*Average weekly slaughter, live weight, while in operation. Small plants 30–99 thousand pounds; medium 100–299; and large over 300.

22

For many years it was the rule that all poultry going into cold storage must be dry-picked, because it would keep much better than scalded poultry. Since about 1926, however, there has been more and more use of the method known as "slack-scalding" or "semi-scalding," in which the birds are bled and debrained as for dry-picking and are then mechanically drawn through a tank of

Fig. 160.—A new type of floating-action on-the-line picker.
(*Courtesy of Poultry Processing and Marketing.*)

Fig. 161.—A view in the Tyson processing plant in Springdale, Arkansas. Capacity is 40,00 broilers a day. (*Courtesy of Poultry Processing and Marketing.*)

moderately hot water, under carefully controlled conditions of time and temperature. The correct temperature seems to be within the narrow range of from 128° to 130° F., the time of scalding being varied according to the age and feathering of the birds being dressed. After scalding, the feathers are picked off, and the carcasses are dried before being frozen. Careful control of all conditions has made it possible to secure by this method some of the advantages of scalding without its serious disadvantages.

FIG. 162.—Ice chilling vats in a poultry processing plant.
(*Courtesy of Poultry Processing and Marketing.*)

TABLE 55.—RECEIPTS OF PROCESSED POULTRY AT FOUR MARKETS, NEW YORK, CHICAGO, PHILADELPHIA AND BOSTON, FROM THE FOUR LEADING STATES, AS A PER CENT OF TOTAL RECEIPTS, 1934, 1944, 1949 AND 1959. CALCULATED FROM DATA REPORTED BY THE U. S. DEPARTMENT OF AGRICULTURE.

	1934 Per cent		1944 Per cent		1949 Per cent		1959 Per cent
State	of total	State	of total	State	of total	State	of total
Iowa	19.1	Iowa	17.0	Delaware	19.6	Georgia	23.5
Minnesota	14.1	Minnesota	15.6	Iowa	10.5	Maine	13.4
Illinois	8.8	Delaware	7.6	Maryland	9.6	Delaware	11.6
Kansas	8.6	Illinois	7.5	Minnesota	9.2	Maryland	11.3
Sum	51.0	Sum	47.7	Sum	48.9	Sum	59.8

FIG. 163.—Mechanical chilling equipment in a modern poultry processing plant. (*Courtesy of Poultry Processing and Marketing.*)

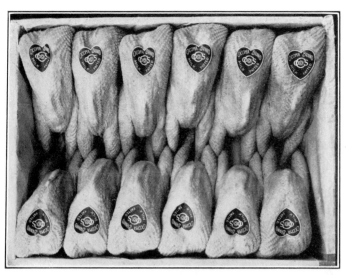

Fig. 164.—For many years dressed poultry was packed in lined wooden boxes, 12 birds to a box. Most poultry today is packed in fiber or wire-bound boxes. (*Courtesy of Institute of American Poultry Industries.*)

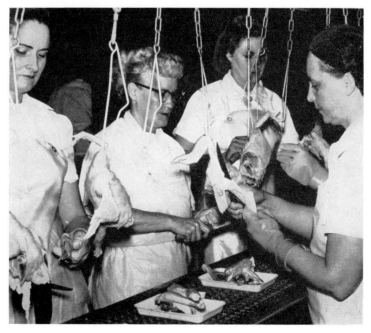

Fig. 165.—Cutting up of processed poultry is an "on-the-line" operation with each person performing a single specific task. (*Courtesy of Poultry Processing and Marketing.*)

Fig. 166.—Cut-up fryers packaged and prepared for freezing at −40° F. After freezing they are packed in the corrugated paper containers shown in the foreground and are ready for shipment. (*Courtesy of Poultry Processing and Marketing.*)

The wax method of plucking has been widely used in connection with slack scalding. The semi-scalded birds are first rough picked, then passed through a drying chamber and dipped automatically, usually twice, in hot wax. The next step is to pass the birds through a cooling chamber in which a cold water spray hardens the wax to a rubbery consistency so that it can be peeled off by hand. Hair and pin-feathers are removed by the wax, leaving a clean, smooth surface, so that singeing is unnecessary.

Fig. 167.—Frozen "turkey dinners" are being placed in cartons for shipment from this C. A. Swanson and Sons plant. (*Courtesy of Poultry Processing and Marketing.*)

With the development and improvement of mechanical picking machines for feather removal, the wax method has been discontinued except in plants processing ducks and geese. Dry picking is no longer used in commercial plants.

Prompt chilling of the dressed or ready-to-cook carcasses is very important, and this is accomplished by immersion in vats containing water and crushed ice. If the water is agitated by compressed air, the total required chilling time is under two hours. New types of chilling equipment which are mechanically operated have reduced chilling time in some plants to less than thirty minutes.

TABLE 56.—States Shipping as Much as Five Million Pounds of Processed Poultry (Not Including Turkeys) to Any One of the Indicated Cities, 1959. As Reported by the U.S. Department of Agriculture.

	Boston	Chicago	Detroit	Los Angeles	New York	Philadelphia	Pittsburgh	San Francisco
				(Millions of Pounds)				
Alabama	—	17	18	35	—	—	—	—
Arkansas	—	6	—	30	—	—	—	6
California	—	—	—	—	—	—	—	8
Connecticut	—	—	—	—	12	—	—	—
Delaware	9	—	—	—	40	11	—	—
Georgia	—	105	42	—	12	—	9	—
Illinois	—	5	—	—	—	—	—	—
Indiana	—	12	—	—	—	—	—	—
Kentucky	—	11	—	—	—	—	—	—
Maine	29	—	—	—	39	—	—	—
Maryland	—	—	—	—	50	6	—	—
Massachusetts	5	—	—	—	—	—	—	5
Mississippi	—	6	5	35	—	—	—	—
Missouri	—	6	—	—	—	—	—	—
New York	—	—	—	—	9	—	9	—
North Carolina	—	—	—	—	18	16	5	—
Ohio	—	—	—	—	—	—	8	—
Pennsylvania	—	—	—	—	13	—	6	—
Tennessee	—	17	15	—	—	—	6	—
Texas	—	—	—	5	—	—	—	—
All other	16	16	12	5	21	11	8	4
Total	59	201	92	108	214	44	45	23

TABLE 57.—STATES SHIPPING AS MUCH AS THREE MILLION POUNDS OF PROCESSED TURKEYS TO ANY ONE OF THE INDICATED CITIES, 1959. AS REPORTED BY THE U.S. DEPARTMENT OF AGRICULTURE.

	Boston	Chicago	Los Angeles	New York	Philadelphia	Pittsburgh	San Francisco
				(Millions of Pounds)			
California			43	9			8
Colorado				4			
Illinois		4			5		
Iowa	6	8		6	4		
Minnesota	4	25		9	5		
Missouri		3					
Nebraska				5			
Ohio						4	
Utah		6		10			
Virginia				4			
Wisconsin		8					
All other	12	10	—	11	10	7	—
Total	22	64	43	58	24	11	8

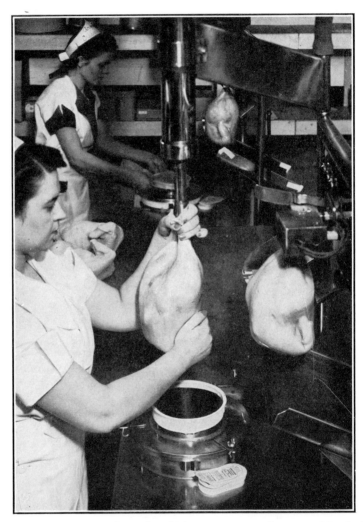

Fig. 168.—Carcasses of roasting chickens are commonly wrapped in plastic before freezing, for better preservation of quality. (*Courtesy of U. S. Egg and Poultry Magazine.*)

Fig. 169.—Insulated trucks are used to make prompt deliveries to retailers from this Columbia, S. C. poultry processing plant. (*Courtesy of Poultry Processing and Marketing.*)

Fig. 170.—Refrigerated truck-trailers are used for long-distance hauling of processed poultry. (*Courtesy of Poultry Processing and Marketing.*)

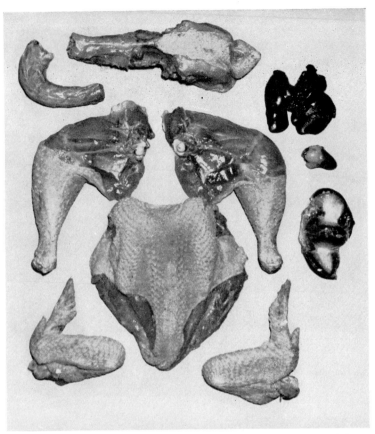

FIG. 171.—Cut up chicken parts ready for wrapping. (*Courtesy of Beacon Milling Company, a Division of Spencer Kellogg and Sons, Inc.*)

FIG. 172.—Chicken parts packaged for sale at retail.
(*Courtesy of Poultry Processing and Marketing.*)

(348)

Millions of pounds of broilers and fryers are prepared for market by being cut up and packaged, ready to cook. This has become possible with the widespread installation of refrigerated counters in retail stores and markets.

There are also many retail markets in which it is possible to buy half a chicken, one quarter of a turkey, or parts of a chicken such as breasts, legs, wings or giblets.

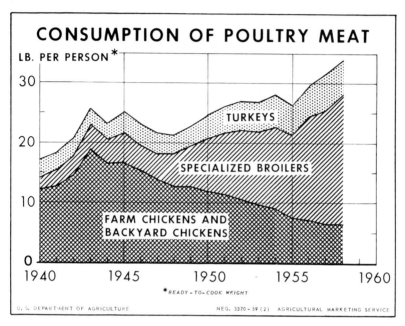

Fig. 173.—Annual consumption of poultry meat, 1940–1958. (*U. S. Department of Agriculture.*)

Killing, Dressing and Eviscerating Losses.—Weight losses represented by inedible parts of the chicken are important to both producer and processor, because they are the basis upon which maximum paying prices should be adjusted in relation to the market price of the final product. They are also related to feeding practices just prior to killing.

Killing and dressing losses consist of feathers and blood. The amount of blood lost is close to 4 per cent of the live weight. This means a tenth of a pound for a $2\frac{1}{2}$-pound broiler and up to a fourth of a pound for a large roaster. The weight loss represented by feathers is more variable, but will average about 5 per cent of the live weight. It is higher for females than for males, and lower for short-feathered chickens such as Cornish than for the more heavily feathered breeds.

Records for twenty lots of 300 chickens each in the 1951 Maine Broiler Production Test, when all were killed and dressed at the same time, showed an average killing loss of 8.8 per cent. The average live weight of these chickens at time of slaughter was 4.94 pounds (cockerels and pullets combined). The lowest shrink for any lot was 6.0 per cent, and the highest 12.4 per cent. For a plant dressing 10,000 head daily, this difference, at 35 cents a pound, represents an extra processing cost of about $1100 a day. The difference between 12.4 per cent and the average of 8.8 per cent, figured at the same price, is over $600 a day for such a plant. It is not surprising that dressing plant operators have definite preferences for certain types of poultry.

TABLE 58.—EXPECTED YIELD IN POUNDS OF DRESSED WEIGHT, EVISCERATED WEIGHT AND EDIBLE MEAT WEIGHT AS RELATED TO LIVE WEIGHT. (CALCULATED FROM DATA PUBLISHED BY THE U.S. DEPARTMENT OF AGRICULTURE AND OHIO STATE UNIVERSITY.)

| Average live weight (pounds) | From 100 pounds live weight | | | | | From 100 pounds dressed weight | |
| | Dressed weight | | Eviscerated (with giblets) | | Edible meat (with giblets) | Eviscerated (with giblets) | Edible meat (with giblets) |
	(a)	(b)	(a)	(b)	(a)	(a)	(a)
2.0	83.2	87.8	65.6	71.7	55.7	78.9	67.0
2.5	84.4	88.4	67.1	72.0	56.7	79.5	67.2
3.0	85.2	88.9	68.1	72.0	57.4	80.0	67.4
3.5	85.7	89.3	68.8	72.1	57.9	80.3	67.5
4.0	86.2	89.5	69.4	72.2	58.2	80.5	67.5
4.5	86.5	89.8	69.8	72.3	58.5	80.6	67.6
5.0	86.8	89.9*	70.1	72.3*	58.7	80.7	67.6
5.5	87.1	90.0*	70.4	72.4*	58.9	80.8	67.6
6.0	87.2	90.1*	70.6	72.4*	59.0	80.9	67.7

(a) McNally and Spicknall, 1949 (chilled weight basis) battery-raised R. I. Red males slaughtered in groups of 25 at bi-weekly intervals.
(b) Jaap, Renard and Buckingham, 1950 (fresh dressed weight basis) over 1600 males from 44 strains, all slaughtered at 12 weeks of age.
* These values are extrapolations beyond the 4.5-pound maximum live weight attained at 12 weeks of age by chickens used in the Ohio tests.

Killing and dressing losses are sometimes complicated by the amount of feed remaining in the crops but under ordinary conditions, when soft feed (as opposed to whole grain) is being fed, a fasting period of four hours prior to slaughter is sufficient. This will allow time for the crop to become empty, and for the intestinal contents to be reduced to a satisfactory point. About 60 per cent of the 24-hour fasting loss of intestinal contents occurs in the first three or four hours.

Eviscerating losses are influenced by the plumpness and degree of finish of the carcasses and, like dressing losses, they tend to be greater with small chickens than with large. Chickens which are grown to market weight on rations high enough in energy to produce a good covering of fat will show a lower eviscerating loss than will chickens which for any reason are somewhat thin or poorly finished.

Not too many reports have been published showing actual yields in terms of eviscerated weights or edible meat. Data from two tests, at Beltsville, Maryland, and Columbus, Ohio, are summarized in Table 58. More information of this sort is needed, especially as related to different degrees of finish.

Fig. 174.—For many years live poultry was shipped to the central markets in special railroad cars such as the one shown here, but by 1950 rail shipments had become negligible. (*Courtesy of Institute of American Poultry Industries.*)

Marketing Live Poultry.—The live-poultry industry is one of considerable magnitude, with New York City as the principal market outlet. Until recent years, only about 20 per cent of the receipts of live poultry in that market came from nearby points. The balance was largely in the form of car-lot shipments from the western producing sections. Freight shipments into New York increased from about 2000 cars a year in 1900-1905 to 12,000 cars in 1927, the highest year of record. From this high point, freight receipts have continued to decline. Only about 1000 cars were received in 1944.

Truck receipts, on the other hand, have steadily increased. Truck and express receipts made up more than 80 per cent of the total at New York in 1943 and 1944. By 1949, over 99 per cent of the live poultry arrived by truck.

It is estimated that about 80 per cent of the live poultry that enters the metropolitan area of New York City is consumed by Jewish people, and the growth of the industry has corresponded rather closely with the growth of the Jewish population. The live-poultry industry in this market is greatly influenced by Jewish customs and religion, and many of the peculiarities of the industry are traceable to them. For example, the orthodox Jewish church

TABLE 59.—HOLIDAYS THAT AFFECT THE DEMAND FOR POULTRY

Holiday	Kinds of poultry particularly desired
New Year's Day	Turkeys, geese, fowls, capons
Purim	Fowls and hen turkeys
Pessach—First Days (Passover)	Heavy fowls, fat ducks, geese, turkeys
Pessach—Last Days (Last Passover)	Prime quality of all kinds
Shevuoth (Feast of Weeks)	Prime quality of all kinds
Rosh Hashanah (Jewish New Year)	Fat fowls, turkeys, ducks, geese
Yom Kippur (Day of Atonement)	All prime stock
Succoth—First Days (Feast of Tabernacles)	Ducks, geese, fat fowls
Succoth—Last Days* (Feast of Tabernacles)	Prime quality of all kinds
Thanksgiving Day	Turkeys, geese, fowls, capons
Hanukka (Feast of Dedication)	Prime quality of all kinds
Christmas Day	Turkeys, geese, fowls, capons

*The last, or ninth, day is also called Simchas-Torah (Feast of Law).

TABLE 60.—DATES OF CERTAIN JEWISH HOLIDAYS, 1961–1970

Year	Purim	First day of Pessach (Passover)	First day of Pentecost (Shevuoth)	Rosh Hashanah (New Year)
1961	Mar. 2	Apr. 1	May 21	Sept. 11
1962	Mar. 20	Apr. 19	June 8	Sept. 29
1963	Mar. 10	Apr. 9	May 29	Sept. 19
1964	Feb. 27	Mar. 28	May 17	Sept. 7
1965	Mar. 18	Apr. 17	June 6	Sept. 27
1966	Mar. 6	Apr. 5	May 25	Sept. 15
1967	Mar. 26	Apr. 25	June 14	Oct. 5
1968	Mar. 14	Apr. 13	June 2	Sept. 23
1969	Mar. 4	Apr. 3	May 23	Sept. 13
1970	Mar. 22	Apr. 21	June 10	Oct. 1

Year	Yom Kippur (Day of Atonement)	First day of Succoth (Feast of Tabernacles)	Simchas-Torah (Feast of Law)	Hanukka (Feast of Dedication)
1961	Sept. 20	Sept. 25	Oct. 3	Dec. 3
1962	Oct. 8	Oct. 13	Oct. 21	Dec. 22
1963	Sept. 28	Oct. 3	Oct. 11	Dec. 11
1964	Sept. 16	Sept. 21	Sept. 29	Nov. 30
1965	Oct. 6	Oct. 11	Oct. 19	Dec. 19
1966	Sept. 24	Sept. 29	Oct. 7	Dec. 8
1967	Oct. 14	Oct. 19	Oct. 27	Dec. 27
1968	Oct. 2	Oct. 7	Oct. 15	Dec. 16
1969	Sept. 22	Sept. 27	Oct. 5	Dec. 5
1970	Oct. 10	Oct. 15	Oct. 23	Dec. 23

Dates for other holidays and other years can be found in *The Centurial* by Rev. E. M. Myers, published by Bloch Publishing Company, New York.

(352)

TABLE 61.—STATES SHIPPING AS MUCH AS ONE MILLION POUNDS OF LIVE POULTRY TO ANY ONE OF THE INDICATED CITIES, 1959. AS REPORTED BY THE U.S. DEPARTMENT OF AGRICULTURE.

	Boston	Chicago	Detroit	New York*	Philadelphia	San Francisco
			(Thousands of Pounds)			
California	—	—	—		—	18,938
Connecticut	774	—	—		—	—
Delaware	—	—	—		1,802	—
Illinois	—	3,086	—		—	—
Indiana	—	6,389	3,989		—	—
Kentucky	—	1,146	—		—	—
Maine	1,457	—	—		—	—
Massachusetts	7,040	—	—		—	—
Michigan	—	2,876	4,811		—	—
New Hampshire	6,038	—	—		—	—
New Jersey	—	—	—		3,263	—
Ohio	—	—	1,155		—	—
Pennsylvania	—	—	—		3,627	—
Wisconsin	—	1,156	—		—	—
All other	45	68	249		480	—
Total	15,314	14,721	10,204	58,450*	9,172	18,938

*Not available by State of origin.

requires that poultry be kosher killed, that is, a deputy of the Jewish rabbi (shochet) must slaughter the bird.

The Jewish feast and fast days greatly influence the demand for live poultry. The principal Jewish holidays come during the early fall and the early spring months, and at these times the quantity of poultry consumed is much greater than usual.

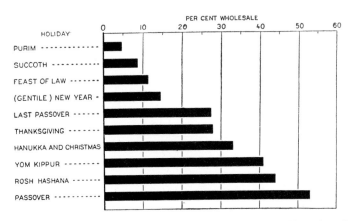

Fig. 175.—Showing the influence of holidays on the weekly sales of live poultry at wholesale in New York City. Increases in sales are here expressed as percentages of the average sales during the two weeks preceding a given holiday. (*After Buechel, 1929.*)

Fig. 176.—A special type of truck designed for hauling live poultry. Soft feed is pumped from the mixing tank to individual feed troughs. (*Courtesy of American Poultry Journal.*)

In the New York wholesale market, more poultry is sold on Wednesday than on any other day in the week, the order of importance of the other market days being Thursday, Tuesday, Friday and Monday. The day of greatest slaughter is Thursday in winter and Friday in summer. Fowls have long been the most important class of live poultry dealt in, making up 80 to 85 per cent of the total receipts. Development of the eastern broiler business in recent years has changed all this so that fowls now make up only about one-third of the total.

Shrinkage during shipment from farm to market represents a part of the marketing cost. It varies widely and is affected by such things as air temperature and humidity; age, weight and kind of chickens; the time chickens are on the road; and whether or not they have feed and water available during the trip to market. Records on 100 loads of poultry moving from eastern Connecticut to the New York live poultry market, a distance of about 150 miles, showed shrinks ranging from 8.5 per cent to as low as 1 per cent.

Other Connecticut tests with 14-week-old broilers showed shrinks of 5 to 7 per cent for chickens cooped without feed for 14 hours, compared with 7 to 8 per cent for similar chickens trucked 300 miles during the same length of time. Males showed consistently greater amounts of shrink than did females. Chickens which had been fed high-energy rations fared better than did those fed what had previously been considered standard mixtures. Shrinkage could be estimated roughly as 1 per cent for each of the first two hours plus $\frac{1}{2}$ per cent of the initial weight for each additional hour on the road.

Chapter 14

The Business of Poultry Keeping

PROFITS in poultry keeping depend mainly on a favorable relationship between the cost involved in producing poultry products and the income received for those products. Some of the items that enter into this relationship are wholly beyond the control of the individual producer, while others can be greatly modified by the adoption of specific practices and methods of management. Both sorts of factors (internal and external) need to be taken into consideration, but it is usually wise for the individual operator to concentrate his attention on those items that will reduce the cost per unit of product, as it is in this direction that he is likely to find the greatest opportunity for increasing his margin of profit.

The General Situation.—The poultry business, like nearly every other productive enterprise, passes through periods of relative prosperity and depression. There are times when the margin between costs and income is so wide that nearly all persons engaged in the business are making money. This sort of relationship may attract others to the industry so that production is soon increased to such an extent as to lower the prices received for the products and to narrow the margin of profit. There are other times when the major items of cost are so high in relation to the prices received for poultry and eggs that only the most efficient operators can make a profit.

TABLE 62.—COMPARISON OF FARM BUSINESS FACTORS ON 32 NEW YORK STATE POULTRY FARMS IN 1957 AND 1958. (DATA FROM CORNELL FARM ECONOMICS, No. 215.)

Production Factor	1957	1958
Average number of layers for the year	3,960	4,698
Eggs produced per layer	210	214
Man equivalent	2.0	2.0
Layers per man	1,990	2,314
Dozens of eggs sold per man	34,123	40,323
Pounds of feed per dozen eggs produced	6.1	5.8

Records on 32 New York State poultry farms for 1957 and 1958 illustrate the type of farm business adjustments which poultrymen are making in order to reduce egg production costs and remain

(356)

competitive. Like poultrymen in many other areas, they are increasing the size of their flocks and adopting practices which will increase average egg production per layer, thereby increasing the number of eggs sold per man employed in the enterprise.

The Effect of Location.—In addition to the economic advantage that may come from a favorable price relationship between cost and income items, as they vary with time, there is the type of economic advantage which results from being in a geographical location that is favorable to poultry and egg production. This may depend upon a freight differential in comparative feed or egg and poultry prices, or it may depend upon the effect of surplus

TABLE 63.—PRICES OF EGGS, CHICKENS AND POULTRY FEED, BY YEARS, 1950–1959, AS REPORTED BY THE U.S. DEPARTMENT OF AGRICULTURE.

Year	Eggs[1] (cents)	Chickens[2] (cents)	Poultry ration[3]	Egg-feed ratio[4]	Chicken-feed ratio[5]
1950	36.3	22.2	$3.59	10.3	6.2
1951	47.7	25.0	4.02	12.0	6.4
1952	41.6	22.1	4.21	10.0	5.4
1953	47.7	22.1	3.87	12.3	5.9
1954	36.6	16.8	3.86	9.4	4.7
1955	38.9	18.6	3.61	10.8	5.2
1956	38.7	15.9	3.54	10.9	4.8
1957	35.8	13.6	3.47	10.3	4.0
1958	38.3	13.9	3.41	11.2	4.1
1959	31.1	10.9	3.39	9.2	3.2

[1]Weighted average farm price per dozen
[2]Weighted average price per pound
[3]Average cost per 100 pounds
[4]Pounds of poultry ration one dozen eggs will buy
[5]Pounds of poultry ration one pound of chicken will buy

or deficit areas in lowering the price of feed or raising the price of poultry products with little relation to transportation costs. Thus in the more densely populated sections of the country the farm price of eggs and of chickens takes on some of the characteristics of a retail price, because many more sales are made direct from producer to consumer, or from producer to jobber. The cost of feed in deficit areas is not so likely, as is the price of eggs, to be above that in surplus areas by more than the difference due to transportation. The final result is a greater difference between cost and income for the poultryman located near the centers of population than exists for the producer who is several hundred miles away. The margin in seven different regions of the United States, calculated from production and price data reported by the U. S. Department of Agriculture, is shown in Table 64.

U.S. Farm Egg Prices 1958–1959

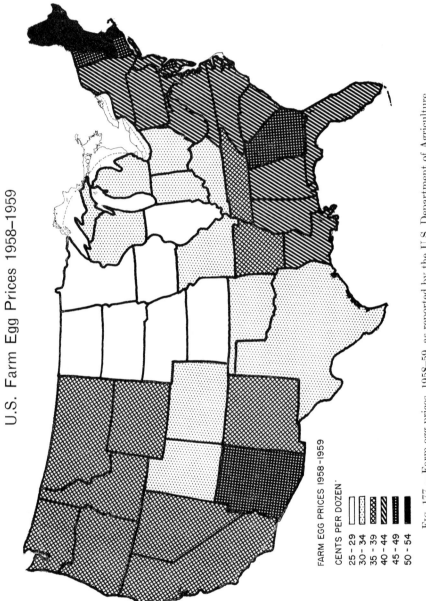

FARM EGG PRICES 1958-1959

CENTS PER DOZEN

25 - 29
30 - 34
35 - 39
40 - 44
45 - 49
50 - 54

FIG. 177.—Farm egg prices, 1958–59, as reported by the U.S. Department of Agriculture.

TABLE 64.—FARM PRICES OF EGGS AND FEED ARE INFLUENCED BY GEO-
GRAPHICAL LOCATION. EGG PRODUCTION ALSO VARIES FROM REGION TO REGION.
(PRICES OF FEED AND EGGS, AND PRODUCTION PER LAYER AS REPORTED BY
THE U.S. DEPARTMENT OF AGRICULTURE.)

Region	Eggs per layer	Price per dozen	Pounds of feed per layer*	Cost of ration per 100 lbs.	Value of eggs per layer	Cost of feed per layer	Differ- ence
			1958				
New England	210	55.6¢	91.0	$4.23	$9.72	$3.85	$5.87
Middle Atlantic	203	44.7	90.0	3.75	7.56	3.37	4.19
East North Central	205	35.0	91.3	3.24	5.98	2.92	3.06
West North Central	206	30.1	91.4	2.79	5.16	2.52	2.64
South Atlantic	193	47.7	88.6	4.01	7.67	3.55	4.12
South Central	176	39.9	86.2	3.44	5.85	2.96	2.89
Mountain	200	38.2	89.6	3.41	6.37	3.05	3.32
Pacific	224	39.2	93.0	3.94	7.32	3.66	3.06
United States	201	38.3¢	89.7	$3.41	$6.42	$3.06	$3.36
			1959				
New England	212	45.8¢	91.3	$4.20	$8.09	$3.83	$4.26
Middle Atlantic	207	36.4	90.6	3.68	6.28	3.33	2.95
East North Central	209	27.6	90.9	3.22	4.75	2.92	1.83
West North Central	208	23.5	90.7	2.83	4.07	2.57	1.50
South Atlantic	200	38.9	89.6	3.90	6.65	3.49	3.16
South Central	182	33.4	87.0	3.36	5.06	2.93	2.13
Mountain	205	32.8	90.3	3.43	5.60	3.09	2.51
Pacific	228	32.4	93.6	3.90	6.16	3.65	2.51
United States	206	31.1¢	90.4	$3.39	$5.34	$3.06	$2.28

*Calculated by the formula $F = 25 + 8W + E/7$, with W assumed to be $4\frac{1}{2}$ pounds.

POULTRY ON THE GENERAL FARM

Production of poultry and eggs has long been considered an essential part of a well-diversified system of farming. On many farms, particularly in the great Mississippi Valley area, the income from poultry has often furnished a large part of the living expenses of the family. But this picture is changing. As pointed out in the opening chapter, the production of poultry and eggs is being concentrated in fewer and fewer hands. In some parts of the country the once common farm flock has virtually disappeared.

According to preliminary reports of the 1959 Census of Agriculture, the number of farms reporting chickens on hand in the nine Northeastern states declined 41 per cent between 1954 and 1959. And in the eight North Central States for which data are available (Ohio, Indiana, Illinois, Wisconsin, Minnesota, Missouri and Kansas) the reduction was 35 per cent. At the same time, the number of chickens sold, including broilers, increased by 14 and 12 per cent, respectively, in the two areas, and the number of eggs sold increased by 5 per cent and 6 per cent. Similar changes have occurred in many other states.

Profit margins have narrowed so that only high-producing and well-managed flocks can yield a fair return, and such flocks must be large enough to make it worth while to find a suitable market outlet for high quality eggs. As more and more states have enacted fresh egg laws in the interest of consumers, the time-honored country store outlet for eggs has ceased to exist, and this has contributed to the decline in farm flock numbers.

TABLE 65.—COSTS OF PRODUCING EGGS IN MINNESOTA, 1959.
(MINNESOTA AGRICULTURAL EXTENSION SERVICE.)

	Per hen	Per dozen eggs (cents)
Operating Cost:		
Pullet cost	$2.03	11.3
Feed (6.1 lbs/dozen @ 2.5¢/lb.)	2.73	15.2
Miscellaneous costs	.25	1.4
Total	5.01	27.9
Less sales of cull hens	.45	2.5
Net operating cost	$4.56	25.4
Ownership Cost:		
Interest:		
Buildings (6 per cent)	.06	0.3
Equipment (6 per cent)	.09	0.5
Depreciation:		
Buildings (3 per cent)	.06	0.3
Equipment (10 per cent)	.30	1.6
Maintenance, insurance, taxes	.12	0.7
Total ownership	$ .63	3.4
Labor Cost:		
One hour/hen @ $1.00/hour	1.00	5.5
Total Cost	$6.19	34.3

Table 65 shows 1959 egg production costs in Minnesota for flocks of 300 to 500 hens averaging 216 eggs per hen. Capital investment was $5 a hen, and the death loss 15 per cent during the laying year.

Pullet replacement cost is shown in Table 65 as $2.03 per hen. This differs from the figure of $1.88 shown in Table 66 because of laying house mortality. With a 15 per cent death loss in both the growing and the laying flock, an operator would have to start 127 pullet chicks in order to house 108 pullets. This would give an average number of 100 pullets in the flock during the laying year.

TABLE 66.—COST OF RAISING REPLACEMENT PULLETS.
(MINNESOTA AGRICULTURAL EXTENSION SERVICE.)

Per pullet housed

Chick cost (115 pullet chicks for each 100 pullets housed @ 50¢) . . .	$ .62
Feed	.73
Miscellaneous	.13
Interest	.05
Depreciation (buildings and equipment) . .	.10
Labor (15 minutes per pullet @ $1.00/hour) .	.25
Total Cost	$1.88

COMMERCIAL EGG FARMING

Commercial egg production is a highly competitive business which involves a substantial investment of capital and a considerable element of risk. The demand for high quality eggs is growing, but the total demand is inelastic so that small changes in total egg production cause sharp declines in the prices which producers receive for eggs. Furthermore, there has been for several years a general downward trend in per capita consumption of eggs. Improved methods of breeding, feeding and management have resulted

FIG. 178.—A flock of 15,000 layers in one half of this 400′ × 52′ four-story house in Middlesex, New York, averaged 262 eggs each in twelve months beginning July 1, 1959. Mortality was 11 per cent, and feed conversion 4.15 pounds of feed for each dozen eggs.

in a spectacular increase in average egg production, as pointed out in the opening chapter. It is therefore inevitable that commercial production will continue to be concentrated in fewer hands, that operating margins will be narrow, and that only the most efficient operators will be able to survive.

During the years from 1915 to 1940, economic studies of poultry farming were concerned with enterprises in which the number of layers was usually under 1000, and the total capital investment was around \$10,000 or \$12,000. Today the average number of layers on commercial egg farms is around 4,000, with many individual farms carrying 15,000 to 20,000, and individual specialized farms running to more than 100,000 layers. Furthermore, this is true whether one looks at poultry farms in the northeast, on the Pacific coast, in the north central states or in the south.

Fig. 179.—In an effort to reduce depreciation charges to a minimum, some poultrymen have turned to aluminum for constructon of laying houses. This one is 500 feet long, 42 feet wide. (*Courtesy of Poultry Tribune.*)

Fig. 180.—Bulk tanks are an aid to keeping feed and labor costs low. Park Leghorn Farm, Warrensburg, Illinois. (*J. C. Allen and Son Photo.*)

FIG. 181.—Automatic feeding and watering equipment is important in helping a poultryman to care for more hens. (*Courtesy of Poultry Tribune.*)

FIG. 182.—A cart like this saves labor in gathering eggs on the Frank Miller ranch in Central California. (*Courtesy of Pacific Poultryman.*)

(363)

The Capital Investment.—A farm flock of 400 or 500 hens may be kept in a relatively low-cost building, but when ten times that number of layers is to be kept, a more expensive building is usually necessary. Furthermore, there must be much more equipment such as an efficient water system, bulk feed tanks, probably an automatic feeder, as well as egg washing and grading equipment, and the like. In Table 67 is shown the breakdown of investment items for a typical 4,000-hen egg farm in California, and in Table 68 a summary of actual investment as determined for 64 New York State egg farms in 1954-55.

TABLE 67.—INVESTMENT ITEMS FOR A TYPICAL 4,000-HEN EGG FARM IN CALIFORNIA. CALIFORNIA AGR. EXP. STATION CIRCULAR 483.

Item	Original cost, 1959	Yearly depre- ciation	Average value Total	Per hen
Land—2 to 5 acres	$ 4,000	$ —	$ 4,000	$1.00
5 Colony cage grow-lay houses, equipped	8,000	500	4,000	1.00
Brooder house, 20′ × 48′, equipped	2,000	100	1,000	.25
Egg room and service building, 20′ × 24′	1,600	80	800	.20
3 Bulk feed tanks of 6-ton capacity	1,200	60	600	.15
Water system, well, pump, etc.	1,000	50	500	.13
Feed cart, tools, misc. equipment	1,000	100	500	.13
Paving of drives and service area	500	—	500	.12
Subtotal—land, bldgs., equipment	$19,300	$ 890	$11,900	$2.98
Poultry stock	7,000	—	7,000	1.75
Feed and miscellaneous supplies	1,100	—	1,100	.27
Total poultry enterprise	$27,400	—	$20,000	$5.00
Dwelling and 0.5 acre of land	12,600	400	6,500	1.62
Total poultry farm	$40,000	$1,290	$26,500	$6.62

TABLE 68.—CAPITAL INVESTMENT IN THE LAYING ENTERPRISE, AND RELATED ITEMS, 64 NEW YORK POULTRY FARMS 1954–55. CORNELL AGR. EXP. STATION A. E. 1052.

Size of flock	Number of farms	Number of layers* Average	Median	Range
Under 3000	22	2380	2413	1506–2887
3000–5000	22	3944	3783	3201–4988
Over 5000	20	6982	6018	5208–17,436
All flocks	64	4356	3766	1506–17,436

Size of flock	Average capital in buildings Per farm	Per layer	Average capital in equipment Per farm	Per layer
Under 3000	$ 9,442	$4.00	$1,347	$.57
3000–5000	17,238	4.23	2,076	.53
Over 5000	29,505	4.32	3,596	.51
All flocks	$18.215	$4.18	$2,280	$.54

*Commercial egg production was the major enterprise on each of these farms, only market eggs were sold, and all flocks consisted of White Leghorns.

Costs and Returns.—Cost of production includes both cash and non-cash items, and although cash costs in the production of eggs are rather high when compared with the cash costs in some other enterprises, they make up only about two-thirds of the total cost. Feed purchased is by far the largest item in cash cost. Farm-grown feed represents about one-half cash cost and one-half non-cash cost. Among the non-cash costs would be included the labor of the operator and that of members of his family, together with interest and depreciation that may be charged against the business.

TABLE 69.—CALIFORNIA POULTRY MANAGEMENT STUDY AVERAGES FOR THE YEARS 1954, 1956 AND 1958. CALIFORNIA AGR. EXP. STA. CIRCULAR 483.

Item	*1954*	*1956*	*1958*
Number of flock records	222	199	203
Average number of hens per flock	3,002	3,742	4,899
Eggs laid per hen	223	231	233
Dozens sold per hen	18.8	19.6	19.4
Hen mortality, per cent	14	13	13
Hens culled, per cent	94	86	78
Feed cost per 100 pounds	$ 3.81	$ 3.72	$ 3.38
Pounds of feed per hen, including replacement pullets	129	128	117
Hours of labor per hen	1.2	1.0	0.8
Average price per dozen eggs	37.6¢	39.7¢	37.5¢
Net cost per dozen eggs	37.7¢	34.9¢	30.7¢
Management income per dozen	−0.1¢	4.8¢	6.8¢

Major Cost Items.—The largest item of cost in the production of eggs is feed. It will normally make up from 50 to 60 per cent of the total cost, though in exceptional cases it may run as low as 45 per cent or as high as 65 per cent. With increased specialization, as on poultry breeding farms, many extra costs are introduced, so that the relative importance of feed becomes less. During periods of extremely high, or very low feed prices, the normal relationship may be temporarily disturbed.

Labor is normally the second largest item of cost, but on some farms it may easily happen that in certain years the cost of depreciation and mortality of laying stock will amount to more than the cost of labor. Other cost items of importance are baby chicks or pullets for replacement, depreciation of buildings and equipment, interest charges, egg packages and express charges. The distribution of costs as recorded for some 200 California flocks in 1954, 1956 and 1958 is shown in Table 70.

Feed is also the principal item of cost in raising pullets for flock replacement. A representative distribution of costs in this part of the egg-farming business is shown in Table 71.

Sources of Income.—Just as feed constitutes the most important item of expense, so market eggs form the chief source of income on

TABLE 70.—EXPENSE AND INCOME ITEMS—CALIFORNIA POULTRY MANAGEMENT STUDY, FOR THE YEARS 1954, 1956 AND 1958. SAME FLOCKS AS TABLE 69.

Item	1954	1956	1958
Income per hen:			
Egg sales	$7.06	$7.76	$7.29
Poultry sales	.51	.50	.37
Miscellaneous income	.05	.05	.04
Increase in poultry inventory	.15	.18	.22
Total Income (A)	$7.77	$8.49	$7.92
Expenses per hen:			
Total feed cost	$4.96	$4.79	$3.99
Poultry stock bought	.50	.49	.51
Miscellaneous costs	.55	.44	.50
Depreciation	.30	.31	.32
Hired labor	.43	.33	.44
Total cash and depreciation (B)	$6.74	$6.36	$5.76
Value of operator's labor	.80	.92	.59
Interest on investment	.25	.26	.25
Total—all costs (C)	$7.79	$7.54	$6.60
Management income per hen (A–C)	−.02	$ .95	$1.32
Farm income per hen (A–B)	$1.03	$2.13	$2.16

TABLE 71.—SUMMARY OF COSTS OF RAISING PULLETS ON NEW YORK FARMS IN 1958 AND 1959. (COURTESY OF C. D. KEARL. DEPT. OF AGR. ECONOMICS, CORNELL UNIVERSITY.)

Costs and returns per 100 chicks started:	1958	1959
Number of farms	6	7
Total number of chicks started	28,956	71,729
Mortality, per cent	4	3
Costs:		
Chicks—cost per 100 started	$ 38.41	$ 35.25
Feed (2,342 lbs. in 1958; 1,945 lbs. in 1959)	91.03	75.00
Labor (8 hours in 1958; 4 hours in 1959)	12.77	6.55
Auto, truck, tractor	3.25	1.18
Poultry equipment	2.91	6.41
Litter	.47	.38
Interest	3.17	2.39
Fuel and electricity	3.97	2.40
Medicine and disinfectants	1.59	.84
Buildings	10.76	6.42
All other	1.82	1.15
Total cost	$170.15	$137.97
Returns:		
Pullets for laying	$183.91	$164.64
Other returns	4.62	8.43
Total Returns	$188.53	$173.07
Gain	$ 18.38	$ 35.10

commercial poultry farms. Hatching eggs, cull hens, and broilers sold for meat are of varying importance as sources of income on individual farms, but in the aggregate they are of only minor significance. This is quite in contrast to the situation on general farms, where the income from poultry meat may approach and occasionally exceed that from market eggs. In a poultry business that is being expanded, the increase in inventory or appreciation in the value of the flock may represent an appreciable percentage of the yearly receipts.

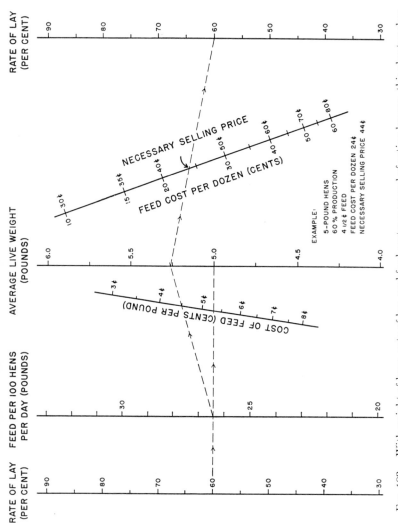

Fig. 183.—With weight of hens, rate of lay, and feed cost per pound of ration known, this chart makes it easy to find the amount of feed required per 100 hens per day, the feed cost of a dozen eggs, and the necessary selling price to provide a margin of 20 cents a dozen over feed cost. If actual feed consumption is known, use of the chart can begin at that point. In either case the live weight line is used as a "turning scale" when finding the feed cost per dozen.

Feed Cost of Egg Production.—Since market eggs furnish the chief source of income, and feed represents the main item of expense, it is evident that the relationship between these two items is of great importance to the poultryman. It is so important, in fact, that many producers are inclined to overlook all costs other than feed and to think of the difference between egg receipts and feed cost as "profit." It is more nearly accurate to speak of the "return above feed cost" or the "feed cost of egg production." A convenient way of arriving at this latter figure for any given flock at a particular time is shown in Figure 183. There is also included on the chart a scale which shows the necessary selling price to provide a margin of 20 cents a dozen above the cost of feed. This is the approximate total of all other costs, including labor, as shown in recent cost account studies.

Major Factors Influencing Profits.—Profits in egg production are influenced by many things, but the most important factors seem to be (1) size of business, (2) egg yield per hen and (3) efficiency in the use of labor. The third factor is directly related to the first in that small flocks can rarely be handled as efficiently as large ones. On the other hand, labor is not always efficiently utilized on large flocks.

Under certain conditions the rate of mortality and depreciation of flocks may outweigh everything else, and again the price received for market eggs, though not often under the control of the operator, may have much to do with the profit on the enterprise.

Size of Business.—Many poultry businesses are less profitable than they might be because they are too small. A small flock can never make a very large profit, nor can it ever cause the owner a very large loss. One who is trying to make a living from poultry must keep a rather large flock, and must assume the risk of a possible large loss in order to have the opportunity of making a reasonably large total net income. Economic studies of poultry farming have shown, without exception, that net income increases almost in direct proportion to the increase in size of flock. Within the limits of flock size that have come under careful study and observation, there has been little evidence of the application of the law of diminishing returns. It seems clear that if one intends to stay in the business of producing market eggs he should plan to maintain a flock that is larger than the average in most, if not all sections of the country.

Not many recent records are available from which to show the effect of flock size on costs and returns per hen, but the data in Table 72, based on 63 New York farms for 1954-55 indicate the relationships. Returns in that year were low because of low egg prices—the U. S. egg-feed ratio at the time was 9.4 as compared with an average of 11.7 for the 10-year period from 1944 to 1954— but this did not greatly affect the distribution of cost items. The

19 farms with flocks averaging 7,066 hens had an average total cost per layer of $7.80 as compared with $8.40 per layer for the 22 farms on which flock size averaged 2,380 hens.

Egg Yield.—Productive livestock has long been recognized as one of the essentials of good farming, and poultry farming is no exception to the rule. High egg yields nearly always mean high costs per hen, but they usually result in low costs per dozen eggs, and of course they mean high gross returns per hen when comparison is made with low-producing flocks. The net result is that egg yield is one of the most important factors in determining the profits to be realized from a poultry farm business.

TABLE 72.—EFFECT OF FLOCK SIZE ON COSTS AND RELATED ITEMS, 63 NEW YORK POULTRY FARMS, 1954–55. CORNELL AGR. EXP. STATION A. E. 1052.

Size of flock

Item	Under 3000	3000–5000	Over 5000	All flocks
Number of farms	22	22	19	63
Average number of layers	2,380	3,944	7,066	4,340
Per cent mortality	191	191	196	193
Eggs per layer	23	21	22	22
Pounds of feed per layer	105	106	107	106
Hours of labor per layer	1.3	1.1	1.0	1.1
Pounds of feed per dozen eggs	6.8	6.7	6.7	6.7
Dozens of eggs sold per farm	37,505	62,943	115,580	69,661
Dozens of eggs sold per hour of labor	12.1	14.5	16.4	14.6
Cost per layer:				
Feed	$4.15	$4.14	$4.04	$4.11
Labor	1.69	1.33	1.11	1.39
Depreciation	1.36	1.35	1.39	1.37
Buildings and equipment	.76	.78	.79	.78
Other	.44	.42	.47	.43
Return per hour of labor	−.10	.16	.41	.12

Data for 135 New York farms in 1946-47, given in Table 73, show the relation of egg yield to costs and returns at that time. Because of better breeding, feeding and management, most commercial egg flocks today are laying as well as the best flocks of a few years ago, and the net effect of a small increase in average egg yield is not so apparent as it was formerly, but the differences are still important. A 1959 egg cost study for San Diego County, California, provides a good example.

Among the 40 cooperators with an average of 7,177 layers per ranch and an average yield of 243 eggs per hen, there were 31 flocks with 4,000 or more hens. The top 9 flocks in this latter group had an average yield of 248 or more eggs per hen. Their net cost averaged 26.5 cents a dozen. At the low production end were 9 flocks with average yields of 237 eggs or less, and their average net

24

cost was 29.5 cents a dozen. The unweighted average egg production for the two groups was 254 and 230 eggs, respectively, enough of a spread to account for a difference of three cents a dozen in net cost. Since the average price received for market eggs that year was only 29.8 cents a dozen, the difference in egg production and in net cost was very important. All of these layers were housed in cages, the most common practice in southern California.

TABLE 73.—RELATION OF EGGS PER LAYER TO COSTS AND RETURNS PER DOZEN EGGS ON 135 FARMS IN NEW YORK STATE, 1946–47. (CORNELL AGR. EXP. STA. BULLETIN 864.)

	Light breeds			Heavy breeds		
	Low	Medium	High	Low	Medium	High
Number of farms	28	27	27	18	18	17
Average number of layers	1,252	1,022	1,006	604	609	629
Eggs per layer	152	178	203	137	188	218
Per cent mortality	13	17	15	21	13	15
Labor per dozen eggs (minutes)	9.3	8.1	7.2	6.8	7.8	9.0
Feed per dozen eggs (pounds)	8.3	7.2	6.8	9.6	7.6	6.7
	Cents	Cents	Cents	Cents	Cents	Cents
Cost per dozen eggs:						
Feed	34.8	29.9	28.3	39.8	31.3	27.3
Labor	9.2	8.9	7.7	11.9	8.4	9.1
Buildings and equipment	3.8	3.6	2.8	3.6	4.2	3.5
Depreciation	6.9	6.1	6.9	2.3	2.9	2.3
Other	2.8	2.9	2.6	4.2	3.6	3.5
Total	57.5	51.4	48.3	61.8	50.4	45.7
Returns per dozen eggs:						
Eggs	54.7	54.4	55.7	51.1	51.4	51.2
Other	0.2	0.4	0.3	0.6	0.6	0.5
Total	54.9	54.8	56.0	51.9	52.0	51.7
Profit per dozen eggs	−2.6	3.4	7.7	−10.1	1.6	6.0

One important reason why high egg yields are profitable is that the feed required for maintenance purposes is constant for hens of any given size, and bears no relation to the number of eggs laid. The amount of feed consumed for each dozen eggs produced is therefore much less in the case of high producing hens or flocks than it is for low producers. Thus a 5-pound hen laying 120 eggs will eat about 8 pounds of total feed for each dozen eggs; whereas a hen of the same size laying 180 eggs will eat 6 pounds of feed for each dozen; and one laying 240 eggs will eat but 5 pounds of feed for each dozen eggs. At four cents a pound for feed, the respective feed costs of a dozen eggs from each of these hens would be 32 cents, 24 cents, and 20 cents. Curves showing how feed per dozen eggs varies with egg production of $4\frac{1}{2}$- and $5\frac{1}{2}$-pound hens are presented in Figure 184.

Labor Efficiency.—Efficient use of labor is important on poultry farms because, as has already been stated, the number of hens kept has a great deal to do with the size of the farm income. For maximum labor efficiency it is necessary also to have good stock, because a high egg yield per hen makes possible the production of a large number of eggs per man. Eggs produced per hour of man labor, or per man employed per year, can be used as an index of labor efficiency.

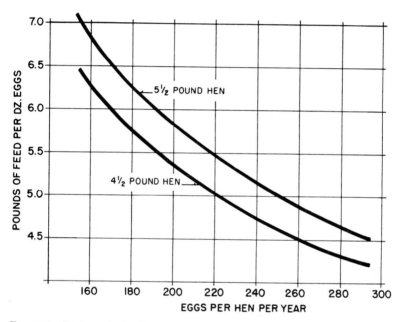

Fig. 184.—High-producing hens are more profitable than low producers because they require less total feed for each dozen eggs laid.

A common cause of low efficiency in the use of labor is the route of travel in doing the necessary daily chores connected with the poultry enterprise. In a study made in Oregon, it was found that the long-distance men on measured chore routes traveled seven to fourteen times as far as the short-distance men. Time saved in chore-route travel can be better expended in taking care of more hens or in finding additional ways to cut costs or increase market returns.

In a study of labor saving on Pennsylvania poultry farms it was found that installation of automatic watering systems saved nearly one-half hour of chore time daily per 1000 layers. Substantial savings in chore time and travel were effected by such changes as removing partitions and rearranging nests.

In a 1957 Illinois report the time required for hand feeding 1000 hens averaged 25 to 30 minutes a day, compared with 10 to 12 minutes a day when self-feeders were used, and 6 minutes a day with mechanical feeders.

Competition has forced poultrymen to find ways of caring for more layers per man, or selling more dozens of eggs per man, or both, in order to get the cost per dozen down low enough to leave a margin of profit with current low market egg prices. The data in Table 74 show the trends in San Diego County, California, from

TABLE 74.—AVERAGE RESULTS OF SAN DIEGO COUNTY POULTRY MANAGEMENT STUDIES, 1950 to 1959. (COURTESY OF ROBERT H. ADOLPH, FARM ADVISOR.)

Year	Average flock size	Eggs per hen	Management income per hen	Price received for eggs	Feed cost per 100 pounds	Hours of labor per hen	Net cost per dozen eggs
1950	2,183	217	$1.41	43.6¢	$3.65	1.4	35.6
1951	2,517	222	2.70	55.2	4.06	1.3	40.3
1952	3,034	231	.99	46.0	4.53	1.2	40.8
1953	3,801	228	2.48	51.5	4.06	1.1	36.3
1954	3,719	235	.53	36.8	3.95	1.0	34.1
1955	3,808	234	1.80	41.3	3.84	1.0	32.1
1956	4,600	236	1.21	38.4	3.63	.9	32.1
1957	5,685	235	1.05	36.3	3.45	.9	30.8
1958	6,426	239	1.73	37.0	3.31	.8	28.3
1959	7,177	243	.33	29.8	3.23	.7	28.1

1950 through 1959. There was a shift to larger flocks and a 12 per cent increase in average egg yield. Labor per hen was reduced by half during the 10-year period. The combination of these factors with lower feed costs enabled producers to cut their net cost per dozen by about 12 cents. In spite of this increased efficiency, the low price received for market eggs in 1959 reduced management income to a mere 33 cents a hen.

Large commercial egg operations are using bulk delivery of feed, automatic feeders to distribute feed to the laying pens, automatic egg washing and grading equipment, and in some cases mechanical belts for gathering eggs—all with the primary objective of saving labor and reducing the cost of each dozen eggs. Even on a well-equipped egg ranch, about half of all labor will be used in egg handling, including gathering, washing and grading. The total time required for these operations can not often be reduced below 30 minutes for each 30-dozen cases of eggs sold. Attempts to increase speed much beyond this may involve the risk of more breakage which can easily offset the saving in labor cost.

Mortality and Flock Depreciation.—One of the most serious problems confronting poultrymen in many sections of the country is the mortality among laying pullets, and to a less extent among

Fig. 185.—Bulk feed delivery saves labor and expense. Farm mixing of grain and concentrate is another means of keeping feed costs low. (*Courtesy of Illinois Farm Supply Company.*)

Fig. 186.—A motor-driven conveyor belt saves labor when cleaning out old litter. (*Courtesy of American Poultry Journal.*)

older hens. Methods of sanitation, as previously pointed out, have enabled flock owners to bring the mortality of young growing chickens reasonably well under control, but the problem of reducing or preventing excessive mortality of laying stock is not yet completely solved. It appears that the most promising method of attack is through breeding and selection for highly resistant strains, but until the vital significance of the problem is fully appreciated, progress is likely to be rather slow.

To the beginner in poultry keeping, the loss of a few fine pullets is little short of tragedy, but the more experienced operator accepts a certain mortality as a matter of course, and looks upon the picking up and disposal of dead hens merely as one of the chores. The practical result is that poultrymen have become accustomed to a mortality loss that would not be tolerated at all in any other livestock business. As long as there was a profit left to the individual operator little was said about the loss, and in the meantime the total cost to the industry has been tremendous.

Mortality among laying flocks not only causes a direct monetary loss amounting to the value of the birds that die, but it results in further indirect losses that may be even more costly in spite of the fact that they are less apparent. Houses, equipment and labor sufficient to care for 1200 hens will be used with decreasing efficiency as the death loss mounts during the year. This is partly obscured by the common practice of making calculations, such as average egg yield, on the basis of the average number of layers in the flock during the year, or on the hen-day basis. A flock that has lost 50 per cent of the original number by death may thus show an average yield well above 200 eggs. If all such calculations were made on the basis of the number of hens and pullets at the beginning of the laying year the picture would often be quite different.

The mortality among commercial flocks observed in some of the economic studies of poultry farming made during the last 45 years was 7 per cent in New Jersey in 1915-1916; 13 per cent in Oregon in 1926-1928; 17 per cent in New Hampshire in 1929-1930; 20 per cent in Utah in 1929–1931, 25 per cent in New York in 1940–1941, and 13 per cent in California in 1956–57–58.

Fortunately there has been substantial improvement in this respect in recent years, and many commercial farms now experience a death loss of no more than 10 per cent. If this is distributed uniformly through the year, the effect on the cost of producing eggs is small, especially with Leghorns or other light breeds with relatively small market value when sold for meat. The difference between the inevitable depreciation and total loss by death is not very great.

Even if the pullets all lived through the first twelve months in the laying house, they would be worth less after a year of production than at the beginning. As potential egg-producers they are worth more when about six months old and ready to lay than at any other time. The normal expectation is that they will continue to be worth less and less as they get older, until their egg-laying value is equal to their meat value. This does not take into account the possible breeding value of certain individuals, but is concerned only with their value as egg layers.

The difference between the value of a pullet at the beginning of the year, and the value of the same individual at the end of the year, is depreciation, and is one of the important costs in commercial egg production. If a pullet is worth $2.00 at the beginning of the year, and will bring but 50c after twelve months of laying,

Fig. 187.—Eggs roll gently out of this wire-floor nest onto a belt which serves two rows of nests back to back. Each nest is 12 × 18 inches. See Figure 188 for a view of the automatic egg gatherer. (*Photograph by Eleanor Gilman.*)

it has clearly cost the poultryman $1.50 just to own her for a year, without considering any expense for feed, labor, housing, interest, and the like. Whether one likes it or not, depreciation is just as much a part of the cost of producing eggs as it is a part of the cost of owning an automobile.

In cost accounting work, depreciation is usually determined by adding together the value of layers at the beginning inventory, the value of any pullets raised and later added to the laying flock, and the value of any pullets purchased, and subtracting from this total the sum of the ending inventory and the value of any layers sold or eaten. With equal death losses, depreciation is higher in Leghorn flocks than in flocks of heavy breeds because of the greater meat value of the latter. For the same reason, death losses are more serious, as measured in dollars, in flocks of heavy breeds.

Price of Market Eggs.—Although price is less completely under the control of the farm operator than the other factors that have been discussed, it is nevertheless true that the average price received for eggs is one of the most important factors in determining the labor income on a poultry farm. A high average price is the result of securing a large proportion of the yearly egg production during the high-price months, or of marketing eggs at premium prices or both. If one can obtain a premium of one cent a dozen on market eggs when selling 20 dozen eggs per layer annually, the difference in income will amount to $800 a year on a flock of 4,000 layers. Going after a price premium may be a very profitable way for a poultryman to spend part of his time.

TABLE 75.—DATA FOR 31 NEW YORK STATE POULTRY FARMS, 1959. DEPARTMENT OF AGR. ECONOMICS, CORNELL UNIVERSITY, A. E. EXT. 90.

Item	15 High Labor Income Farms	16 Low Labor Income Farms
Average farm inventory	$39,633	$41,289
Total receipts	37,596	34,053
Total expenses	31,537	33,643
Farm income	$ 6,032	$ 410
Interest on capital @ 5%	1,982	2,064
Labor income per farm	$ 4,050	$-1,654
Average number of layers	4,657	4,539
Eggs produced per layer	221	201
Layer mortality, per cent	11	13
Man equivalent	1.8	1.9
Dozens of eggs sold per man	44,764	38,765
Price received per dozen (cents)	37.1	34.4
Feed per dozen eggs produced (pounds)	4.8	5.6

Although several other factors were involved, the data for 31 New York poultry farms shown in Table 75 suggest that the price received for eggs was important in determining labor income. If the 73,653 dozens of eggs sold from each of the low-labor-income farms could have been sold at the price received by the high-labor-income group it would have meant an extra $1989 in case receipts, or enough to change the negative labor income of $1654 to a plus labor income of $335 per farm.

The Replacement Cycle.—On most large commercial egg farms today chicks to be grown out as replacement pullets are started two to five times a year instead of only once in the spring. This is important in order to be able to maintain a fairly uniform weekly or monthly egg production all through the year. It also simplifies the problem of labor distribution, and keeps brooding and rearing equipment, as well as laying houses, filled to near capacity most of the year.

It is more profitable to replace layers when they are 17 to 20 months of age than to keep the longer. Young birds lay at a higher rate and produce eggs of better shell quality than do older hens. To maintain a laying flock of 8,000 pullets, it will be necessary to start about 8,000 pullet chicks in batches of 2,000 four times a year. This will allow for normal mortality and some slight culling.

Fig. 188.—Eggs from three floors are gathered by conveyor belts moving at six feet a minute. Picture shows how eggs are picked up by the vertical conveyor and taken to the grader on the second floor. Coll's Poultry Farm, East Jaffrey, N.H. (*Photograph by Eleanor Gilman.*)

When the pullets are 2 to $2\frac{1}{2}$ months old they can be moved to a growing-laying house that has been emptied and cleaned. Here they will be kept for about 15 months until they are removed to make room for a new lot of pullets. Obviously they should be kept as long as they are profitable because income on such a farm or ranch can come only from egg sales. As each group of layers approaches 17 months of age, both their performance and the current market situation should be studied before deciding on the exact age at which to sell them. Since brooding and rearing are on a year-round basis, it is sometimes better to skip a hatch and carry a good flock of layers for an extra three months than to replace them arbitrarily. This is one way of keeping the cost of eggs low when conditions warrant.

The program suggested for a flock averaging 8,000 layers would require a brooder house and five growing-laying houses. This is to avoid mixing of two lots at any time or having chickens of more than one age in any one house. If any one lot is carried to a full 21 months of age it may be desirable to double the size of one hatch in anticipation of the replacement of two groups at one time. Under the old-style program of hatching once a year, no such adjustment was possible. In any event, the brooder house is normally in use for 8 to 10 months out of the year, and the five growing-laying houses are filled except at the normal recurring clean-up time.

An alternative procedure followed by many producers in some parts of the country is to buy started pullets from a dependable source instead of raising their own.

Poultry Farm Organization.—Perhaps the most significant, and at the same time the most encouraging fact growing out of the various analyses that have been made of poultry farm records is that whether the labor income is high or low depends almost exclusively on the operator himself. The possibilities seem to be limited only by the extent to which he will adopt profitable practices and a profitable farm organization.

Aside from the necessary physical qualifications, the operator of a specialized commercial egg enterprise should have more or less natural aptitude for attention to details. Permanent success in specialized poultry farming is, to a considerable degree, a matter of constant and sharp attention to a great many details, the neglect of any one of which may lead to serious losses. Men who do not like to bother with too much detail are not naturally well fitted for success in specialized poultry farming. Persistent attention and genuine interest in details are necessary qualifications for the poultry business.

The accumulation of a reserve fund for tiding over an occasional bad year is a prime essential of permanent success in any type of specialized farming. Every enterprise has a bad year occasionally, sometimes owing to circumstances beyond the operator's control. The large cash expenditures required for feed make it especially necessary for the specialized poultry farm to have a reserve fund.

From a dollars viewpoint, the requirements for a successful egg-farming business can be simply stated. They are about as follows:

1. Have productive stock. This means hens with the genetic makeup and the physical stamina necessary for high annual egg production. High production is essential if the feed cost of each dozen eggs is to be kept at a profitable level.

2. Keep enough hens—as many as one can care for. This is necessary in order to make possible a reasonably large gross income, and to be able to reduce the man labor requirement below one hour per layer per year.

3. Provide comfortable housing, so as to permit year-round production. This means protection from extremes of both heat and cold, along with the necessary safeguards to flock health.

4. Feed a well-balanced ration. A close corollary is found in doing everything possible to encourage maximum feed consumption.

5. Practice quantity buying of feed and other supplies so as to permit maximum savings in costs. Bulk delivery of feed is an example.

6. Find and maintain a market outlet which pays a premium price for high quality eggs.

BROILER PRODUCTION

The proportion of the total chicken meat supply furnished by commercial broilers has risen steadily from about 5 per cent in 1935 to nearly 50 per cent in 1951 and then to 84 per cent in 1959. During the last ten years of this period the trend in broiler prices has been downward. The average price received by producers in 1935–1939 was about 20 cents a pound, live weight. It rose to a high of 36 cents in 1948 and since then has declined almost steadily to 16.1 cents in 1959. This is in large part the result of year-round production and availability of fresh ready-to-cook broilers.

There are well-defined broiler-producing areas in Delmarva, North Georgia, Northwest Arkansas, Texas, Virginia, North Carolina, Alabama, Mississippi and in parts of New England, and similar if less extensive areas in several other states. Since nearly all commercial producers depend on hatcheries for their supply of chicks, and since they can change sources promptly if performance is not satisfactory, there are many hatcheries and breeding farms which specialize in the production and sales of broiler chicks.

Total placements of broiler-type chicks in 1959 were 1,844 million. Two-thirds of these went into the nine states of Delaware, Maryland, Virginia, North Carolina, Georgia, Alabama, Mississippi, Arkansas and Texas. New lots of broilers are started in large numbers every week in the year. The seasonal index of broiler chick placements for thirteen important broiler areas, based on the five years 1952 through 1956, dropped as low as 90 in only ten weeks, with the actual minimum at 84 during the first week in September, and reached a level of 110 in only ten weeks, with the maximum at 115 during the first week in March.

The Broiler Business.—Many broiler farms have lost money— sometimes because of disease, more often because of inefficient management, and at times simply because the market price of broilers

FIG. 189.—Inside view of a 48′ × 230′ broiler house in Mississippi.
(*Courtesy of Broiler Business.*)

FIG. 190.—Wooden blocks make it easy to adjust feed troughs to any desired
height in this broiler house. (*Courtesy of Broiler Business.*)

at the time of sale was too low in proportion to the cost of feed which had gone into their production. The total production of broilers is enormous, and the business is well established in many areas, but it is none the less true that only the more efficient operators are in a position to make substantial profits.

The broiler business requires a relatively large investment in short-term capital. From 40 to 50 per cent of the total capital may be invested in chicks, feed, fuel, labor and other cash costs. Furthermore, the amount of such capital increases rapidly as each lot of broilers approaches market age or weight. This is because feed represents about 60 per cent of the total cost of production. It

Fig. 191.—Automatic feeders save labor and reduce feed wastage, especially on broiler plants. A 40-foot house requires two loops to provide ample feeding capacity. (*Courtesy of U.S. Egg and Poultry Magazine.*)

takes about 40 tons of feed to raise a lot of 10,000 broilers to market weight. They may eat only three-fourths of a ton during the first week, but will require seven or eight tons during the final week, depending on the type of ration used, how well they have grown and the weight at which they are sold.

Efficiency of feed utilization in the production of broilers has been increasing steadily for a number of years, partly because of the selection and breeding of chickens capable of rapid growth, and partly because of improved rations. Better management, which has resulted in lower mortality, is also responsible for part of the improvement. The following data for selected years of the Maine Broiler Test are typical:

Year	Days required to reach 3.5 pounds	Pounds of feed for each pound of gain
1951	73	3.12
1954	67	2.66
1957	62	2.25
1960*	53	2.12

*First test only

The U. S. Department of Agriculture makes an annual report on the units of feed consumed by various classes of livestock and poultry. The reported figures show continued improvement in broiler feed utilization but, as yet, no general improvement in feed conversion by laying hens and pullets. Individual flock owners have, however, made substantial improvement in this respect.

TABLE 76.—FEED UNITS CONSUMED IN POULTRY AND EGG PRODUCTION FOR SELECTED YEARS AS REPORTED BY THE U.S. DEPT. OF AGRICULTURE.

Year	Hens and pullets (Pounds of feed per 100 eggs)	Broilers (Pounds of feed per 100 pounds of meat)
1933	60	528
1938	59	465
1943	64	451
1948	60	410
1953	58	351
1958	60	302

Since feed consumption increases with a decrease in environmental temperature, broiler growers are faced with the very practical question of whether it is cheaper to provide some artificial heat in order to keep feed consumption at a minimum, than to keep the broilers in unheated houses where they are certain to consume more feed. Workers at the University of Connecticut undertook to find an answer to this question. They found that with 2-pound broilers, as the temperature dropped below 75° F., feed consumption increased by 0.6 pound of feed per 1000 broilers per day for each drop of one degree in temperature. Simultaneously, feed conversion became less efficient at the rate of 0.1 pound of feed per pound of grain, with each decrease of one degree in environmental temperature. The nomogram shown in Figure 192 was constructed from their data. It shows for the specified conditions the fuel requirement in gallons per 1000 broilers per day to maintain any desired difference in temperature between inside and outside air for three different ventilation rates expressed as cubic feet of air per minute per bird.

Rate of Feed Conversion.—Since feed is the largest single item of cost in broiler production, it follows that the rate at which feed is converted into poultry meat is an important measure of efficiency. In Table 77 are shown data for 456 lots of broilers grown in Maine between July 1, 1959 and June 30, 1960, and marketed at 77 days of age or less. Records of the 456 lots were sorted according to rate of feed conversion. It is clear that as the amount of feed required per pound of broiler increased, the total cost per pound of finished broiler also increased. When the sort is made on this basis there is relatively little change in either age or weight at time of sale.

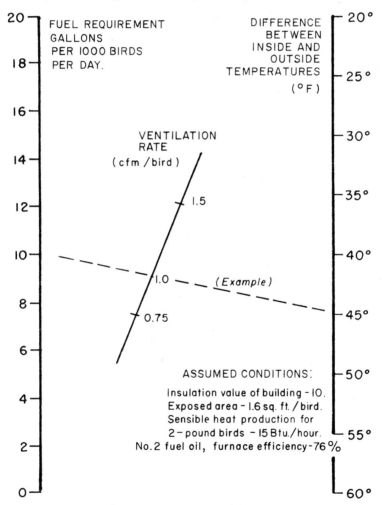

Fig. 192.—Fuel required to maintain indicated temperature differences in a broiler house, with three different specified ventilation rates. Based on data of Prince, Irish and Potter, University of Connecticut.

Another analysis of the effect of feed conversion on costs is shown in Figure 193. It is based on 47 lots, about 10 per cent of the total, which were sold at 69 days of age. As shown by the equation of the straight line, an improvement of 0.1 pound in feed conversion accounted for a reduction of slightly more than 0.8 cent in total cost per pound of broiler meat. Since these lots averaged slightly above 15,000 broilers and were sold at an average weight of 3.56 pounds, a

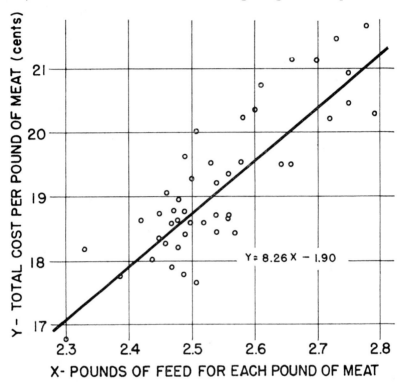

$$Y = 8.26 X - 1.90$$

FIG. 193.—The rate of feed conversion is an important factor in determining costs and returns in broiler growing. Plotted points are for 47 different lots of broilers in 1959–60. All lots contained the same kind of chicks, all were fed the same brand of feed, and all were marketed at 69 days of age. (*Courtesy of R. F. Saunders, Maine Agr. Exp. Station.*)

gain in feed efficiency of one tenth of a pound was worth about $440 four times a year. This explains why successful operators have learned to purchase the kind of chicks that will grow rapidly, to use efficient rations, and to keep both feed wastage and mortality at a minimum.

Broiler growers must also make decisions as to the age or weight at which to sell their flocks. In Tables 78 and 79 the records of the same lots of Maine broilers have been sorted according to age and weight at time of sale. As age at time of sale increased from about nine to about eleven weeks, average weight increased sharply, while rate of feed conversion and cost per pound were only slightly affected. But as weight at time of sale increased—the sort being made on that basis in constructing Table 79—cost per pound of broiler decreased steadily, with almost no change in the rate of feed conversion. This clearly suggests that in a market which pays as well for heavy as for light broilers, many growers could increase their returns by carrying broilers to heavier weights than is current practice in the industry.

TABLE 77.—FEED CONVERSION AS RELATED TO COSTS IN BROILER PRODUCTION. (UNPUBLISHED DATA, MAINE AGR. EXP. STA., COURTESY OF R. F. SAUNDERS.)

Feed conversion	Number of lots	Average age when processed (days)	Average weight (pounds)	Total cost per pound (cents)
Under 2.40	41	67.0	3.56	17.91
2.40–2.49	101	70.5	3.71	18.11
2.50–2.59	145	71.8	3.76	18.66
2.60–2.69	86	72.4	3.75	19.18
2.70–2.79	57	71.9	3.67	19.93
2.80–2.89	18	73.2	3.62	20.87
Above 2.90	8	73.4	3.59	22.01
All	456	72.2	3.71	18.88

TABLE 78.—AGE AT PROCESSING AS RELATED TO COSTS IN BROILER PRODUCTION. (UNPUBLISHED DATA, MAINE AGR. EXP. STATION, COURTESY OF R. F. SAUNDERS.)

Age when sold (Days)	Number of lots	Average weight (pounds)	Feed conversion	Total cost per pound (cents)
Under 66	21	3.33	2.34	18.39
66–68	68	3.44	2.51	19.14
69–71	151	3.64	2.56	19.02
72–74	141	3.81	2.59	18.87
75–77	75	4.01	2.61	18.49
All	456	3.71	2.56	18.88

TABLE 79.—WEIGHT AT PROCESSING AS RELATED TO COSTS IN BROILER PRODUCTION. (UNPUBLISHED DATA, MAINE AGR. EXP. STATION, COURTESY OF R. F. SAUNDERS.)

Weight when processed (pounds)	Number of lots	Feed conversion	Age when sold (days)	Total cost per pound (cents)
Under 3.20	13	2.50	65.9	20.35
3.20–3.39	48	2.58	68.4	19.84
3.40–3.59	106	2.56	69.4	19.32
3.60–3.79	107	2.55	71.0	18.77
3.80–3.99	107	2.58	73.2	18.61
4.00–4.19	54	2.55	74.2	17.97
4.20 and over	21	2.56	75.1	17.74
All	456	2.56	72.2	18.88

25

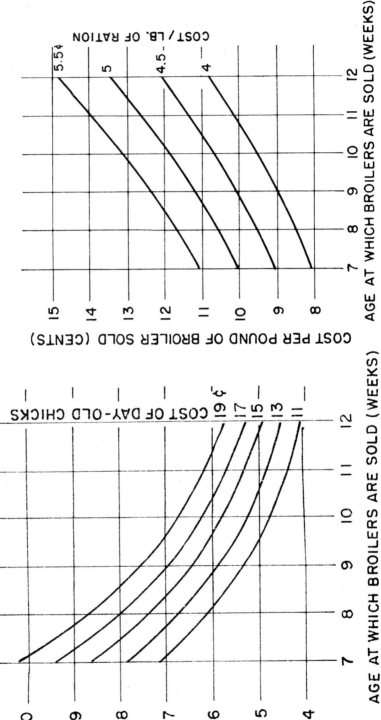

FIG. 194.—Showing the effect of chick cost (left) and of feed cost (right) on the cost per pound of broiler at different ages. To find total cost, add the values for selected points on the two parts of this chart. See text for discussion. The data are given in Table 80.

As further evidence of this, some Maine growers are actually producing roasters at an average cost per pound of live weight only 1.4 cents above the average cost of producing broilers. Data for 306 lots of over 15,000 roasters each, processed at 15 weeks of age when they weighed 6½ pounds each, showed a feed conversion of 3.12 pounds and a production cost of 20.23 cents a pound. These roasters were grown between July 1, 1959, and June 30, 1960.

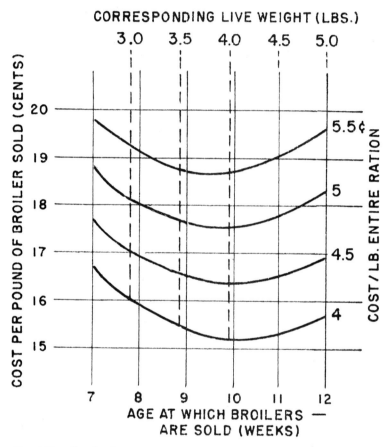

Fig. 195.—Showing how total cost per pound of broiler sold varies with age and cost per pound of feed when chick cost and other fixed costs are held constant. See text for discussion, and Table 80 for data.

Sorts of the kind just mentioned are helpful in showing what happens to different groups of growers, but they still do not explain why the differences occurred, and they may sometimes lead broiler operators to make wrong decisions or to adopt unprofitable practices.

What is needed is a breakdown which will show how the accumulated cost is changing from week to week, or with each added fraction of weight, so that an individual producer can have a reasonable basis for deciding when to sell. Not many data of this kind are available, but Table 80, and Figures 194, 195 and 196 prepared from the same data, will serve as an example.

An inspection of the curves shows that the higher the cost of feed, the earlier broilers must be sold if the grower is to obtain the maximum margin over feed cost per pound. On the other hand, high fixed or initial costs, such as a high price paid for chicks, make it

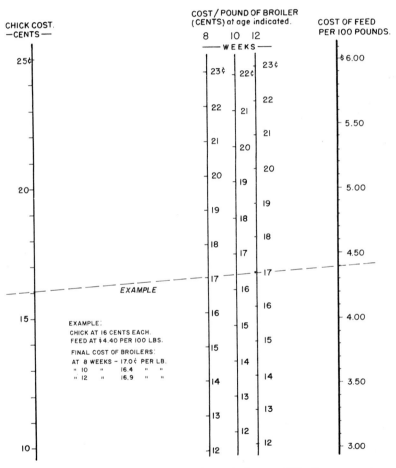

Fig. 196.—For any assumed cost and any feed cost within the ranges given, this nomogram shows the age at which to sell for maximum profit per pound of broiler. It is based on the growth rate and feed conversion data shown in Table 80, with labor at 50¢ per 1000 head per day and other fixed costs at 5 cents per chick started.

necessary to sell at a later time (in terms of age or weight) in order to distribute these costs over more pounds of broiler and thus obtain a maximum margin. One set of costs increases, and the other decreases, the longer the chickens are kept, and the broiler grower is faced with the nice problem of deciding for each lot he raises when the combination of the two is at a minimum. The whole problem is often further complicated by the prospect of a declining market.

TABLE 80.—COST PER POUND OF BROILER WILL VARY ACCORDING TO THE AGE OR WEIGHT AT WHICH BROILERS ARE SOLD, AS WELL AS WITH THE COST OF FEED. THESE DATA FOR STRAIGHT-RUN BROILERS, TAKEN IN PART FROM DELAWARE AGR. EXP. STA. BUL. 328, WERE USED IN PREPARING FIGURES 194 AND 195.

Age in weeks	Average weight (pounds)	Cumulative feed consumption (pounds)	Labor and fixed costs* per head (cumulative) (cents)
7	2.60	5.26	22.45
8	3.11	6.61	22.80
9	3.61	8.09	23.15
10	4.10	9.70	23.50
11	4.56	11.46	23.85
12	4.96	13.35	24.20

*Chicks @ 15¢ each
Other fixed costs 5¢ per chick started
Labor calculated at 50¢ per day per 1000 chickens

The chart shown in Figure 196 brings together the relationships shown in Figures 194 and 195 so that their combined effect can be determined. On the basis of the growth, feed consumption and other cost data shown in Table 80, it is possible to determine for any chick cost and any cost of feed the age at which to sell broilers for the maximum margin per pound. This chart is based on mixed sexes or straight-run chicks. For lots of broilers which have a different rate of feed conversion, the final result might be quite different.

When they are bought at the same price as day old chicks, pullets should be sold earlier than cockerels in order to obtain the maximum margin for each. If, on the other hand, cockerel chicks are bought at a low price and pullets at a high price, the most profitable selling times might be reversed.

In the language of the economist, this approach represents an analysis of input-output relationships in order to maximize returns from the broiler enterprise in terms of the margin between the total cost per pound of broiler sold and the current selling price. It involves the whole concept of marginal cost and marginal revenue. More complete data than are now available are needed on weight gains and feed consumption, by both cockerels and pullets, over the entire range of increasing marketable weights, so that broiler growers can be provided with background material as an aid in making correct decisions. The average weight at which broilers are marketed has been increasing in all but one of the ten leading broiler States (Table 81). In many individual instances it would be profitable to grow broilers to still heavier weights.

TABLE 81.—AVERAGE WEIGHTS AT WHICH BROILERS WERE MARKETED IN SELECTED STATES, 1955–1959. (FROM THE U.S. DEPT. OF AGRICULTURE.)

	1955	1956	1957	1958	1959
			Pounds		
Alabama . . .	3.1	3.1	3.2	3.2	3.3
Arkansas . . .	2.8	2.8	2.9	2.9	3.1
Delaware . .	3.1	3.3	3.4	3.5	3.5
Georgia . .	2.9	3.1	3.2	3.2	3.3
Maine. . . .	3.6	3.6	3.8	3.7	3.8
Maryland . .	3.1	3.3	3.4	3.4	3.5
Mississippi . .	2.8	2.9	3.1	3.1	3.1
North Carolina .	3.0	3.1	3.1	3.3	3.3
Texas	2.9	3.0	3.0	3.0	3.1
Virginia . . .	3.1	3.2	3.1	3.1	3.1
United States .	3.1	3.2	3.2	3.2	3.3

TABLE 82.—ADDITIONAL PRICE PER POUND NECESSARY TO MAKE BROILERS OF EACH INDICATED WEIGHT AS PROFITABLE AS BROILERS OF THE MOST PROFITABLE WEIGHT UNDER THE ASSUMED PRICES AND CONDITIONS. (AFTER HANSEN AND MIGHELL, 1956, U.S.D.A. TECH. BUL. 1154.)

System of Operation

Weight (pounds)	Single lot, with market price of:		Continuous production, labor limited		Continuous production, space limited	
	25¢	30¢	25¢	30¢	25¢	30¢
2.25	3.6¢	7.3¢	1.7¢	2.6¢	0.2¢	*
2.50	2.4	5.3	1.0	1.6	*	0.3
2.75	1.6	3.8	0.6	0.9	0.1	0.7
3.00	1.0	2.5	0.3	0.6	0.3	1.4
3.25	0.4	1.5	0.1	0.2	0.4	1.9
3.50	0.1	0.7	*	*	0.8	2.7
3.75	*	0.2	0.1	0.1	1.3	3.7
4.00	0.1	*	0.5	0.4	2.0	4.9
4.25	0.4	*	1.0	0.9	3.0	6.4

*Most profitable market weight under assumed prices and conditions.
Mortality estimated @ 0.5 per cent per week.
Feed calculated @ $5.00 per 100 pounds, including feed used by non-surviving birds.
Chicks @ 20¢ each, plus 2¢ for fuel and medicines.
Space limitation: 5000 sq. ft. available, to be utilized @ 0.5 sq. ft. per broiler sold @ 2.25 lbs., increased by 0.07 sq. ft. per broiler for each additional 0.25 lb. of finished weight.
Labor limitation: 10,000 chicks started per lot.
Continuous production assumes two weeks between lots.

Growers who are able to buy crossbred cockerel chicks, and who use well-formulated rations, often find it profitable to carry such chickens to much heavier weights than would be profitable for mixed sexes. Since both cost and selling price are variable, it should be obvious that each grower must keep track of his individual costs in order to arrive at correct decisions affecting his own operations.

Labor Efficiency.—Efficient use of labor is an important means of increasing profits in the broiler business, because more broilers raised per man means more total dollar income per man. Size of business is therefore the most important contributing factor in labor efficiency. If only a few broilers are grown one cannot afford to install expensive labor-saving equipment, but if the flock size warrants, there are many devices which will simplify chore work and reduce the number of hours required for each 1000 broilers raised. Automatic watering systems alone may cut the chore labor in half, and the use of feed carriers or automatic feeding equipment will produce additional savings.

Maximizing Annual Returns.—The foregoing discussion has emphasized returns per pound of broiler for a single lot. Assuming that there is no appreciable price discount for broilers sold at the heavier weights, it has been shown that as the price of feed decreases, or the price of broilers increases, flocks should be carried to heavier weights. Many growers are tempted to do just the opposite—sell at lighter weights in order to take advantage of a good market. The charts and tables in the preceding section should help them to analyze the current situation and to make the right decision.

It is always a mistake to top out or "cream" a flock of broilers. The birds that are doing best are not the ones to sell first. Neither should cockerels be sold before pullets. Greater returns can usually be realized by selling pullets as much as a week younger than cockerels when both are ready for market at about the same time.

For growers who are following a system of continuous year-round production, there is another important question to be answered. Will the total annual returns be greater if individual lots are sold just enough short of the point of maximum returns to permit growing out an extra lot each year? This, too, will be influenced somewhat by the cost of feed and the price received for each pound of broiler. The curves shown in Figures 197 and 198 are based on an analysis of this problem using growth and feed conversion data from Delaware Bulletin 328 and the indicated feed cost and broiler price figures. Actual figures would vary under other sets of conditions, but the principles would not be different.

Finally, in Table 83 are given production information and cost data for over 29 million broilers grown out during the 1959–60 year in five different broiler areas. They will serve as background information.

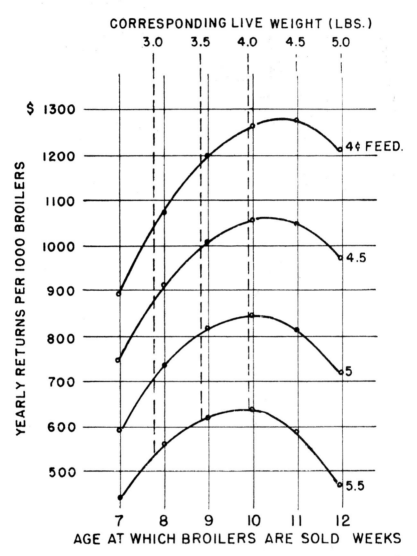

Fig. 197.—Yearly returns per 1000 broilers under continuous production of straight-run broilers. All sales at 21¢ a pound. Feed cost at 4¢ to 5.5¢ a pound. Other out-of-pocket costs estimated at 18¢ per bird. Chart prepared from data on 144 lots of commercial broilers, as reported in Delaware Agr. Exp. Sta. Bulletin 328.

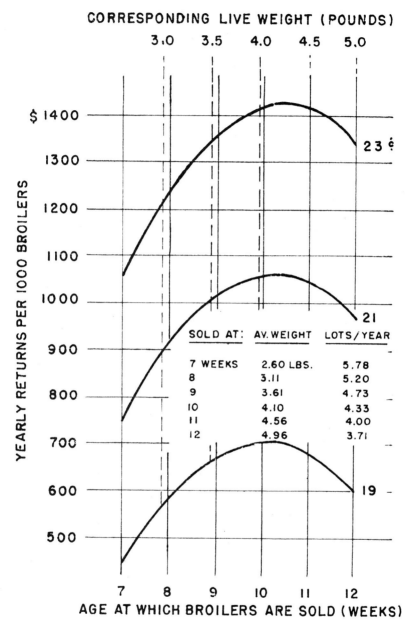

CORRESPONDING LIVE WEIGHT (POUNDS)

SOLD AT:	AV. WEIGHT	LOTS/YEAR
7 WEEKS	2.60 LBS.	5.78
8	3.11	5.20
9	3.61	4.73
10	4.10	4.33
11	4.56	4.00
12	4.96	3.71

AGE AT WHICH BROILERS ARE SOLD (WEEKS)

FIG. 198.—Yearly returns per 1000 broilers under continuous production of straight-run broilers. Feed cost assumed to be 4½¢ apound. Other out-of-pocket costs estimated at 18¢ a bird. Selling price 19¢, 21¢ or 23¢ a pound. Chart prepared from data on 144 lots of commercial broilers, as reported in Delaware Agr. Exp. Sta. Bulletin 328.

TABLE 83.—COST DATA AND SELECTED PRODUCTION INFORMATION FOR COMMERCIAL BROILERS GROWN IN FIVE DIFFERENT AREAS, 1959-60.

Item	Maine	New York and northern Pennsylvania	Del-Mar-Va Peninsula	Shenandoah Valley Virginia	Arkansas
Number of lots	494	553	774	1,538	83
Av. number started per lot	15,984	8,904	11,766	3,840	16,577
Age when processed (days)	72	67	68	63	70
Weight when processed (pounds)	3.76	3.70	3.48	3.29	3.20
Feed conversion	2.57	2.35	2.48	2.25	2.48
Mortality (per cent)	2.3	2.0	5.0	1.5	2.9
Cost per pound live weight					
Feed	11.89¢	10.49¢	11.48¢	10.64¢	12.34¢
Chicks	3.42	3.04	3.31	3.68	4.78
Fuel	.43	.62	.56	.57	.07
Litter	.12	.25	.22	.19	.10
Medication	.12	.07	.08	.07	.49
Grower payment and flock supervision	2.77	2.61	2.16	2.08	2.28
Total cost	18.82¢	17.08¢	17.81¢	17.23¢	20.06¢

Note: All operations covered a full year, except Arkansas, which was for September, 1960 only.

The Future of the Poultry Business.—Whenever there is temporary overproduction of poultry and eggs, the question of the future prospects for the business comes uppermost in the minds of many producers. In a business that is nation-wide, every producer comes into more or less direct competition with producers in many other sections of the country. Certain sections have a price advantage in the selling of eggs and poultry, while others have an advantage in the way of low costs of production.

In the long run, the producer who will best be able to meet competition, and to survive recurring periods of depression in the industry, will be the one whose cost of production is lower than that of his competitors, and who is able through individual initiative or collective organization to receive a premium price for high quality products.

The poultry business has become firmly established as a part of the agricultural production of this country. As pointed out in the opening pages of this book, poultry keeping exists as an industry because poultry and eggs are prized as human food. If the industry is to maintain and improve its position in the national economy, it is essential that there be continued improvement in the quality of poultry and eggs which reach the consumer's table.

Index

7 26